45.50

Advances in Infrared and Raman Spectroscopy

VOLUME 3

Advances in Infrared and Raman Spectroscopy

Edited by R. J. H. Clark and R. E. Hester

Contents of Previous Volumes

Advances in Infrared and Raman Spectroscopy

VOLUME 3

Edited by

R. J. H. CLARK
University College, London

R. E. HESTER
University of York

London · Bellmawr N.J. · Rheine

Heyden & Son Ltd., Spectrum House, Alderton Crescent, London NW4 3XX
Heyden & Son Inc., Kor-Center East, Bellmawr, N.J. 08030, U.S.A.
Heyden & Son GmbH, Münsterstrasse 22, 4440 Rheine/Westf., Germany

ISBN 0 85501 183 1

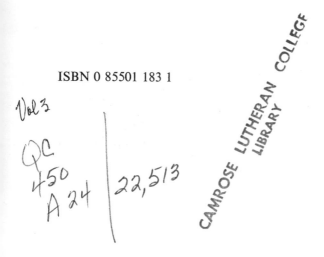
Set by Eta Services (Typesetters) Ltd., Beccles, Suffolk.
Printed and bound in Great Britain by W & J Mackay Ltd, Lordswood,
Chatham, Kent.

CONTENTS

CHAPTER 1: Recent Techniques in Raman Spectroscopy—
W. Kiefer

CHAPTER 2: Advances in Far-Infrared Interferometric
Spectroscopy—
N. W. B. Stone and G. W. Chantry

CHAPTER 3: Force-Constant Calculations—The State of the Art—
P. Gans

LIST OF CONTRIBUTORS

G. W. CHANTRY, Department of Industry, National Physics Laboratory, Teddington, Middlesex TW11 0LW, U.K. (p. 43).

P. GANS, Department of Inorganic and Structural Chemistry, The University, Leeds LS2 9JT, U.K. (p. 87).

D. J. GARDINER, Newcastle upon Tyne Polytechnic, Department of Chemistry, Ellison Building, Ellison Place, Newcastle upon Tyne NE1 8ST, U.K. (p. 167).

W. KIEFER, Sektion Physik der Universität München, Schellingstr. 4, D-8 München 40, Germany (p. 1).

M. LAPP, General Electric Company, Corporate Research and Development, Schenectady, New York 12301, U.S.A. (p. 204).

C. M. PENNEY, General Electric Company, Corporate Research and Development, Schenectady, New York 12301, U.S.A. (p. 204).

I. W. SHEPHERD, Physics Department, Manchester University, Manchester M13 9PL, U.K. (p. 127).

N. W. B. STONE, Department of Industry, National Physics Laboratory, Teddington, Middlesex TW11 0LW, U.K. (p. 43).

PREFACE TO VOLUME 1

There are few areas of science which have not already benefited from the application of infrared spectroscopic methods, and progress in this field remains vigorous. Closely related information on chemical and biological materials and systems is obtainable from Raman spectroscopy, though there are also many important differences between the types of information yielded and the types of materials and systems best suited to study by each technique. The close relationship between these two sets of spectroscopic techniques is explicitly recognised in this Series. Advances in Infrared and Raman Spectroscopy contains critical review articles, both fundamental and applied, mainly within the title areas; however, we shall extend the coverage into closely related areas by giving some space to such topics as neutron inelastic scattering or vibronic fluorescence spectroscopy. Thus the Series will be firmly technique orientated. Inasmuch as these techniques have such wide ranging applicability throughout science and engineering, however, the coverage in terms of topics will be wide. Already in the first volume we have articles ranging from the fundamental theory of infrared band intensities through the development of computer-controlled spectrometer systems to applications in biology. This integration of theory and practice, and the bringing together of different areas of academic and industrial science and technology, constitute major objectives of the Series.

The reviews will be in those subjects in which most progress is deemed to have been made in recent years, or is expected to be made in the near future. The Series will appeal to research scientists and technologists as well as to graduate students and teachers of advanced courses. The Series is intended to be of wide general interest both within and beyond the fields of chemistry, physics and biology.

The problem of nomenclature in a truly international Series has to be acknowledged. We have adopted a compromise solution of permitting the use of either English or American spelling (depending on the origin of the review article) and have recommended the use of SI Units. A table on the international system of units is given on p. xiii for reference purposes.

August 1975

R. J. H. CLARK
R. E. HESTER

PREFACE

The present volume continues the policy established by the Editors for Volumes 1 and 2 of this Series of commissioning critical review articles in both fundamental and applied aspects of infrared and Raman spectroscopy, as well as in topics closely allied to these. The first chapter emphasizes the great advances which have been made in the past few years in instrumentation and technique of Raman spectroscopy. The Munich Physics Department has been at the forefront of a great many of these advances, and it is fitting that one of their number should contribute a Review on this topic. The leading role of the NPL group in developing instruments for Fourier transform interferometric spectroscopy is recognized in the second chapter. FTS remains in a state of active development, and many aspects of instrumentation, as well as novel applications of the technique (e.g. to the monitoring of the trace gases in the atmosphere from Concorde) are discussed in this chapter. By contrast with these technical subjects, the third chapter is concerned with the long established subject of force-constant calculations. This review is concerned less, however, with the mechanics of carrying these out, than with a detailed assessment of the state of the art of the subject. The fourth chapter is concerned with the use of Raman polarization techniques in the study of macro-molecules. These techniques have only recently been recognized as being able to play an important role in our understanding of polymer structure, and the review is both novel and intriguing. The fifth chapter on the vibrational spectra of non-aqueous solvents complements two previous reviews in Volume 2 of this Series which dealt with vibrational studies of ionic species in vapours, liquids, glasses and aqueous electrolyte solutions. The present review consists of a wide ranging survey of many solvent systems and of the molecules and ions which may be present therein. Finally a review of the Raman spectra of flames focuses attention on Raman scattering as a probe of combustion systems with the object of determining the temperatures and densities of the main constituents.

As with earlier volumes, we have favoured IUPAC nomenclature and the use of SI Units. To aid the reader, a table of SI units and conversion factors from other systems commonly in use is included on pages xiii–xv.

February 1977   R. J. H. CLARK
                                                        R. E. HESTER

THE INTERNATIONAL SYSTEM OF UNITS (SI)

Physical quantity	Name of unit	Symbol for unit
SI Base Units		
length	metre	m
mass	kilogram	kg
time	second	s
electric current	ampere	A
thermodynamic temperature	kelvin	K
amount of substance	mole	mol
SI Supplementary Units		
plane angle	radian	rad
solid angle	steradian	sr

SI Derived Units having Special Names and Symbols

energy	joule	$J = m^2\,kg\,s^{-2}$
force	newton	$N = m\,kg\,s^{-2} = J\,m^{-1}$
pressure	pascal	$Pa = m^{-1}\,kg\,s^{-2} = N\,m^{-2} = J\,m^{-3}$
power	watt	$W = m^2\,kg\,s^{-3} = J\,s^{-1}$
electric charge	coulomb	$C = s\,A$
electric potential difference	volt	$V = m^2\,kg\,s^{-3}\,A^{-1} = J\,A^{-1}\,s^{-1}$
electric resistance	ohm	$\Omega = m^2\,kg\,s^{-3}\,A^{-2} = V\,A^{-1}$
electric conductance	siemens	$S = m^{-2}\,kg^{-1}\,s^3\,A^2 = \Omega^{-1}$
electric capacitance	farad	$F = m^{-2}\,kg^{-1}\,s^4\,A^2 = C\,V^{-1}$
magnetic flux	weber	$Wb = m^2\,kg\,s^{-2}\,A^{-1} = V\,s$
inductance	henry	$H = m^2\,kg\,s^{-2}\,A^{-2} = V\,s\,A^{-1}$
magnetic flux density	tesla	$T = kg\,s^{-2}\,A^{-1} = V\,s\,m^{-2}$
frequency	hertz	$Hz = s^{-1}$

SOME NON-SI UNITS

Physical quantity	Name of unit	Symbol and definition

Decimal Multiples of SI Units, Some having Special Names and Symbols

length	ångström	$\text{Å} = 10^{-10}$ m $= 0.1$ nm $= 100$ pm
length	micron	$\mu\text{m} = 10^{-6}$ m
area	are	$\text{a} = 100$ m^2
area	barn	$\text{b} = 10^{-28}$ m^2
volume	litre	$\text{l} = 10^{-3}$ m$^3 = $ dm^3 $= 10^3$ cm^3
energy	erg	$\text{erg} = 10^{-7}$ J
force	dyne	$\text{dyn} = 10^{-5}$ N
force constant	dyne per centimetre	$\text{dyn cm}^{-1} = 10^{-3}$ N m^{-1}
force constant	millidyne per ångström	$\text{mdyn Å}^{-1} = 10^2$ N m^{-1}
force constant	attojoule per ångström squared	$\text{aJ Å}^{-2} = 10^2$ N m^{-1}
pressure	bar	$\text{bar} = 10^5$ Pa
concentration	—	$\text{M} = 10^3$ mol m^{-3} $= $ mol dm^{-3}

Units Defined Exactly in Terms of SI Units

length	inch	$\text{in} = 0.0254$ m
mass	pound	$\text{lb} = 0.453\ 592\ 27$ kg
force	kilogram-force	$\text{kgf} = 9.806\ 65$ N
pressure	standard atmosphere	$\text{atm} = 101\ 325$ Pa
pressure	torr	$\text{Torr} = 1$ mmHg $= (101\ 325/760)$ Pa
energy	kilowatt hour	$\text{kW h} = 3.6 \times 10^6$ J
energy	thermochemical calorie	$\text{cal}_{\text{th}} = 4.184$ J
thermodynamic temperature	degree Celsius[a]	$°\text{C} = \text{K}$

[a]Celsius or "Centigrade" temperature θ_C is defined in terms of the thermodynamic temperature T by the relation $\theta_C/°\text{C} = T/\text{K} - 273.15$.

OTHER RELATIONS

1. The physical quantity, the wavenumber (units cm^{-1}), is related to frequency as follows:

$$\text{cm}^{-1} \approx (2.998 \times 10^{10})^{-1} \text{ s}^{-1}$$

2. The physical quantity, the molar decadic absorption coefficient (symbol ε) has the SI units m^2 mol^{-1}. The relation between the usual non-SI and SI units is as follows:

$$\text{M}^{-1} \text{ cm}^{-1} = 1 \text{ mol}^{-1} \text{ cm}^{-1} = 10^{-1} \text{ m}^2 \text{ mol}^{-1}$$

3. It appears that for many years to come a knowledge of the 'electromagnetic CGS' unit system will be a necessity for workers in various fields of spectroscopy, but for practical purposes it is usually sufficient to note that for magnetic flux density, 1 gauss (G) corresponds to 10^{-4} T and for electric dipole moment, 1 debye (D) corresponds to approximately 3.3356×10^{-30} C m.

The SI Prefixes

Fraction	Prefix	Symbol	Multiple	Prefix	Symbol
10^{-1}	deci	d	10^{1}	deca	da
10^{-2}	centi	c	10^{2}	hecto	h
10^{-3}	milli	m	10^{3}	kilo	k
10^{-6}	micro	μ	10^{6}	mega	M
10^{-9}	nano	n	10^{9}	giga	G
10^{-12}	pico	p	10^{12}	tera	T
10^{-15}	femto	f	10^{15}	peta	P
10^{-18}	atto	a	10^{18}	exa	E

Chapter 1

RECENT TECHNIQUES IN RAMAN SPECTROSCOPY

W. Kiefer

Sektion Physik der Universität München, Schellingstr. 4, D-8 München 40, Germany

1 INTRODUCTION

The renaissance in Raman spectroscopy began with the application of reliable laser excitation sources; since then, many new techniques have been developed which permit the recording of Raman spectra of a great variety of compounds, from deeply coloured or even black materials, to highly fluorescent molecules. Besides this, many very helpful instrumental methods were introduced into Raman spectroscopy from other spectroscopic fields. A typical example is the two-channel technique which, for instance, enables difference or addition Raman spectroscopy to be carried out, as well as the automatic scanning of the depolarization ratio. Double beam spectrometers are common in infrared spectroscopy, but it was only recently that this two channel method was applied in inelastic light scattering. Another example is the use of differential methods, where the first derivative of the spectrum is scanned as a function of the Raman shift. This method, well known in the field of modulation spectroscopy, has proved to be highly effective in the investigation of electronic band structures of solids. Many of these new techniques are very useful, in many cases they are inexpensive to set up, and they can be adapted to nearly any existing laser Raman spectrometer. These developments can be regarded as a contribution to automatization in this field of spectroscopy.

This article attempts to collect and discuss some recent innovations in Raman instrumentation and techniques. However, this review is not intended to be comprehensive. Only some typical, but highly efficient instrumental novelties will be discussed which are of considerable use for the practical spectroscopist.

Two recent, more technically oriented reviews in this Series have already concentrated on digital computer methods[1] as well as on time-resolved and space-resolved techniques in Raman spectroscopy,[2] to which the interested reader is referred.

1

2   DYNAMICAL SAMPLE TECHNIQUES

One of the main limitations in Raman spectroscopy is with respect to samples that absorb the exciting radiation. Dark or coloured materials have, until recently, produced mostly unusable results because of localized overheating of the sample. To overcome this difficulty, a variety of effective techniques have been developed whose common idea is that of relative motion between sample and focused laser beam. This can be done either by rotating the sample in the laser beam to present continuously cooled material to the beam or by scanning the focused beam over the surface of the absorbing material. These rotating sample or surface scanning techniques not only avoid thermal decomposition of the sample but also eliminate the thermal lens effect which would otherwise prevent the laser beam from coming to a sharp focus in highly absorbing static media; the consequence of this would be less collected Raman light. If Raman spectra of short-lived, absorbing species are to be obtained (as could be the case for instance for some reaction intermediates), a third dynamical method, the continuous-flow technique, can be employed. This method does not influence the reaction rate by sample heating but nevertheless permits the use of long recording times even though the species under investigation is stable only for seconds or fractions of a second.

2.1   Rotating Sample Techniques

The rotating sample technique introduced to Raman spectroscopy for the first time by Kiefer and Bernstein[3,4] has become a powerful tool for exciting spectra of highly absorbing liquids or solids. Since then, many applications, particularly for the study of the laser-excited resonance Raman effect, have been described in the literature.[5,6] Many modifications of the original design for the rotating sample device have been developed. Examples can be found in Refs (5) and (6), in which arrangements for 90° as well as for 180° scattering geometries are shown for samples in the liquid or solid state.

Recently, a universal rotating system for Raman spectroscopy has been described,[7] which is suitable for recording the spectra of rotating liquid or solid samples and the difference Raman spectra of liquids or solids (see Section 3.1) as well as for the automatic scanning of the depolarization ratio (see Section 3.3) using only one mechanical unit. This instrument was constructed in such a way that all of these procedures could be carried out with the minimum of adjustment and the maximum of flexibility and stability. Furthermore this instrument can be mounted on any optical bench and be used in connection with any Raman spectrometer with 90° viewing optics.

The arrangement of the system for the recording of Raman spectra of rotating liquid samples is very similar to that for the recording of difference Raman spectra (Section 3.1), and a description of it is therefore not included in this section. Figure 1 shows schematically the universal rotating system, set up to record

Raman spectra of rotating crystal powders in a 90° scattering arrangement. The crystal powder is pressed with a special pressing tool into a circular channel of the solid sample cell (4, Fig. 1) which is then put on a holder (3, Fig. 1). The latter is directly fixed on the motor axis. The motor is held by a motor block which is turned at an angle of between 45 and 75° with respect to the direction of observation. The laser beam comes up from below and is focused on to the sample surface. Scattered light is observed at 90°. The rotating system can be

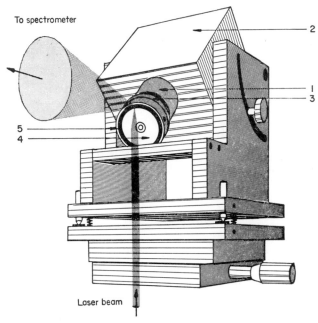

To spectrometer

Laser beam

Fig. 1. Universal rotating Raman system adjusted for excitation of solid samples. 1, motor; 2, motor block; 3, holder for solid sample cell; 4, solid sample cell; 5, solid sample (Kiefer *et al.*, Ref. 7).

adjusted very precisely in all directions by a kinematic mount and an *X-Y*-precision moving stage. Rotation rates can be chosen from 0 to 3000 r.p.m. Further details, in particular for cell devices, are given in Kiefer *et al.*[7]

The optimum operating conditions for a rotating sample system for absorbing crystal powders have been worked out in terms of the radius of the ring-shaped crystal pellet, the focal length of the focusing lens, and the properties of the material studied (i.e. specific heat, thermal conductivity, etc.).[4] It was found that the greatest influence on the temperature at the sample surface comes from the focal length of the focusing lens of the laser beam. For not too small focal lengths (≈ 5 cm), rotation rates of the order of 2000 r.p.m. for solid sample cells with a diameter of approximately 3–4 cm are sufficiently high to keep the temperature increase on the sample surface of most samples sufficiently small for no thermal decomposition to occur. This was also found to be the case experimentally for many samples.[8]

The diameter of the solid sample cell should be moderately large for the reasons indicated above; the amount of sample can be kept very small by reducing the width of the circular channel of the sample holder to 1 mm or less. Long et al.[9] have found that it is possible to obtain useful Raman spectra from a solid sample of about 1 mg only if the sample is pressed on top of a layer of KBr which had been previously pressed into the sample holder. This application of the rotating sample technique to semimicro samples was demonstrated with spectra of solid $KMnO_4$.

Thermal decomposition of the sample may arise also when the latter is in the vapour phase. This results in a gradual lowering of band intensities with time and can also produce spot or film deposits of solids on the wall of the sample cell, mainly at the spot where the laser beam enters the cell. A device which overcomes these problems has been described by Clark et al.[10] Using a rotating, sealed Pyrex or silica tube, which incorporated identations of the Vigreux type, the authors were able to record the vapour phase Raman spectrum of a sample of the compound ICF_3 at room temperature. In this way the sample was stable for a day or more, whereas in a static cell it decomposed in the beam of a focused argon ion laser within five minutes.

2.2 Continuous-Flow Techniques

An alternative procedure to overcome sample decomposition due to overheating is to flow the liquid through a capillary at a velocity of 5–10 cm s^{-1}. This technique was first applied by Mortensen[11] who studied resonance Raman spectra of iodine/chloroform solutions. Woodruff and Spiro[12] used a circulating sample in order to control the sample temperature. This was achieved with a peristaltic pump which circulates the sample solution through the capillary and also through a bath with constant temperature for heat exchange. Although the circulating sample technique is simple and inexpensive and allows the control of the sample temperature, it has one major drawback compared to the rotating sample technique. Since flow velocities are nearly zero in liquid layers close to the capillary wall, the focused laser beam can destroy the absorbing sample in this area leaving spot deposits on the cell wall, which would then appreciably decrease the exciting laser power.

Continuous-flow techniques have, nevertheless, proved to be extremely useful when applied to the Raman spectroscopic study of reaction intermediates.[13–15] In this method, reactant solutions (A and B) are pumped continuously at a known rate into a mixing chamber, from where the reaction mixture (A + B) flows into a Raman capillary cell (see Fig. 2). The flow velocity is controlled by a peristaltic pump connected to the exit part of the Raman cell. In Fig. 2 the laser beam is directed longitudinally through the capillary and the scattered light is collected at right angles. In the case of absorbing solutions the transverse excitation in the capillary cell[14] is more advantageous. Also, a better reaction-time resolution may be obtained by this method.

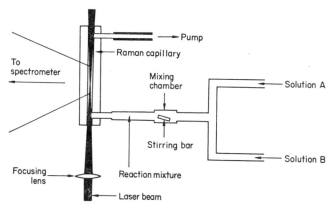

Fig. 2. Schematic diagram of a Raman flow apparatus. (Adapted from Carey and Schneider, Ref. 15).

2.3 Surface-Scanning Techniques

The rotating sample technique, discussed above, has proven to be a general solution for the study of highly absorbing materials at ambient temperatures. However in some cases, for instance at very low temperatures, it is complicated or even impossible to rotate the sample and keep it cold at the same time. Some methods have been developed in this direction for moderately low temperatures.[16,17]

Instead of rotating the sample, the problem of recording Raman spectra of absorbing samples at very low temperatures is perhaps best solved by a method where the sample is kept fixed and the overheating is avoided by scanning the focused laser beam on the surface of the sample either in a linear[18] or a circular path.[19] Koningstein and Gächter[18] have described a technique whereby the surface is scanned by placing a rotating refractor plate between the sample and the focusing lens (L1) (see Fig. 3). Then the laser beam is repeatedly made to scan the surface in a linear pattern. The collecting lens (L2) projects the scattered radiation onto the entrance slit of the monochromator. Thus the image of the focused laser beam on the sample moves along the entrance slit of the spectrometer in a sawtooth-like time function. The authors[18] used this technique to obtain a Raman spectrum of $CsCuCl_3$, which was impossible to obtain using the 514.5 nm line of the argon ion laser without relative motion of the focused laser beam and the sample.

In order to get a uniform relative motion between the static sample and the focused laser beam, a situation which is not achieved by Koningstein and Gächter's method,[18] Zimmerer and Kiefer[19] have developed a rotating, surface-scanning technique which has, in addition, the advantage that the image of the illuminated sample region does not move along the slit, but is kept fixed in its centre. A schematic diagram of this technique is given in Fig. 4. Photographs of the device, in which the cryogenic system with the sample has been replaced by a thin glass plate in order to display the focal ring produced by the laser beam, are shown in Plate 1.

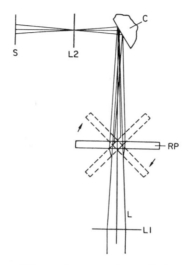

Fig. 3. Schematic diagram of the surface-scanning technique with a rotating refractor plate (after Koningstein and Gächter, Ref. 18). C, crystal; L, laser beam; L_1, focusing lens; L_2, collecting lens; S, spectrometer slit.

The principle of the rotating, surface-scanning technique is as follows (compare Fig. 4). The laser beam comes from below (any direction approximately perpendicular to the optical axis of the system is possible) and is reflected at 90° by a dielectrically coated mirror whose size is of the order of the beam diameter. It travels along the optical axis and hits eccentrically a lens (L1) with a relatively short focal length. This lens refracts and focuses the laser beam through a flat window onto the surface of the sample, which, in the case shown, consists of a pressed, ring-shaped pellet of the crystalline powder placed in a circular channel which is grooved into a copper block. The latter is connected to a cooling system. The distance between lens L1 and the sample surface corresponds to the focal length of the lens. Suppose lens L1 is turned by 180° around the optical axis of the system, then the laser beam is refracted onto a spot on the sample surface, the position of which is symmetric with respect to the optical axis. The extreme upper and lower positions of the lens are indicated in Fig. 4. If lens L1 is continuously rotated around the optical axis, the focus of the laser beam scans over the sample surface in a circular pattern, the radius of which corresponds to the distance d between lens centre (L1) and the spot where the laser beam hits the lens. Thus, a displacement of the laser beam toward the centre of L1 allows one to obtain 'focus rings' of any desired smaller diameter. Lens 1 serves at the same time as a collecting lens for the backward-scattered Raman light, which leaves the lens as a parallel beam. The latter is focused by a second lens (L2) onto the entrance slit of the spectrometer. The diameter and focal length of L2 are chosen to match the aperture of the spectrometer. The arrangement of a rotating lens, which simultaneously combines the task of focusing the laser beam and collecting the Raman light, together with a static lens, results in the fact that the collected Raman light excited by the rotating laser beam is focused onto a fixed, small spot at the centre of the entrance slit.

A miniaturization of the focus ring and hence of the amount of sample is easy to accomplish and therefore plane surfaces of small single crystals can also be surface-scanned by this method.

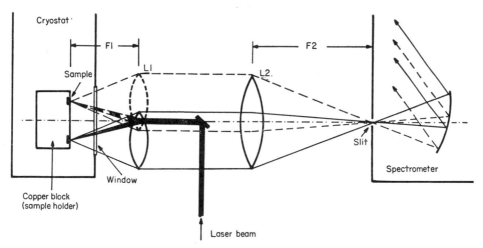

Fig. 4. Schematic diagram of the rotating, surface-scanning apparatus. L1 is the rotating lens which focuses the laser beam onto the surface of the sample and which collects simultaneously the backward-scattered Raman light. Lens L2 focuses the Raman light onto the spectrometer slit. F is the focal length of the lens. $- \cdot - \cdot -$ marks the optical axis (Zimmerer and Kiefer, Ref. 19).

The improvement in the signal-to-noise ratio of Raman spectra by using this technique, in connection with cooling of the sample and the appropriate choice of laser wavelengths, is demonstrated in Fig. 5. Using static samples no Raman spectrum of solid $KMnO_4$ can be obtained with excitation in the blue or green region.[20] With red lasers (Fig. 5a, b), spectra can be recorded, but with only a low signal-to-noise ratio.[4,20] The latter increases considerably when the rotating sample technique is employed (Fig. 5c), and, in addition to the totally symmetric stretching vibration at 843 cm^{-1}, two peaks can be observed in the region of the anti-symmetric stretching vibration around 915 cm^{-1}.[4] The spectrum in this region can be clearly resolved into three bands at 906, 916 and 920 cm^{-1} at liquid-nitrogen temperature using the surface-scanning technique.[19] Comparing spectrum (d) with spectrum (a), one can observe a dramatic improvement in signal-to-noise ratio when the appropriate technique and a suitable laser source are employed for Raman spectroscopic studies of absorbing solid samples.

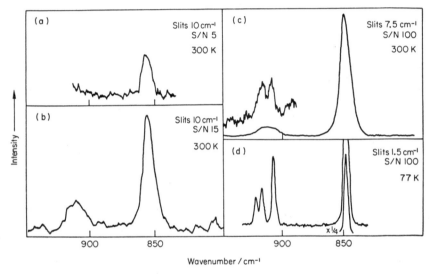

Wavenumber / cm^{-1}

Fig. 5. Raman spectra of solid KMnO$_4$ obtained under different conditions. (a) Static sample; He—Ne laser, 50 mW, 632.8 nm.[20] (b) Static sample; Ruby laser, 500 mW, 694.3 nm.[4] (c) Rotating sample technique; Argon laser, 1 W, 514.5 nm.[4] (d) Rotating surface-scanning technique; Krypton laser, 700 mW, 647.1 nm.[19] (S/N is the signal-to-noise ratio).

Highly absorbing liquids can also be investigated using the rotating, surface-scanning technique. This was demonstrated[19] with the system described above for pure liquid bromine, which is opaque throughout the visible region up to about 700 nm. Figure 6 shows spectra excited with the 647.1 nm line of a krypton ion laser for the static (upper field) and the dynamic (lower field) cases.

The application of this device for resonance Raman studies of solids and liquids, and for matrix isolation studies, as well as for Raman studies of any absorbing materials which are also air- or moisture-sensitive, is recommended. In addition, the rotating, surface-scanning technique (in connection with a cryostat) is useful for Raman excitation of very heat-sensitive compounds where the relative motion between sample and laser focus alone is not sufficient to prevent sample decomposition.

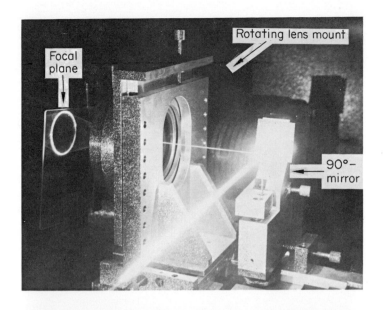

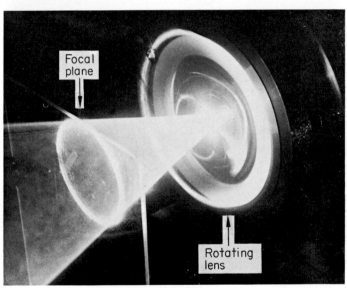

Plate 1. Photographs of the rotating, surface-scanning device developed by Zimmerer and Kiefer (Ref. 19).

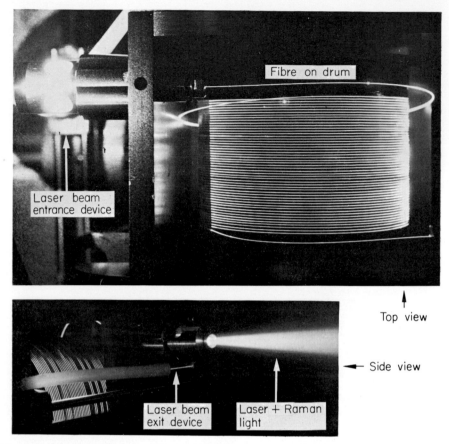

Plate 2. Photographs of a Raman liquid-core, optical-fibre device developed by Schmid, Ref. 76. Top view shows the fibre on the drum ($\approx$ 20 m long). Side view shows the emerging laser and Raman radiation from the fibre end.

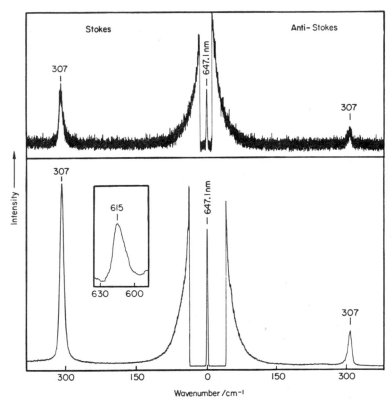

Fig. 6. Raman spectra of liquid bromine obtained by the rotating, surface-scanning technique. The upper field shows the spectrum obtained with a fixed laser beam and reduced (*ca.* 35 mW) laser power in order to avoid boiling and bubbles in the liquid. Lower field, spectrum with the rotating device where the laser power could be increased to 700 mW of 647.1 nm excitation, slits 2 cm⁻¹, time constant 0.25 s. Inset on lower field, the first overtone of Br_2 (Zimmerer and Kiefer, Ref. 19).

3 TWO-CHANNEL RAMAN SPECTROSCOPY

In many fields of spectroscopy 'two-channel' experiments are carried out in order to eliminate, for example, unwanted components of the spectra. In infrared spectroscopy, for instance, the absorption by water vapour or CO_2 in air is often compensated for by the use of double-beam spectrometers. Further, the spectrum of the host or the solvent can be removed from that of an impurity species or solution, respectively, by double-beam techniques. Such two-channel methods were unknown in Raman spectroscopy until a few years ago, the only exception being a difference Raman method for mercury excitation proposed by Zubov *et al.*[21] Recently, several techniques were invented to perform difference and addition laser-Raman spectroscopy, and to correlate the scattered Raman light excited by light of two different states of polarization. The ratio of the Raman intensities obtained from two laser beams with linear polarization perpendicular to each other (i.e. the depolarization ratio) can now be directly scanned as a function of the Raman shift.

If the ratio of the difference and the sum of the scattering intensities excited by two oppositely circularly polarized light sources is taken, then measurements of c.i.d.s (Circular Intensity Differential) are possible. This section reviews several simple two-channel methods. Typical spectra are given to show the performance of the various techniques.

3.1   Difference Raman Spectroscopy

Difference laser Raman spectroscopy has been pioneered by Bodenheimer *et al.*[22] They have demonstrated the basic advantage of this kind of spectroscopy over conventional Raman spectroscopy in two ways: cancellation of unwanted Raman bands of the solvent in the spectrum of the solution and accurate determination of small environmental frequency shifts. In the double-beam instrument described by them, a rotating half-mirror was used to split the laser source into two beams which were focused by separate lenses into different sample cells. An optical system of three lenses and a recombination mirror focuses the Raman scattered light into the monochromator. Detection was by lock-in amplification synchronized to the chopping mirror. Although this method has been checked for CBr_4/CCl_4 mixtures it appears that it suffers from difficulties in matching the two separate optical systems. A much simpler system, introduced by Kiefer,[23] in principle gives double the intensity given by the method of Bodenheimer *et al.*, because of the elimination of the recombination mirror used for their double beam instrument. The main features of this technique, together with possible electronic systems, will be discussed in the following section.

3.1.1   Difference Raman Spectroscopy with a rotating cell
3.1.1.1   THE MECHANICAL-OPTICAL SYSTEM
The very simple optical arrangement of the rotating sample technique (see Section 2.1) may also be used in difference Raman spectroscopy. The principal idea[23] is to rotate a cylindrical cell which is divided into two equal parts, one containing, for example, solution and one solvent, so as to present to the spectrometer alternately signals from the two different liquids. Such an arrangement[7,23] is shown in Fig. 7, in which the rotating two-chamber cylindrical cell (9) is fixed on an axis (10) which also holds a trigger wheel (11) driven by a rubber wheel (not shown). The latter is fixed on the motor axis and drives the trigger wheel on its periphery. The complete system is placed in front of the spectrometer. The incident laser beam can come down from above or, as shown in Fig. 7, from below, and is focused by a lens into the cell. The liquid is forced to the outer part of the cell during rotation, and the scattered Raman light is viewed horizontally by a condensing lens. The trigger wheel has a hole (12) which is

slightly larger than the diameter of the laser beam. As the wheel rotates, the hole passes through one of the two opto-electronic arrays (14) each time one half of the cell has passed the focused laser beam. Simultaneously the detection system is blocked for a short time when the separation wall passes the focal region.

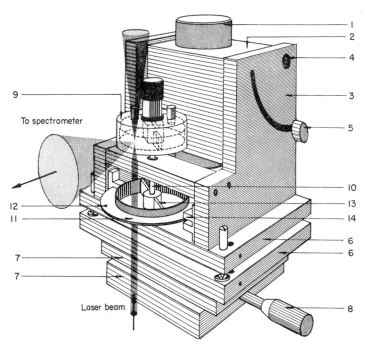

Fig. 7. Rotating system for difference Raman spectroscopy of liquids. 1, motor; 2, motor block; 3, side parts; 4, motor block axis; 5, set screw; 6, kinematic mount; 7, X-Y-precision ball movement; 8, adjustment screw; 9, liquid cell for difference Raman spectroscopy; 10, axis for trigger wheel and for holders of liquid cells; 11, trigger wheel; 12, trigger hole; 13, bar; 14, opto-electronic array consisting of a luminescence diode and phototransistor (Kiefer *et al.*, Ref. 7).

3.1.1.2 Switching Circuit

To separate from each other the scattered light arising from the two different halves of the cell, one needs a digital switching signal which follows exactly the rotation of the cell. This is achieved by means of a digital electronic system, which is shown schematically in Fig. 8. The weak trigger signals generated in the phototransistors (PT) each time the hole (12) passes by one of the PTs are amplified by an operational amplifier (OA) and fed into a Schmitt trigger (ST). A digital circuit consisting of two gates (G1, G2) and one flip-flop generates at the output of G1 and G2 two rectangular signals which are out of phase with respect to each other by exactly 180° and which can be used to trigger a gated two-channel electronic system.[23-25]

In this manner the two signals originating from the two different liquids are separated. The duration of the activating rectangular signals (t_1, t_1', Fig. 8) are slightly shorter than their intermissions (t_2, t_2'). By adjusting the diameter of the hole, the differences $t_2 - t_1$ or $t_2' - t_1'$ can be adjusted in such a way that they correspond exactly to the time the focused laser beam needs to pass through the separation wall. This adjustable 'electronic bar' is important for blocking off the scattered light from the separation wall.

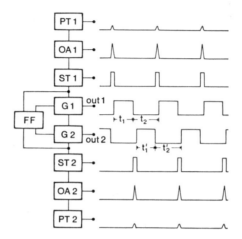

Fig. 8. Block diagram of an electronic switching circuit for general application in two-channel Raman spectroscopy. PT, phototransistor; OA, operational amplifier; ST, Schmitt trigger; G, gate; FF, flip-flop. Left part, switching circuit; right part, monitor outputs (Kiefer *et al.*, Ref. 7).

3.1.1.3   Two-Channel Electronic Systems

For difference Raman spectroscopy there are several possibilities to process electronically the two input signals. One is the use of a phase-sensitive detection system as mentioned above. The most inexpensive approach for a suitable difference Raman detection system is a gated 'DC'-electronic system,[23,26,27] the principle of which is shown in Fig. 9. This signal circuit consists of an amplifier (A), two linear gates (LG1, LG2), a differential amplifier (DA), an RC-integrator (RC), and a chart recorder (REC). A detailed description of these parts, which can be completely designed and built as one unit with operational amplifiers, has been given by Kiefer.[27] Besides the integrator and recorder all components have pulse rise-times in the microsecond range. This is fast enough, since the switching times of the gates are about four orders of magnitude longer. Gate 1 is opened exactly during the time when the part of the cell which contains the mixed system (e.g., solution) is exposed to the laser beam. At the same time LG2 is closed, blocking the signals which arise from Raman lines of the solvent. For the next half-rotation period the situation is vice versa: LG2 is opened, and

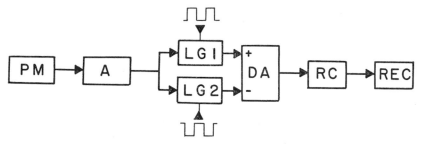

Fig. 9. Block diagram of a simple electronic system for difference Raman spectroscopy. PM, photomultiplier; A, amplifier; LG, linear gate; DA, differential amplifier; RC, RC-integrator; REC, chart recorder.

LG1 is closed. This is achieved by feeding the output signals of the switching circuit (Fig. 8) to the trigger inputs of the linear gates. By this arrangement the DC signal, formed by the RC-integrator, is independent of the rotation rate of the cell. Difference spectra are generated by the differential amplifier which has two inputs (+ and −) with independently variable gain stages, allowing the cancellation of Raman lines of the solvent in the spectrum of the solution.

In Fig. 10 a block diagram of an electronic system[24,25,28] for general application in two-channel optical spectroscopy is given. The central functional elements are a gated two-channel photon counter and a computing unit which processes the signals A and B, which have been separated from each other by the gated photon-counting system, to form a digital signal C which can be either A − B, B − A, A/B (for depolarization measurements), B/A, or (A − B)/(A + B) (for c.i.d. measurements). For exact measurements the dark current of the detector has to be eliminated from the signals A and B before processing. Furthermore fluctuations of the exciting source should be cancelled with a reference signal D. Note that the latter is not necessary for ratio measurements. The digital signals A, B, and C can either be stored in a multi-channel analyser or converted separately into an analogue signal with a digital-to-analogue converter (DAC, see Fig. 10). Thus, with the use of a chart recorder with three

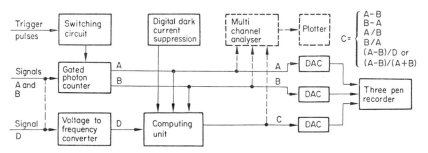

Fig. 10. Block diagram of an electronic system for general application in two-channel Raman spectroscopy. For explanation see text. (Partially adapted from Ref. 25).

pens, all three signals (A, B and C) can be recorded simultaneously on one chart, allowing the Raman spectroscopist to get complete information from only a single scan.

3.1.1.4 Difference Raman Spectra of Liquids

To illustrate the efficiency of a difference Raman system the spectrum of a $1:1$ (by volume) mixture of CCl_4 and $CHCl_3$ was examined by comparing it to the spectrum of the pure liquids.[23] The result is given in Fig. 11. The upper field shows the Raman spectrum of the mixture (A + B), the second field the Raman

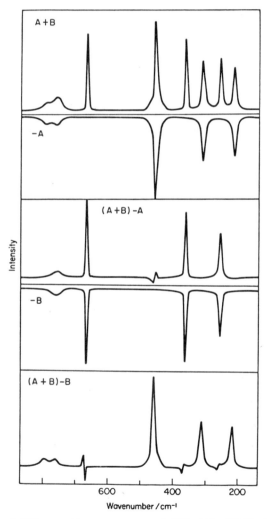

Fig. 11. Raman and difference Raman spectra of CCl_4 (A), $CHCl_3$ (B), and a mixture of CCl_4 and $CHCl_3$ (A : B = 50 : 50 volume per cent) (Kiefer, Ref. 23).

spectrum of pure CCl_4 $(-A)$, while in the middle field the difference Raman spectrum of the mixture compared to pure CCl_4 $((A+B)-A)$ is displayed. The CCl_4 Raman bands at 218 and 314 cm^{-1} are completely cancelled in the difference spectrum. This is not the case for the ν_1 band at 459 cm^{-1}, where a derivative-shaped feature can be seen which is caused by small frequency shifts due to inter-molecular interactions (see Section 3.1.2). The lower field of Fig. 11 is the difference spectrum of the mixture when $CHCl_3$ is the reference liquid.

It is often impossible to obtain a Raman spectrum of a compound in solution without having a large contribution due to the solvent. An example,[23] where the solvent spectrum partially obscures the solute spectrum, is given in Fig. 12.

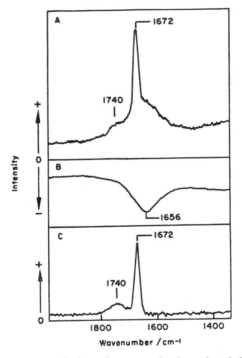

Fig. 12. Illustration of the cancellation of unwanted solvent bands by difference Raman spectroscopy in the region of the first overtone of the ν_1 vibration of the $[MnO_4]^-$ ion in water. A, Raman spectrum of the solution (10^{-3} M in H_2O); B, bending mode of H_2O (negative scale!): C, difference spectrum of A and B (Kiefer, Ref. 23).

Here, part of the resonance Raman spectrum of a $KMnO_4/H_2O$ solution[23,30] is shown in which the first overtone ($2\nu_1$) at 1672 cm^{-1} and the combination band $\nu_1+\nu_2$ at 1740 cm^{-1} of the $[MnO_4]^-$ ion overlap with the broad bending mode of H_2O at 1656 cm^{-1}. In Fig. 12B only the water band is displayed (negative scale!). The difference spectrum, leaving only the Raman spectrum of the $[MnO_4]^-$ ion, is shown in Fig. 12C. It should be mentioned that the Raman signal from the bending mode of pure H_2O is one order of magnitude larger than the corresponding signal from the solution. This is due to the high absorption of the incident laser beam by the dissolved material. The large discrepancy between the signals obtained from the highly absorbing solution and from the non-absorbing solvent can be equalized electronically by matching one of the gains in the two-channel electronic processing system.

3.1.2 Measurement of small frequency shifts

For specific studies, such as of intermolecular interactions, the precise know-ledge of small vibrational frequency shifts is required. Owing to instrumental errors, such small shifts can barely be detected in conventional Raman spectro-scopy, (at least for relatively broad bands). It has been shown[22,23,31] that difference Raman spectroscopy is a very sensitive method for the elucidation of very small wavenumber shifts, because any failure caused by an improperly working spectrometer drive is cancelled by the instantaneous comparison of the two frequencies of interest. Moreover, small changes in wavenumber or band shape give rise in a difference spectrum to the effect of 'derivative' line shapes, whose positive and negative peaks are separated by a distance d which is approximately one order of magnitude larger than the actual band shift $\Delta\tilde{v}$. This is illustrated in Fig. 13 where the $v_2(a_1)$ band of $CHCl_3$ at 668 cm^{-1} in a 1:1 mixture with CCl_4 (I_2, positive band) is compared with the Raman line of the neat liquid (I_1, negative).[23] For this case, $\Delta\tilde{v}$ is only about 1 cm^{-1} whereas $d = 6$ cm^{-1}. In the following it is shown how the actual wavenumber shift, $\Delta\tilde{v}$, can be determined from the difference Raman trace.[31]

To a first approximation the intensities of the two Raman bands (I_1, I_2), as a function of wavenumber, can be written as

Gaussian:
$$I_1 = I_0 \exp(-\tilde{v}^2/2a^2) \tag{1}$$
$$I_2 = I_0 \exp(-(\tilde{v}+\Delta\tilde{v})^2/2a^2) \tag{2}$$

or as

Lorentzian:
$$I_1 = I_0/(1+(2\tilde{v}/W)^2) \tag{3}$$
$$I_2 = I_0/(1+(2\{\tilde{v}+\Delta\tilde{v}\}/W)^2) \tag{4}$$

where a is the standard deviation, W is the band width at half height, and I_0 is the maximum value of either I_1 or I_2.

Referring to Fig. 13, the difference trace may be expressed as

$$I_{\text{diff}} = I_2 - I_1 \approx (\partial I_1/\partial\tilde{v}).\Delta\tilde{v}. \tag{5}$$

This form arises from a Taylor expansion of the expression for individual band intensities. It can be shown[31] that the maximum or minimum intensity, D, of the difference trace is reached at approximately the turning points of the Gaussian or Lorentzian curves. Therefore we obtain the following expressions for d.

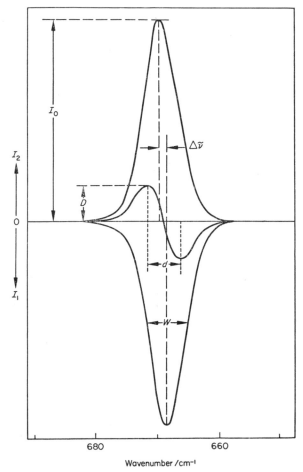

Fig. 13. Derivative features in a difference Raman spectrum caused by small frequency shifts. Parameters indicated are used for the analysis of Raman difference spectra:[31] $\Delta\tilde{\nu}$, actual wavenumber shift; d, distance between the maximum and minimum points in the difference Raman trace; W, bandwidth at half height; D, intensity minimum or maximum in the difference trace; I, intensity of the Raman band (Kiefer, Ref. 23).

Gaussian: $\qquad\qquad\qquad d = 2a = W/\sqrt{(2\ln 2)}$ $\qquad\qquad$ (6)

Lorentzian: $\qquad\qquad\qquad d = W/\sqrt{3}$ $\qquad\qquad\qquad\qquad$ (7)

If we calculate I_{diff} (eqn. 5) for $\tilde{\nu} = d/2$, we finally obtain the following equation

$$\Delta\tilde{\nu} = C(DW/I_0)$$ (8)

with $C = e^{0.5}/2\sqrt{(2\ln 2)} = 0.70$ for a *Gaussian* function, and $C = 4\sqrt{3}/9 = 0.77$ for a *Lorentzian* function.

Thus the constant C for these two types of band shape differs only by 10%.

By determining experimentally the ratio d/W, which is $1/\sqrt{(2 \ln 2)} = 0.85$ for a pure *Gaussian* and $1/\sqrt{3} = 0.58$ for a pure *Lorentzian* function, one can recognize which function best describes the actual Raman trace and consequently one can choose the appropriate constant C. However, in most cases the observed profile of a Raman band will be the convolution of a *Gaussian* and a *Lorentzian* function.[32] This convolution is known as the *Voigt* function, and it has long been used in the analysis of Doppler-broadened spectral lines in astrophysics and absorption spectroscopy.[32,33] According to this, values for C in formula (8) which are between 0.70 and 0.77 will therefore give the most accurate data for $\Delta\tilde{v}$. It should be mentioned that this analysis is limited to cases where the frequency shifts $\Delta\tilde{v}$ are small compared to the Raman-band width at half height W and where the intensities I_1 and I_2 have very similar functional forms.[31] Since the application of the difference technique in Raman spectroscopy is of interest predominantly for the determination of only small shifts, these conditions are fulfilled, as has been found experimentally by Gardiner *et al.*[31] for the difference Raman spectra of electrolyte solutions in formamide.

Complicated difference Raman spectra may arise when a Raman band, having fine structure or being overlapped by other lines, shifts in frequency. For such a situation the simple analysis described above cannot be applied. Then an alternative method is to determine the frequency shift in a graphical way.[23] As an example, the difference Raman spectrum is shown in Fig. 14 of the isotopic structure of the v_1 band of CCl_4 in a mixture with $CHCl_3$ and in the pure liquid. Here the wavenumbers of the three isotopically split components $C^{35}Cl_2{}^{37}Cl_2$, $C^{35}Cl_3{}^{37}Cl$ and $C^{35}Cl_4$ have shifted by only 0.3 cm^{-1} to lower values, the difference spectrum being displayed in field B, and, with higher gain, in field C of Fig. 14.

3.1.3 Absorption correction for Raman intensities

Difference Raman spectroscopy offers a method[23] for absorption corrections for Raman or resonance Raman (r.R.) intensity measurements, where the exciting line and the Raman spectrum are in a region of strong and varying absorption. If the laser beam is at a given distance d away from the cell wall, the observed intensity of a Raman band is given by $I = I_0 \, 10^{-\varepsilon cd}$, where I_0 is the Raman intensity at the region of the laser focus, ε is the extinction coefficient (molar decadic absorption coefficient), and c is the concentration. In most cases one Raman band of the solvent is taken as the internal standard band and the intensities of r.R. bands which are at different wavenumber shifts are then compared with that of the solvent band. If the concentration c, the extinction coefficient change $\Delta\varepsilon$ between standard band and r.R. band, and the distance d are high, large intensity errors could occur. However, when a difference Raman spectrum of a highly absorbing solution is recorded, where the compensation has been carried out for a solvent band at a certain wavenumber, solvent bands at other wavenumbers will not be cancelled if $\Delta\varepsilon$ is not zero. On the other hand, the remaining intensity (positive or negative, depending on the sign of $\Delta\varepsilon$) of the

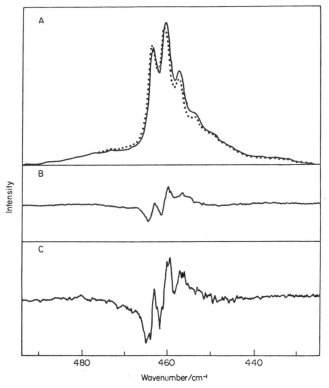

Fig. 14. Difference Raman spectrum of the ν_1 band of CCl_4; A, solid curve, CCl_4 in $CHCl_3$ (1:1 volume per cent); dotted curve, pure liquid CCl_4. B, difference band of solid and dotted curves in A. C, same as in B, but with higher gain (Kiefer, Ref. 23).

solvent bands can be used to calculate the intensity correction factor if the absorption spectrum is known. This method is illustrated in Fig. 15, where in the upper field a Raman spectrum of a highly absorbing solution (iodine in chloroform) is shown[35] together with the corresponding part of the visible absorption band. Excitation with the green argon-ion laser line yields, as shown, a strong r.R. spectrum with many overtones of the iodine stretching vibration at 211 cm^{-1}. In the lower field of Fig. 15 a difference spectrum is shown in which the intensity difference for the solvent band at 668 cm^{-1} is exactly balanced to zero by appropriately setting the input gains of the difference detection system. In the region of the C—H-stretching vibration of chloroform at 3019 cm^{-1} there is almost no absorption by the iodine molecule. Hence, we have a large value for $\Delta\varepsilon$ when this Raman band is compared to the one at 668 cm^{-1}. The remaining intensity of the band at 3019 cm^{-1} in the difference Raman spectrum therefore indicates the intensity error due to the absorption of the scattered Raman light at different spectral positions. In practice, the proposed method can be used either to determine the minimum distance at which no intensity correction is necessary or, if this is not possible (in the case of too high a concentration of sample), the remaining intensity of the solvent band in the difference Raman spectrum can be used to calculate an effective pathlength, d, which then, together with the knowledge of the absorption curve and the relative intensities of the bands in the pure solvent, makes it possible to make the required correction for absorption.

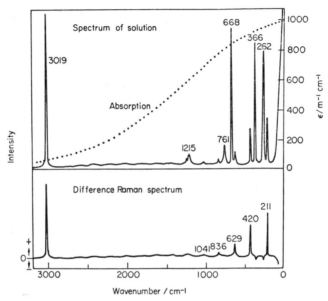

Fig. 15. Upper field: the resonance Raman spectrum of an iodine/chloroform solution.[35] Excitation 514.5 nm; concentration 10^{-2} M. Dotted line: part of the visible absorption spectrum of the iodine/chloroform solution. Lower field: difference Raman spectrum for a case where exact compensation has been carried out for the chloroform line at 668 cm^{-1} and where the Raman radiation excited in the solution has to penetrate through a pathlength d of absorbing liquid.

3.1.4 Solid state difference Raman techniques

Difference Raman spectra of solid samples[36] (e.g. doped versus undoped materials) can also be scanned directly, when the rotating solid sample cell described in Section 2.1 is split into two equal parts and a 180° back-scattering arrangement, which is shown in Fig. 16, is used. Here, the solid sample holder, the separate halves of whose annular groove are loaded with two different materials (4, Fig. 16), is mounted on the axis of a trigger wheel (see Section 3.1.1.1) for exact time correlation of the difference detection system. In this case the laser beam comes from above and passes through a small hole in a 90° mirror. The latter serves to reflect the back-scattered Raman light from the sample surface to the spectrometer.

Combination of the surface scanning (Section 2.3) with the difference Raman techniques allows direct comparison of two static solid samples, which are located in adjacent positions in the focal plane of the laser beam. The latter then alternately scans the surfaces of the two different solids, which can either be pressed pellets of crystalline powders or single crystals. Clearly the electronic detection system has again to be time-correlated in a similar way as discussed in Section 3.1.1.

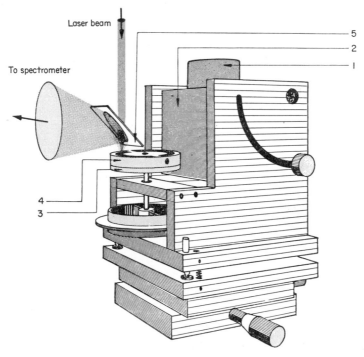

Fig. 16. Rotating Raman system for difference Raman spectroscopy of crystal powders. 1, motor; 2, motor block; 3, holder for solid sample cell; 4, divided solid sample cell; 5, 90° mirror (Kiefer *et al.*, Ref. 7).

Bodenheimer *et al.*[22] have suggested a Raman difference method which can be applied to study single crystals under various orientations in order to subtract (for example) *a* type modes from spectra containing $(a+e)$ modes. To do this they have split the laser beam and directed the light into two different single crystals, which are oriented differently with respect to the direction of polarization of the laser beam, and collected, alternately, the Raman scattered light with two different optical detection systems. A similar experiment can be performed with only one single crystal and without splitting the laser beam, by a method which produces, alternately, two perpendicular states of polarization for the exciting laser beam. This can be achieved by a rotating polarizer (see Section 3.3).

3.2   Addition Raman Spectroscopy

In Ref. 23 it was suggested that the split-cell rotating Raman technique used for difference spectroscopy may also be suitable for intensity measurements where *external* standard Raman lines are taken as reference. This addition Raman spectroscopy was realized by Covington and Thain[37] who illustrated the use of a divided rotating cell to superimpose spectra from sample and standard without the necessity of adding the standard to the sample solution. Intensity measurements with reference to external rather than to internal standards are to be preferred when the addition of the standard will disturb the system of interest. Even if a suitable standard with high Raman intensity can be found, it is necessary to add about 10% of the standard to achieve sufficient Raman signal therefrom. This amount of addition of a reference substance often may influence the Raman intensity of certain bands of the liquid under investigation. This is particularly the case in the study of solution equilibria by laser Raman spectroscopy.[37] Covington and Thain[37] have shown that the degree of dissociation of nitric acid as determined by quantitative measurements of relative Raman intensities with a rotating cylindrical double cell with separate compartments for sample and reference is in good agreement with values obtained by other methods. The choice of an internal standard would have yielded slightly higher values because of a salt effect on the position of equilibrium.

For addition Raman spectroscopy there is no need to use special electronic switching or detection systems as long as the time constant applied while scanning the spectrum is high enough compared to the rotation time of the split cell. An example[37] of an addition Raman spectrum is shown in Fig. 17 where one side of the cell contained carbon tetrachloride and the other toluene.

3.3   Automatic Scanning of the Depolarization Ratio

For the measurement of the depolarization ratio in Raman spectroscopy several different schemes have been used.[24,38–46] Most methods[38–44] require two successive spectral scans, between which (for example) either the polarization of the incident light or the orientation of the analyser is changed. The depolarization ratio is then calculated from either peak or integrated intensities. Because the integration is taken over the entire band, the resulting depolarization ratio is therefore an average over the total band, which in some cases can consist of overlapping and unresolved Raman bands. In these cases the depolarization ratio may be meaningless.

Recently several techniques[24,45,46] have been reported which allow an automatic recording of the depolarization ratio during a single scan of a Raman spectrum. By these techniques, which will be described below, the depolarization ratio can be measured as a function of the Raman shift.

In a commercially available system[46] the incident laser beam is chopped mechanically by a rotating sector mirror, then alternately transmitted to and reflected by two different illumination systems. While the reflected laser beam has the same polarization direction as the incident laser beam, the polarization of the transmitted beam is rotated by 90°. Then the two laser beams with polarization planes perpendicular to each other are recombined in respect to their direction and focused into the sample cell, so that the spectrometer receives alternately Raman scattering signals originating from $I_\perp$ and $I_\parallel$. An electronic system automatically records the ratio of the parallel and perpendicular components to give the depolarization ratio. The disadvantage of this optical system is that the laser beam is split up into two beams with different directions and

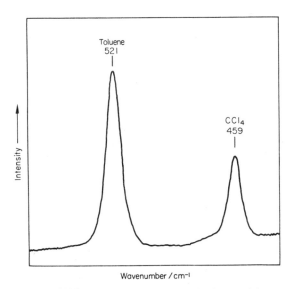

Fig. 17. Example of an addition Raman spectrum obtained with a rotating cylindrical double cell with separate compartments for sample and external standard, allowing Raman intensity measurements to be carried out without disturbing the system of interest (Covington and Thain, Ref. 37).

these have to be recombined, which is not easy to accomplish when high accuracy is required.

In a second method[45] an electro-optic modulator of the Pockels type is used to switch the polarization of the laser beam between two directions perpendicular to each other. Here the rotation of the polarization state is achieved without changing the direction of the beam. When an appropriate square-wave voltage is applied to the Pockels cells, the spectral signal oscillates between $I_\perp$ and $I_\parallel$. The signals are then read into a computer, programmed to separate the two spectra, compute the ratio and plot the depolarization ratio. However, this method is not a real-time technique. All information, i.e. the whole spectrum, has to be collected before it can be plotted. Also the need for a computer makes the method expensive.

A third technique[24] involves the use of a mechanical-optical system which has simpler optics than the methods mentioned above and an electronic system which is able to make a real-time scan of the depolarization ratio ($\rho = I_\perp/I_\parallel$) as well as a simultaneous scan of both polarization components, $I_\perp$ and $I_\parallel$. Although the technique is in principle similar to the method used by Proffitt and Porto, it differs from the latter in the way of switching the polarization states and of processing the data obtained. The former is achieved by a rotating polarizer where for the latter a gated two-channel photon-counting sytem is used.

3.3.1 Optical arrangement

The optical arrangement of the technique developed by Kiefer and Topp[24] is shown in Fig. 18. The y-axis polarized laser beam incident from above (z-axis)

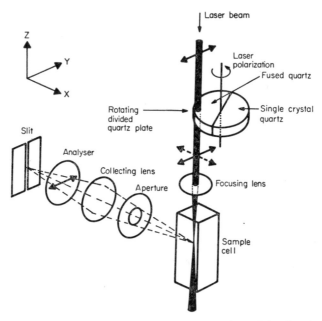

Fig. 18. An optical arrangement for the automatic scanning of the depolarization ratio in Raman spectroscopy. A rotating, divided, polarization rotator oscillates the polarization state of the laser beam in the sample between two mutually perpendicular directions (Kiefer and Topp, Ref. 24).

passes a rotating divided quartz plate on its periphery and is focused by a lens into the sample cell. The rotating quartz plate consists of two equal sized parts. One half is a single-crystal quartz plate with the optic axis perpendicular to its surface; owing to the optical activity of quartz the polarization direction of the laser beam is rotated by 90° if the thickness of the plate is chosen to accord with the wavelength of the laser beam. The second part consists of a fused quartz plate to balance the weight for smooth rotation. This part of the rotating device does not turn the polarization of the laser beam. The divided disc rotates with a frequency of about 50 Hz, so that the sample is illuminated alternately with laser light whose polarization state oscillates between y- and x-polarization. The scattered light is collected at 90° (x-axis) with a second lens. To reduce the error due to aperture effects, an iris diaphragm is placed between the cell and the collecting lens. An analyser (y-polarized) in front of the spectrometer slit eliminates the error due to different polarization sensitivities of the spectrometer.

Rotation of the divided quartz plate can be accomplished with the universal rotating system shown in Fig. 7. Instead of the rotating liquid cell the rotating polarization rotator is mounted on top of the axis of the trigger wheel. Switching circuits for exact time correlation, and suitable electronic detection systems for this two-channel ($I_\perp$, $I_\parallel$) technique, have been described in Sections 3.1.1.2 and 3.1.1.3.

3.3.2 Examples for simultaneous scanning of $I_\perp$, $I_\parallel$ and ρ

The performance of the simple optical system shown in Fig. 18 was tested[24] on a variety of examples. Two typical spectra are displayed in Figs 19 and 20.

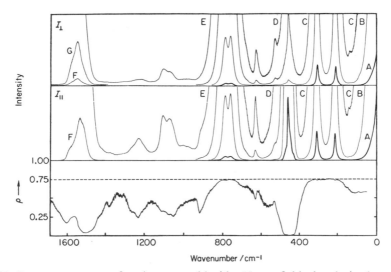

Fig. 19. Raman spectrum of carbon tetrachloride. Upper field, depolarized spectrum ($I_\perp$); central field, polarized spectrum ($I_\parallel$); lower field, depolarization ratio ρ as a function of the Raman shift. Excitation 514.5 nm, power 1.4 W; slits 3 cm^{-1} (except for E slits 10 cm^{-1}). A, gain 1; B, gain 16; C, gain 256; D, gain 2048; E, gain 512; F, gain 64; G, gain 512 (Kiefer and Topp, Ref. 24).

Figure 19 shows the Raman spectra (upper field $I_\perp$, middle field $I_\parallel$) and the depolarization ratio ρ (lower field) of carbon tetrachloride as a function of the Raman shift. To make the overtone and combination bands clear, the region

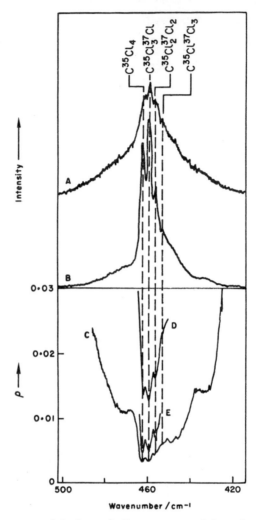

Fig. 20. Raman spectrum of the isotopic fine structure of the ν_1 band of carbon tetra-chloride. Slit width 1 cm⁻¹, exciting wavelength 514.5 nm, power 1 W. A, $I_\perp$, gain 220; B, $I_\parallel$, gain 1; C, ρ (scale on ordinate corresponds to C); D, gain of $I_\perp$ increased by a factor of 4, scale for ρ has therefore to be divided by 4; E, gain for $I_\perp$ increased by factor 2, scale for ρ has therefore to be divided by 2; collection angle was decreased from 30° down to 4° (Kiefer and Topp, Ref. 24).

above about 800 cm⁻¹ was recorded also with higher gain. The scan of the depolarization ratio is nearly noise free in the case of high signal in the denominator ($I_\parallel$). When no Raman signal is present, the noise increases, as can be seen, for example, in the CCl₄ spectrum around 1300 cm⁻¹. Therefore, the positions of Raman lines can also be detected in the ρ scan where the noise is strikingly lower than in other parts of the spectrum.

In this spectrum the depolarization ratio for the doubly degenerate mode v_2 at 218 cm^{-1} was adjusted to be 0.75, and the whole spectrum was then scanned. One can see that ρ stays exactly at 0.75 between v_2 and the triply degenerate mode v_4 at 314 cm^{-1}. The depolarization ratio then decreases to near zero around 460 cm^{-1} indicating the presence of a highly polarized Raman band. This region is shown again with higher resolution in Fig. 20. In the trace of the depolarization ratio in Fig. 19, overtones or combination bands can also be located. Examples for this can be seen at 530 cm^{-1} $(v_2 + v_4)$ and 629 cm^{-1} $(2v_4)$. The overtone of the totally symmetric stretching vibration v_1 at 918 cm^{-1} can barely be detected in the normal Raman scan, because this weak line is overlapped by the relatively strong wing of the depolarized Fermi resonance doublet. In the scan of the depolarization ratio, however, because $2v_1$ is highly polarized, this line shows up clearly with a negative peak at 918 cm^{-1}. This means that in some cases, namely when a weak polarized band is overlapped by a strong depolarized Raman one, the ρ scan may have higher resolution than the normal Raman spectrum.

The isotopic fine structure of the v_1 band of CCl_4, often taken as a test for resolution of Raman spectrometers, has also been investigated with this technique.[24] The result is shown in Fig. 20. Trace A represents the depolarized spectrum $(I_\perp)$ with a gain higher by a factor of 220 than that of trace B, which represents the polarized spectrum $(I_\parallel)$. Trace C is the scan of the ratio of $I_\perp$ and $I_\parallel$. To confirm that the small peaks in the ρ scan (C) are not due to noise the region around the maxima of the isotopic components was rescanned with four-fold higher gain (trace D). Definitely four negative peaks (trace D) mark the position of the v_1 bands which correspond to the isotopic species $C^{35}Cl_4$, $C^{35}Cl_3{}^{37}Cl$, $C^{35}Cl_2{}^{37}Cl_2$, and $C^{35}Cl^{37}Cl_3$. Traces C and D were obtained with an angle of collection of 30°. To decrease the polarization depth, the collection angle was reduced to 4° (trace E). Very low values for ρ for these four isotopic bands (0.002–0.003) were found[24] which indicate a high degree of polarization for this technique. From the point of view of symmetry, the v_1 band which corresponds to the species $C^{35}Cl_4$ should have the lowest depolarization ratio, which was determined[24] to be 0.0023. However, the same value was found for the species $C^{35}Cl_3{}^{37}Cl$. Apparently, because the $v_1(C^{35}Cl_4)$ band is closer to a more depolarized difference band $(v_1 + v_4) - v_4$ at 468 cm^{-1}, some portion of this depolarized wing is included in the ρ measurement of the $v_1(C^{35}Cl_4)$ band and this increases slightly its ρ-value. A broad peak in the ρ trace at 436 cm^{-1} indicates the presence of another more depolarized Raman band which is an overtone of v_2 with symmetry $a_1 + e$.

The advantages of the automatic (real-time) scanning of the depolarization ratio as well as the simultaneous recording of the polarized and depolarized Raman spectrum accrue because the three spectra are taken simultaneously; source fluctuations are thus automatically cancelled and no error due to laser power variations or due to de-adjustment of the optical set-up during the scan time can affect the value of ρ. The measurement of depolarization ratios of isolated Raman bands is therefore more accurate by this method than by the technique of two successive scans of the polarized and depolarized Raman spectrum, between which the source power or optical alignment can vary slightly. As shown above in special cases, namely when a weak polarized band is overlapped by a strong depolarized one, the scan of the depolarization ratio may have higher resolution than the normal Raman spectrum. Furthermore, the method is time saving because the depolarization ratio is taken while recording and does not have to be calculated after the spectra are completed. The method therefore offers a convenient way of getting all the necessary information with just one spectral scan.

The direct scanning of the depolarization ratio may not be helpful for the case in which the spectral band-pass is still larger than the actual width of the Raman band. In this case the actual depolarization ratio is smaller than the one determined experimentally, because the amount of collected depolarized light (due to too large a slit width) is too high. Thus the measured depolarization ratio is dependent on the slit width. Therefore care to has be taken to use as small a slit width as possible. On the other hand, when it happens that the slits cannot be closed very much, as in the case of too low a Raman signal, one can use the simultaneously recorded parallel and perpendicular components for the determination of the depolarization ratio in the usual way. The advantage of being free of errors due to de-adjustment of the optical system still holds. A similar situation occurs for complex (overlapping or unresolved) Raman bands whose components have not the same symmetry. As an alternative one can take again the simultaneously recorded $I_\perp$ and $I_\parallel$ spectra, deconvolute the bands and calculate the depolarization ratio for the resulting bands. However, it is well known that deconvolution involves large errors. The problem may be solved best if a method could be found to deconvolute directly the scan of the depolarization ratio across the complex band, similar to the treatment for frequency shifts in difference Raman spectra (see Section 3.1.2).

By combining the method of the rotating divided quartz plate with the difference Raman technique discussed in Section 3.1, it is possible to subtract the anisotropic scattered light ($I_\perp \sim 3\gamma'^2$) from the $I_\parallel$ ($\sim 45\bar{\alpha}'^2 + 4\gamma'^2$) spectrum. In this way one is able to scan directly the isotropic scattered Raman light.[47] A nice example is given in Fig. 21 where part of the vibrational-rotational spectrum (Fermi-resonance) of gaseous CO_2 is displayed.[47] The three spectra shown were again simultaneously recorded with the electronic system described in Section 3.1.1.3. The upper field of Fig. 21 shows the anisotropic part, the middle field the $I_\parallel$ spectrum (anisotropic + isotropic) and the lower field the pure isotropic part which is obtained from the difference $I_\parallel - 4/3\, I_\perp$ which is proportional to $45\bar{\alpha}'^2$. The strong lines displayed in the lower field represent the Q-branches of the $2\nu_2{}^{12}CO_2$ and the $\nu_1{}^{13}CO_2$ vibrations. The lines at 1366.0, 1376.3 and 1385.3 cm^{-1} are probably due to hot bands and/or fundamental bands of isotopic species of CO_2. A great advantage of this method is demonstrated with the line at 1376.3 cm^{-1} which nearly exactly coincides with one of the

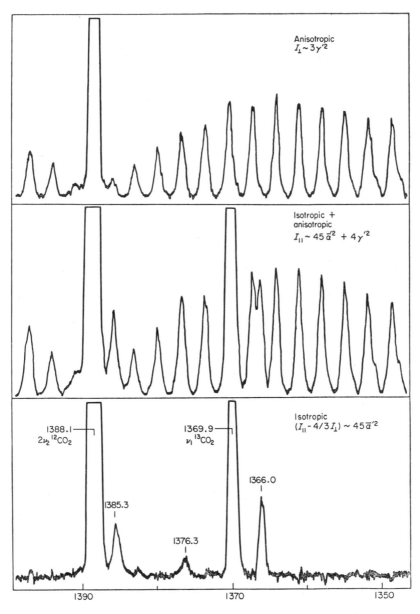

Fig. 21. Part of the vibrational-rotational Raman spectrum of CO_2. Gas pressure 1 atm. Excitation 514.5 nm, 1 W. Slit width 1 cm^{-1}. All three spectra were recorded simultaneously. Upper field: $I_\perp$; middle field: $I_\parallel$; lower field: the direct recorded isotropic ($\bar{\alpha}'^2$) part of the spectrum (Klöckner *et al.*, Ref. 47).

vibrational-rotational lines. Whereas it is difficult to recognize this line in the $I_\perp$ or $I_\parallel$ spectrum because of the overlap with the vibrational-rotational line, it shows up clearly in the difference spectrum as a Q-branch.

Taken altogether, the method of simultaneously scanning of $I_\perp$, $I_\parallel$ and ρ, or the pure isotropic part of the spectrum, can be regarded as a useful supplementary technique to the standard ones in Raman spectroscopy.

3.4   Techniques for Circularly Polarized Raman Spectroscopy

3.4.1   C.I.D. techniques

Excitation of Raman spectra with circularly polarized light has become an important method for the study of vibrational optical activity.[48] This effect, which originates in the interference between electromagnetic waves scattered through the electronic polarizability and the electronic optical activity of the molecule[49] can be studied through the difference between the intensity of the Raman scattering from right and left circularly polarized incident light. A suitable experimental quantity may be expressed by the normalized circular intensity differential (c.i.d.) as[50]

$$\Delta_\alpha = (A - B)/(A + B) \tag{9}$$

where $A = I_\alpha^R$ and $B = I_\alpha^L$ are the scattered intensities for right and left circularly polarized incident light and α denotes the polarization of the observed Raman light. An appropriate experimental technique has been described by Barron and Buckingham.[48] It involves the use of a Pockels cell, modulated so as to produce right or left circularly polarized light, and two synchronized photon counters from which the sum $(A + B)$ and the difference $(A - B)$ is taken per spectral point. An alternative method is to use a quarter-wave plate that can be rotated by $\pm 45°$ with respect to the laser polarization to give right or left circularly polarized light incident on the sample.

With the use of an additional quarter-wave plate (or Pockels cell with constant quarter-wave voltage) in connection with the method described in Section 3.3, it is possible actually to scan the c.i.d.s as a function of Raman shift.[51] The optical arrangement for this technique is shown in Fig. 22. A rotating divided quartz plate oscillates the polarization of the laser beam between two perpendicular directions (x and y). The quarter-wave plate, whose optical axis is parallel to the bisector of the x- and y-axes, then produces alternately right and left circularly polarized light which is focused into the sample. The scattered light, observed at 90° (alternately signal A or B) can be processed with a gated, two-channel, photon-counting system[25] (see Fig. 10), which is modified for direct scanning of the quantity $(A - B)/(A + B)$. By this, c.i.d.s can be scanned automatically as a function of Raman shift and also simultaneously with the signals A and B by means of a chart recorder with three pens.

3.4.2 Reversal coefficient techniques

Besides the measurement of c.i.d.s there has been recently also a need for the experimental realization of complete polarization studies, which means excitation with linearly as well as with circularly polarized light, in order to get independently all three invariants of the Raman scattering tensor, i.e. the isotropy $\bar{\alpha}'$, the symmetric anisotropy γ_s', and the anti-symmetric anisotropy γ_{as}'. This fact was recognized as early as 1934 by Placzek[52] and re-emphasized

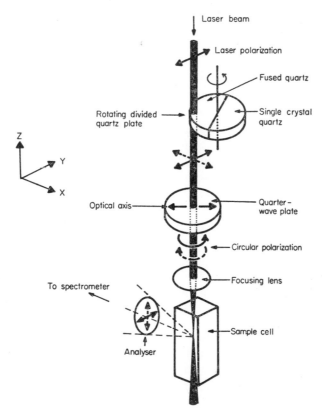

Fig. 22. Optical arrangement for automatic scanning of c.i.d.s (Nitsch and Kiefer, Ref. 51).

by McClain[53] in 1971. While Placzek uses for these invariants the isotropic component ($g^\circ = 3\bar{\alpha}'^2$), the quadrupole component ($g^s = (2/3)\gamma_s'^2$), and the magnetic dipole component ($g^a = (2/3)\gamma_{as}'^2$), McClain has proposed a different set of invariants ($\delta_F, \delta_G, \delta_H$) which are linearly related to the traditional[54] set by the relations $\bar{\alpha}'^2 = (1/9)\,\delta_F$, $\gamma_s'^2 = (3/4)(\delta_G + \delta_H) - (1/2)\delta_F$ and $\gamma_{as}'^2 = (3/4)(\delta_G - \delta_H)$.

Since for a symmetric Raman tensor, γ_{as}' is equal to zero, the measurement of $I_\perp \propto 3\gamma_s'^2$ and $I_\parallel \propto (45\bar{\alpha}'^2 + 4\gamma_s'^2)$ is usually sufficient to determine the two invariants $\bar{\alpha}'^2$ and $\gamma_s'^2$. However, for the r.R. effect[55] or for the electronic Raman effect[56] the restriction to a symmetric tensor is no longer valid and the depolarization ratio, $\rho = I_\perp/I_\parallel$ for polarized incident radiation then becomes[52,57]

$$\rho = (3\gamma_s'^2 + 5\gamma_{as}'^2)/(45\bar{\alpha}'^2 + 4\gamma_s'^2) \tag{10}$$

Additional information concerning the tensor invariants is therefore required. This can be achieved by the measurement of the reversal coefficient P, which is defined[52,53] as

$$P = I_{co}/I_{contra} = (6\gamma_s'^2)/(45\bar{\alpha}'^2 + \gamma_s'^2 + 5\gamma_{as}'^2) . \tag{11}$$

Complete polarization studies, i.e. the measurement of $I_\perp$, $I_\parallel$, I_{co} and I_{contra}, have already been performed under resonance conditions for ferrocytochrome c by two groups,[58,59] both using a 180° back-scattering configuration. A quarter-wave plate[58] or a Fresnel rhomb[59] were used, either of which could be rotated with respect to the direction of polarization of the incident laser beam, to give either plane or circularly polarized light. Two different states of polarization of the incident beam permitted the determination of four polarization spectra, which were scanned separately in four successive runs. Again, it is possible to scan[60] automatically the reversal coefficient as a function of Raman shift by combining the methods of Pezolét et al.[58] or Nestor et al.[59] with the technique developed for direct scanning of the depolarization ratio.[24] The reversal coefficient can then be obtained independently of experimental errors such as spectrometer drift, laser power variation, optical de-adjustment, etc. and simultaneously with the intensities I_{co} and I_{contra}. These potential sources of error can take effect when two successive runs are performed, but their influences are automatically cancelled when the ratio of I_{co}/I_{contra} at a specific Raman shift is taken.

For both methods, whose optical arrangements are displayed in Figs 23 and 24, the general idea is to produce circularly polarized light with a quarter-wave plate or a Fresnel rhomb and to use the same device to retransform the circularly polarized, backwards scattered Raman light into linearly polarized light which is then decomposed into its linearly polarized components with an analyser. The automatic scanning of the reversal coefficient is then achieved by collecting alternately the two linearly polarized signals and by processing them by the method, and with the electronic system, described in Section 3.3.

Figure 23 shows the set-up which uses a quarter-wave plate. Suppose the polarization direction of the incident laser beam is switched by the rotating quartz plate (x-axis) so as to produce right circularly polarized light after the laser beam has passed through the quarter-wave plate. The back-scattered Raman light with co-rotating polarization has linear z-polarization after having been reflected by a 90° mirror and collected with a lens. If the analyser is set to transmit z-polarized light, the co-rotated intensity I_{co} is observed with the detection system. The contra-polarized back-scattered Raman light, produced by right circularly polarized laser light incident on the sample, is blocked by the analyser because of its linear y-polarization. In the second half-period of rotation of the quartz plate, left circularly polarized laser light is incident on the sample and excites backward-scattered, left (I_{co}) and right (I_{contra}) circularly polarized Raman light, the polarization states of which are y and z, respectively, after

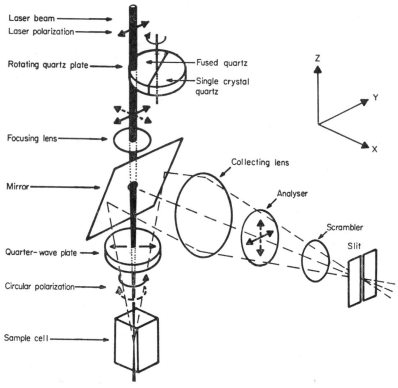

Fig. 23. Optical arrangement for automatic scanning of the reversal coefficient. (Use of a quarter-wave plate) (Kiefer and Nitsch, Ref. 60).

having been reflected by the mirror. Therefore, if the analyser is kept in the same position as above (transmission for z-polarized light), only the contra-rotated component of the Raman light (I_{contra}) is detected. By fast rotation of the divided quartz plate, signals are collected by the spectrometer and detection system which correspond alternately to I_{co} and I_{contra}.

Although the set-up which uses a Fresnel rhomb (Fig. 24) instead of a quarter-wave plate (Fig. 23) to produce circularly polarized laser light is more complicated, it has the advantage of being independent of the wavelength of the laser light. The method for automatically scanning the reversal coefficient using this device is very similar to the one discussed above for the quarter-wave plate (compare Fig. 24 with Fig. 23). Since in Fig. 24 the Fresnel rhomb is rotated by

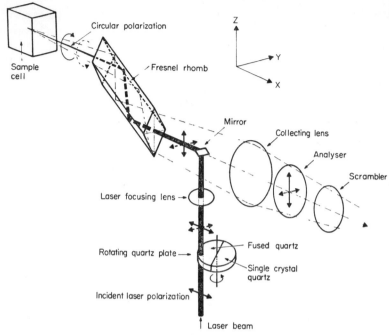

Fig. 24. Optical arrangement for automatic scanning of the reversal coefficient irrespective of the exciting wavelength. (Use of a Fresnel rhomb) (Kiefer and Nitsch, Ref. 60).

45° with respect to the direction of polarization of the incident laser beam, the co-rotated intensity I_{co} (the contra-rotated intensity, I_{contra}) is observed for z-polarized (y-polarized) laser light incident on the Fresnel rhomb when the analyser is transmitting in the z-direction.

4   DERIVATIVE RAMAN SPECTROSCOPY

Although the derivative spectral method has been applied for about 20 years to polarography,[61] mass spectroscopy,[62] infrared spectroscopy,[63] ultraviolet spectroscopy[64] and to general modulation spectroscopy,[65] it was only recently that this technique was used as a tool for the measurement of Raman spectra.[66] The advantage of derivative spectra over conventional spectra is the fact that multiplet structure caused by overlapping bands is more easily recognized and that peak positions can be determined more accurately. For instance, structure which appears only as a change of slope in the conventional spectra, appears as a step in the first derivative and as a peak in the second derivative.[65] Nice examples have been found by Collier and Singleton[63] of first- and second-derivative infrared spectra.

Wavelength derivative spectra can be obtained in principle from the normal wavelength spectrum by use of an on-line computer which performs a differentiation with respect to time while the wavelength is swept linearly in time. However, this method does not have the noise-rejection features which can be achieved by modulation techniques[65] based, for instance, on phase-sensitive detection; furthermore, this method can be regarded, in principle, as equivalent to taking the derivative spectrum after the non-derivative spectrum has been taken. This kind of derivative spectrum from a Raman set-up has been discussed by Downey and Janz.[1]

The measurement of the derivative with respect to wavelength of the scattered light is of particular benefit for the study of second-order Raman scattering in solids.[67] While in first-order Raman scattering in solids only phonons with wavevector $k \approx 0$ are excited, in second-order scattering phonons throughout the whole Brillouin zone are accessible (the selection rule is now $k_1 + k_2 \approx 0$). Phase-space arguments and the relative isotropy of the dispersion curves usually make energies corresponding to phonons near the edge of the Brillouin zone dominate the scattering process. Overtone (two phonons of the same branch) and combination (two phonons of different branches) processes are possible and give rise to many transitions. Thus the structure in a second-order Raman spectrum is very detailed. Many overlapping bands can occur which can more easily be located in a derivative than in a direct Raman spectrum.

Furthermore, Yacoby et al.[66] have shown that this type of modulation spectroscopy gives information on the Van Hove[68] critical points of the combined two-phonon energy function, since peaks in the spectrum of the derivative of the intensity of the Raman scattered light $(=dI_R/d\lambda)$ as a function of the difference between the photon energy E of the incident and the scattered light appear at values of E for which the combined energy function of pairs of phonons has an ordinary critical point.[66] The shapes of the derivatives of the density-of-states function G with respect to frequency ν, $dG/d\nu$, which have been evaluated by Van Hove[68] and Phillips[69] in the neighbourhood of ordinary critical points, are different for different types of critical points (minimum, saddle point, maximum). In these regions the shape of $dI_R/d\nu$ (which is correlated to $dI_R/d\lambda$ by the relation $dI_R/d\nu = -(\lambda^2/c)(dI_R/d\lambda)$ as a function of E is similar to that of $dG/d\nu$.[66] Therefore, the derivative spectrum gives the additional information mentioned above.

Several schemes for obtaining wavelength derivative spectra by a modulation method have been reported.[65] The most ingenious method probably is the one suggested by Drews[70] and applied by Yacoby et al.[66] to Raman spectroscopy. It utilizes a vibrating, transparent, plane-parallel plate which is placed inside the monochromator close to either the entrance or the exit slit. The wavelength modulation is achieved by the modulation in the lateral shift produced by the angular vibration of the plate around an axis parallel to the slit. The shift in wavelength, as a function of the angle of incidence, θ, is given by[66] the expression

$$\Delta\lambda = d\,r\{\tan^{-1}\theta - (n^2/\sin^2\theta - 1)^{-1/2}\} \tag{12}$$

where d is the thickness of the plate, n is the refractive index and r is the resolution of the monochromator.

The direct measurement of $dI_R/d\lambda$ can be achieved by means of a phase-sensitive detection system which is synchronized to the vibration frequency ω of the plate. The rotation of the plate produces, besides the wavelength modulation, a modulation in the intensity of the light because of the variation of the reflectivity of the plate surface with θ. However, this varies with frequency 2ω and is therefore out of phase with the wavelength modulation.

An example of a derivative Raman spectrum is given in Fig. 25, where the first derivative with respect to wavelength of the first- (140, 170 and 231 cm^{-1})

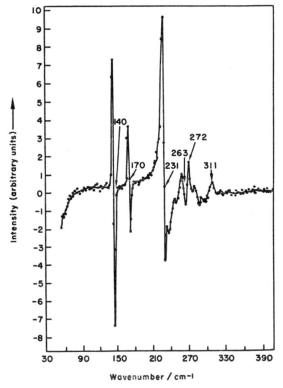

Fig. 25. Derivative first- and second-order Raman spectrum of SrTiO$_3$ at 10 K (Yacoby *et al.*, Ref. 66).

and second-order (263, 272 and 311 cm^{-1}) Raman displacements of SrTiO$_3$ are displayed.[66] Labelled peaks for second-order structure could be interpreted as combinations of longitudinal and transverse optical or acoustical phonons at various points of the Brillouin zone.[66] With this spectrum the usefulness of derivative measurements, particularly of second-order Raman spectra, was

demonstrated and it was also shown that considerable new information could be
obtained using this method.[66]

5   OPTICAL-FIBRE RAMAN SPECTROSCOPY

Solid-core or hollow, liquid-filled fibres have received considerable attention in
communication systems due to their favourable transmission properties.
Typical losses are of the order of 20 dB/km[71] if the medium does not have
absorption at the laser wavelength. The advantages of high collection efficiency
and intensification of spontaneous Raman scattering provided by long, liquid-
core optical fibres of low loss was first recognized and exploited by Walrafen and
Stone.[72-74] Raman gain measurements in glass optical waveguides have been
also performed by Stolen and Ippen.[75]

   This fibre-optics technique for Raman spectroscopy uses a capillary optical
fibre, having a refractive index n_c, filled with a liquid of refractive index n_l,

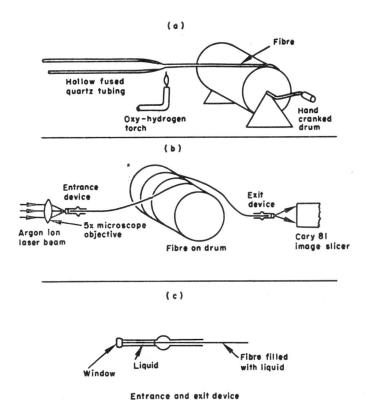

Fig. 26. Schematic diagram of the Raman liquid-core, optical-fibre device developed
by Walrafen and Stone, Ref. 72. (a), simplified fibre-pulling arrangement; (b), optical
arrangement for Raman excitation; (c), details of entrance and exit device.

which is larger than n_c in order that, due to total internal reflection of laser as well as Raman light, all light is trapped in the core and therefore travels inside the capillary. If the capillary is long enough ($\approx 10–25$ m) and the losses are low, very high spontaneous Raman intensities are obtained. The optimum length L of the liquid optical-core fibre depends on the loss coefficient α for light travelling in the fibre by $L = 1/\alpha$.[72] Spectral intensifications by factors of 10^3 compared to conventional techniques were demonstrated with Raman spectra of liquid benzene and tetrachloroethylene.[72] This very high gain factor could be verified for benzene with a fibre-optical Raman device developed by Schmid.[76]

In Fig. 26 the technique of pulling hollow, fused-quartz fibres as well as that of exciting Raman spectra with the use of optical-core fibres are shown.[72] In the lower part of Fig. 26 the entrance and exit device are shown schematically. More details may be found in Walrafen and Stone.[72]

A photograph (Plate 2) of the liquid-core, optical-fibre set-up built by Schmid[76] shows the liquid fibre (20 m long) on the drum (12 cm in diameter),

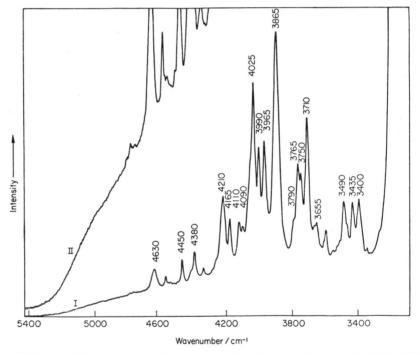

Fig. 27. Forward Raman scattering spectrum from benzene in an optical fibre (20 m long, 60 μm inner diameter). The overtone and combination band region from 3400 to 5400 cm^{-1} is shown. Excitation 200 mW at 514.5 nm; scan rate 200 cm^{-1}/min; slit width 6 cm^{-1}; time constant 0.25 s (the lowest available time constant is determined by the rise time of the recorder). Photon counting, full range 10 count/s for spectrum I, 1.25×10 count/s for spectrum II. A Schott filter RG5 was employed. Spectra were obtained with the device developed by Schmid, Ref. 76.

the entrance and exit device, and the emerging laser (+ Raman) light. With this system, parts of the Raman spectrum of liquid benzene were obtained as demonstrated in Figs 27 and 28. In Fig. 27 the overtone and combination band

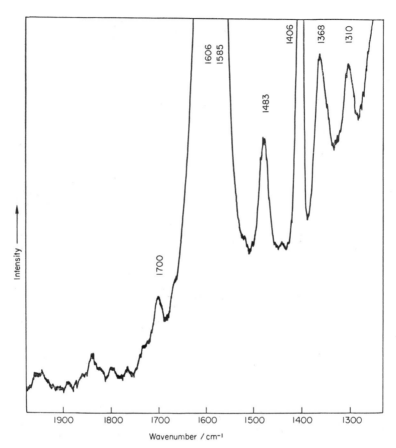

Fig. 28. Part of the anti-Stokes region (1300–1900 cm⁻¹) of the forward Raman scattering from benzene in an optical fibre. Experimental conditions were the same as those given for Fig. 27 except for scan rate 50 cm⁻¹/min, time constant 1 s; full range 10⁴ count/s. The anti-Stokes second-order band at 1700 cm⁻¹ is approximately 2000 times lower in intensity than the corresponding Stokes Raman band.

region above 3400 cm⁻¹ (compare also the spectrum shown in Ref. 74) is displayed; this spectrum was recorded with scanning data (see figure caption) normally used for first-order bands. The displayed spectral range (2000 cm⁻¹) could be scanned within 10 min by use of a time constant of 0.25 s (rise time of the recorder). This demonstrates the very high gain obtained with the liquid-core, optical-fibre technique, because these bands have not been observed previously by use of conventional sample techniques. In order to get an estimate of the real gain factor of the fibre technique compared to the conventional sample technique, the anti-Stokes region between 1300 and 1900 cm^{-1} of benzene was measured. The signal-to-noise ratio of this spectrum (Fig. 28) compares well with the hitherto best published[77] spectrum obtained by conventional sample techniques, excited on the Stokes side. However, the factor $I_{Stokes}/I_{anti-Stokes}$ for the 1700 cm^{-1} line is of the order of 2000.

Walrafen[74] has also demonstrated that this technique can be extended in order to build a slitless laser-Raman spectrometer because the fibre end (diameter 50–100 μm) can be employed directly as an entrance aperture for the spectrometer. Although the optical-fibre method has some disadvantages (no measurements of the depolarization ratio are possible, restrictions to low-loss liquids and to those with their refractive index $n > 1.46$ when quartz fibres are used), it represents a technique which has brought up the sensitivity of detecting weak Raman signals by three orders of magnitude, thus enabling the Raman spectroscopist to record also second- or third-order bands with the same kind of signal as was previously possible only for first-order bands. Thus complete assignments of vibrational spectra are facilitated.[77]

6   CONCLUDING REMARKS

Several simple Raman spectroscopic techniques have been reviewed which range from sample handling ones to ones which permit the automatic and simultaneous recording of quantities important for Raman spectroscopy. Each method described relates to progress in a special technical domain. It is clear that the advantages of different methods can be exploited by using them together in one operation. In particular, the author would like to refer again to the methods reviewed by Bridoux and Delhaye[2] and by Downey and Janz[1] in this book series. As an example, the combined use[78] of the fibre optic technique and the advanced technology of image intensifiers and multi-channel detection systems, may bring up the sensitivity of Raman spectroscopy to very high levels. The technological progress achieved in the last few years seems to make laser Raman spectroscopy now one of the dominant tools in the field of molecular spectroscopy.

ACKNOWLEDGMENTS

The author is grateful to Prof. H. W. Schrötter for critical reading of the manuscript and helpful remarks. He also wishes to thank Mr. W. J. Schmid for supplying information on his optical-fibre device before publication. Financial support from the Bundesministerium für Forschung und Technologie and from the Deutsche Forschungsgemeinschaft is gratefully acknowledged.

REFERENCES

(1) J. R. Downey and G. J. Janz, in *Advances in Infrared and Raman Spectroscopy*, Vol. 1, (R. J. H. Clark and R. E. Hester, eds), Heyden, London, 1975, p. 1.
(2) M. Bridoux and M. Delhaye, in *Advances in Infrared and Raman Spectroscopy*, Vol. 2, (R. J. H. Clark and R. E. Hester, eds), Heyden, London, 1976, p. 140.
(3) W. Kiefer and H. J. Bernstein, *Appl. Spectrosc.* **25**, 501 (1971).
(4) W. Kiefer and H. J. Bernstein, *Appl. Spectrosc.* **25**, 609 (1971).
(5) W. Kiefer, *Appl. Spectrosc.* **28**, 115 (1974).
(6) R. J. H. Clark, in *Advances in Infrared and Raman Spectroscopy*, Vol. 1, (R. J. H. Clark and R. E. Hester, eds), Heyden, London, 1975, p. 143.
(7) W. Kiefer, W. J. Schmid and J. A. Topp, *Appl. Spectrosc.* **29**, 434 (1975).
(8) H. J. Sloane and R. B. Cook, *Appl. Spectrosc.* **26**, 589 (1972).
(9) G. J. Long, L. J. Basile and J. R. Ferraro, *Appl. Spectrosc.* **28**, 73 (1974).
(10) R. J. H. Clark, O. H. Ellestad and P. D. Mitchell, *Appl. Spectrosc.* **28**, 575 (1974).
(11) O. S. Mortensen, *J. Mol. Spectrosc.* **39**, 48 (1971).
(12) W. H. Woodruff and T. G. Spiro, *Appl. Spectrosc.* **28**, 74 (1974).
(13) P. R. Carey and H. Schneider, *Biochem. Biophys. Res. Commun.* **57**, 831 (1974).
(14) W. H. Woodruff and T. G. Spiro, *Appl. Spectrosc.* **28**, 576 (1974).
(15) P. R. Carey and H. Schneider, *J. Mol. Biol.* **102**, 679 (1976).
(16) R. J. Gillespie, J. Sawa and B. Cutforth, personal communication.
(17) J. B. R. Dunn, D. F. Shriver and I. M. Klotz, *Proc. Nat. Acad. Sci. U.S.A.* **70**, 2582 (1973).
(18) J. A. Koningstein and B. F. Gächter, *J. Opt. Soc. Am.* **63**, 892 (1973).
(19) N. Zimmerer and W. Kiefer, *Appl. Spectrosc.* **28**, 279 (1974).
(20) P. J. Hendra, *Spectrochim. Acta* **24A**, 125 (1968).
(21) V. A. Zubov, G. G. Petrash and M. M. Sushchinskii, *Opt. Spectrosc. U.S.S.R.* **6**, 541 (1959).
(22) J. S. Bodenheimer, B. J. Berenblut and G. R. Wilkinson, *Chem. Phys. Lett.* **14**, 523 (1972).
(23) W. Kiefer, *Appl. Spectrosc.* **27**, 253 (1973).
(24) W. Kiefer and J. A. Topp, *Appl. Spectrosc.* **28**, 26 (1974).
(25) Photonic, model PC 07A, as an example of a commercially available, two-channel, photon-counting system.
(26) W. Kiefer and H. W. Schrötter, *Z. Angew. Phys.* **25**, 236 (1968).
(27) W. Kiefer, *Chem. Instrum.* **3**, 21 (1971).
(28) W. Kiefer, W. J. Schmid and J. A. Topp, *GIT Fachz. Lab.* **17**, 1018 (1973).
(29) W. Kiefer and H. J. Bernstein, *Chem. Phys. Lett.* **8**, 381 (1971).
(30) W. Kiefer and H. J. Bernstein, *Mol. Phys.* **23**, 835 (1972).
(31) D. J. Gardiner, R. B. Girling and R. E. Hester, *J. Chem. Soc. Faraday Trans 2* **71**, 709 (1975).
(32) T. Sundius, *J. Raman Spectrosc.* **1**, 471 (1973).
(33) M. W. Zemansky, *Phys. Rev.* **36**, 219 (1930).
(34) H. C. van de Hulst and J. J. M. Reesinck, *Astrophys. J.* **106**, 121 (1947).
(35) W. Kiefer and H. J. Bernstein, *J. Raman Spectrosc.* **1**, 417 (1973).
(36) R. B. Girling and R. E. Hester, personal communication.
(37) A. K. Covington and J. M. Thain, *Appl. Spectrosc.* **29**, 386 (1975).
(38) J. Brandmüller, K. Burchardi, H. Hacker and H. W. Schrötter, *Z. Angew. Phys.* **22**, 177 (1967).
(39) A. Lau, *Exp. Tech. Phys.* **16**, 253 (1968).
(40) H. H. Claassen, H. Selig and J. Shamir, *Appl. Spectrosc.* **23**, 8 (1969).

(41) W. R. Hess, H. Hacker, H. W. Schrötter and J. Brandmüller, *Z. Angew. Phys.* **27**, 233 (1969).
(42) J. R. Scherer and G. F. Bailey, *Appl. Spectrosc.* **24**, 259 (1970).
(43) C. Allemand, *Appl. Spectrosc.* **24**, 348 (1970).
(44) P. Dawson, *Spectrochim. Acta* **28A**, 715 (1972).
(45) W. Proffitt and S. P. S. Porto, *J. Opt. Soc. Am.* **63**, 77 (1973).
(46) Jeol, Ltd., Tokyo, Brochure, Laser Raman Spectrometer, Model JRS-S1.
(47) W. Klöckner, W. Kiefer and H. W. Schrötter, *Appl. Spectrosc.* **31** (1977) in press.
(48) L. D. Barron and A. D. Buckingham, *Annu. Rev. Phys. Chem.* **26**, 381 (1975) and references therein.
(49) L. D. Barron, *Nature* **255**, 458 (1975).
(50) L. D. Barron and A. D. Buckingham, *Mol. Phys.* **20**, 1111 (1971).
(51) W. Nitsch and W. Kiefer, unpublished work.
(52) G. Placzek, Rayleigh-Streuung und Ramaneffekt, in *Handbuch der Radiologie*, Vol. 6, part 2, (E. Marx, ed.), Leipzig, 1934, p. 205.
(53) W. M. McClain, *J. Chem. Phys.* **55**, 2789 (1971).
(54) E. B. Wilson, J. C. Decius and P. C. Cross, *Molecular Vibrations*, McGraw Hill, New York, 1955.
(55) J. Behringer, in *Raman Spectroscopy*, Vol. 1, (H. A. Szymanski, ed.), Plenum, New York, 1967, p. 168.
(56) O. S. Mortensen and J. A. Koningstein, *J. Chem. Phys.* **48**, 3971 (1968).
(57) T. G. Spiro and T. C. Strekas, *Proc. Nat. Acad. Sci. U.S.A.* **69**, 2622 (1972).
(58) M. Pezolét, L. A. Nafie and W. Peticolas, *J. Raman Spectrosc.* **1**, 455 (1973).
(59) J. Nestor and T. G. Spiro, *J. Raman Spectrosc.* **1**, 539 (1973).
(60) W. Kiefer and W. Nitsch, *Appl. Spectrosc.* **31** (1977) in press.
(61) H. M. Davis and J. E. Seaborn, *Electr. Eng.* **25**, 314 (1953).
(62) J. D. Morrison, *J. Chem. Phys.* **22**, 1219 (1954).
(63) G. L. Collier and F. Singleton, *J. Appl. Chem.* **6**, 495 (1956).
(64) E. C. Olson and C. D. Alway, *Anal. Chem.* **32**, 370 (1960).
(65) M. Cardona, *Modulation Spectroscopy*, Academic Press, New York, 1969.
(66) Y. Yacoby, I. Wagner, J. Bodenheimer and W. Low, *Phys. Rev. Lett.* **27**, 248 (1971).
(67) W. Kiefer, W. Richter and M. Cardona, *Phys. Rev. B* **12**, 2346 (1975).
(68) L. Van Hove, *Phys. Rev.* **89**, 1189 (1953).
(69) J. C. Philipps, *Phys. Rev.* **104**, 1263 (1956).
(70) R. E. Drews, *Bull. Am. Phys. Soc.* **12**, 384 (1967).
(71) J. Stone, *Appl. Phys. Lett.* **20**, 239 (1972).
(72) G. E. Walrafen and J. Stone, *Appl. Spectrosc.* **26**, 585 (1972).
(73) G. E. Walrafen, *Phys. Bl.* **12**, 540 (1974).
(74) G. E. Walrafen, *Appl. Spectrosc.* **29**, 179 (1975).
(75) R. H. Stolen and E. P. Ippen, *Appl. Phys. Lett.* **22**, 726 (1973).
(76) W. J. Schmid, University of Munich, unpublished work.
(77) H. W. Schrötter and J. Bofilias, *J. Mol. Struct.* **3**, 242 (1969); and H. W. Schrötter, J. Bofilias, H. J. Falge, H. H. Hacker and J. Brandmüller, *Vijnana Parishad Anusandhan Patrika* **14**, 31 (1971).
(78) W. J. Schmid and H. W. Schrötter, unpublished work.

Chapter 2

ADVANCES IN FAR-INFRARED INTERFEROMETRIC SPECTROSCOPY

N. W. B. Stone and G. W. Chantry

Department of Industry, National Physical Laboratory, Teddington, Middlesex TW11 0LW, U.K.

1 INTRODUCTION

Although it is probably true that Michelson[1] himself understood all the intrinsic advantages of Fourier transform spectroscopy (FTS), he could not exploit this knowledge fully since he did not have available to him the necessary computational techniques. Nevertheless he was able to develop the method of visibility† measurement to obtain limited spectral information from the visible region and to construct a simple harmonic analyser with which he was able to illustrate the form of interferogram which would result from a few simple frequency combinations. However, with the invention of the fast digital computer, the situation changed radically and FTS rapidly became a practical proposition. Its realization can be said to date from 1952 when Fellgett[2] pointed out the advantages of its multiplex operation at the Ohio State Symposium in Columbus. This multiplex feature is now often called the Fellgett advantage. At about the same time, Jacquinot[3,4] drew attention to the extended light grasp which can be achieved with the circular symmetry of a two-beam interferometer. The attention of the spectroscopic world was drawn to the emerging technology of FTS by the early work of the Connes in the near infrared and by the work of Gebbie and his group in the far infrared. Gebbie's introductions of beam dividers made of stretched polymeric film, stepping motor drives and the use of Golay cells as detectors are still commonplace in far infrared FTS.

FTS is no longer a novel topic. Indeed 1977 is its jubilee year and experimental techniques have progressed steadily in these twenty-five years. The tentative efforts of the pioneers in the late 1950s have led the way to the superb

---

† The visibility $\mathscr{V}(x)$ of interference fringes produced by an interferometer, at a path difference x, is defined by $\mathscr{V}(x) = (I_{\max}(x) - I_{\min}(x))/(_{\max}(x) + I_{\min}(x))$ where $I_{\max}(x)$ and $I_{\min}(x)$ are the maximum and minimum values in the vicinity of x. The form of the visibility curve can be used to deduce fine structure in spectral lines and also the widths of isolated lines.

near-infrared planetary spectroscopy now achieved by Connes and Connes[5] and to the development of high-radiometric precision, high-resolution spectro-radiometry in the submillimetre-wave region.[6] In parallel with developments in experimental technique, the computational problems of extracting more and more precise quantitative spectrometric information from the recorded inter-ferograms have received closer and closer scrutiny. Additive and multiplicative noise, the effects of displaced sampling and instrumental misalignment, and a multitude of other major and minor facets of the problem have been analysed in detail.[7] The Aspen Conference of 1970[8] perhaps represents a milestone in the development of the subject.

Progress in the art continues at a steady rate and the twenty-fifth anniversary of Fellgett's paper seems a suitable time at which to review some of the more recent achievements of Fourier spectroscopy in the applied field. The topics selected for this brief resumé include high precision intensity and wavenumber measurements on gases and the monitoring of trace gases in the high atmosphere, measurements (using both transmission and reflection techniques) of the di-electric properties of strongly absorbing solids and liquids, and the time-resolved spectrometry of transient plasmas.

Finally we have outlined several advances in instrumentation developed during recent years and have striven to provide a comprehensive if incomplete bibliography which it is hoped will form an entré to the literature for those readers who would like to probe further.

2 HIGH-RESOLUTION FOURIER SPECTRORADIOMETRY

2.1 Laboratory Studies of Submillimetre-Wave Absorption in Gases

From the earliest days of FTS, gas absorption spectra have received close attention. The pure-rotation spectra of all light molecular gases, many of which are present in the atmosphere as major, minor or trace constituents, fall prin-cipally in the submillimetre region. Fourier methods have effectively filled the gap between microwaves and the infrared and have permitted the study of the complete rotational spectrum. The submillimetre part of the spectrum of a light molecule can often be predicted with good accuracy from the rotational constants derived from measurements on the few lines accessible to microwave techniques, or else can be deduced from combination differences in the infrared spectrum, but there is much complementary information available if the spec-trum can be measured directly with sufficient resolution and at a high enough signal-to-noise ratio. Thus one may determine centrifugal distortion para-meters,[9] collisional perturbation effects,[10] isotope shifts[11] and magnetic splittings,[12] etc.

Recent environmental requirements, arising from the need to monitor possible deleterious consequences of atmospheric pollution, have added a practical urgency to activity in this area since it has become necessary to have laboratory spectra of all possible atmospheric constituents, determined to high intensity and wavenumber precision, so that the complicated emission spectra recorded in the atmosphere can confidently be interpreted. These spectra, of both the lower and the middle stratosphere, have been extensively studied in recent years[13] using Fourier spectroradiometers mounted both in aircraft and in balloons.[14] In order to obtain accurate and reliable estimates of total trace-gas content and vertical concentration profile from the recorded data, laboratory spectra are required from which the wavenumber can be determined to 0.001 cm^{-1}

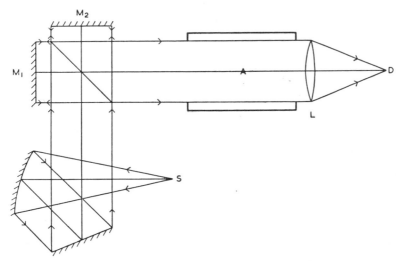

Fig. 1. Schematic diagram of the high-resolution far-infrared interferometer used by Fleming at the National Physical Laboratory (NPL). Gaseous specimens are enclosed in the long (~ 1 m) absorption cell A. S—Source; D—Detector; L—Lens; M—Mirrors.

and absolute line intensities to a few percent. By close attention to detail, it has become possible to obtain standard far-infrared spectra to these accuracies, and detailed studies of many known atmospheric trace gases have now been carried out[15–17]. Interest has centred on the very long-wave end of the far-infrared spectrum, because the rotational spectrum of water vapour becomes much less intense at low wavenumber, and problems of overlapping spectra in atmospheric observation are greatly eased.

The line diagram of Fig. 1 serves to illustrate the main features of the Michelson interferometer built at the National Physical Laboratory by Fleming for determining these standard spectra in the long submillimetre-wave region, and Plate 1 shows a photograph of the equipment. It was constructed from units of the basic NPL/Grubb-Parsons (Messrs Sir Howard Grubb-Parsons and Co. Ltd., Walkergate, Newcastle-upon-Tyne) modular-cube design, though there are several other elegant and sophisticated instruments available commercially (The Beckman, Nicolet, Digilab, EOCOM and Polytec Companies all offer equipment suitable for the far infrared) which could readily be adapted to perform standards work of this quality. General descriptions of the modular instrumentation have been given previously[18] and the main features to note with regard to this particular installation are as follows:

(a) The source is a stabilized d.c. current, high-pressure mercury-arc discharge in a silica envelope. Stabilization has been found[19] to give, at these wavelengths, approximately a 3:1 increase in signal-to-noise ratio in the recorded interferograms compared with those obtained from a lamp in series with a choke and driven from a saturable-core (i.e. constant voltage) mains transformer.

(b) Some modifications were made to the design to accommodate an indium-antimonide bolometer-detector of the helium-cooled Rollin-type.[20] These detectors have detectivities two orders of magnitude higher than any available room-temperature detector, having NEPs (noise equivalent powers) of about 10^{-12} W Hz$^{-1/2}$, but they are restricted in their use to the region below 40 cm^{-1}. Other detectors are available but, in selecting a detector for a particular purpose in the far infrared, speed of response as well as detectivity may have to be considered. In recent years there have been many advances and although much of the work has been published,[21] detailed information about the very latest techniques may not be easily obtainable. The indium-antimonide photoconductive detector due to Putley,[22] which has a response time shorter than 1 μs, is readily available commercially and can be used up to about 100 cm^{-1}. Josephson-type detectors,[23] which will respond to nanosecond pulses, have not yet reached the state of development where they can be offered commercially and are most likely to be used only in heterodyne receiver systems where their fast response is needed. The germanium bolometer-detector[24] is relatively slow but does have a very broad spectral response.

(c) Gas samples of different lengths can be used in the equipment and installed with reasonable facility. Cell lengths between 10 cm and 5 m can be accommodated at the moment and the cells can be maintained at elevated temperatures (ca. 100°C). Longer path lengths could be arranged by the use of a specially adapted White-type cell.[25]

(d) The moving mirror M_1 is driven by a stepping motor (being stationary for the recording of the time-averaged value of each interferogram ordinate) and can be traversed to a maximum displacement of 5 cm from the ZPD (zero path difference) position. This gives a resolution in the unapodized computed spectra[26] of approximately 0.07 cm^{-1}. This relatively simple procedure is adequate in the region from 10 to 40 cm^{-1}, but in the middle and near-infrared regions much more sophisticated methods would be necessary to ensure the required accuracy of sampling.

(e) The radiation source is located as accurately as possible at the focus of the off-axis collimating mirror, so that the radiation traversing the instrument is essentially parallel. If this precaution is not taken a contraction of the wavenumber scale appears in the computed spectrum which can greatly exceed the accuracy and reproducibility with which line-centre positions can be determined.[27] There is, of course, always a small residual scale contraction due to the finite size of that part of the source which is focused onto the detector, and to the consequent inevitable reception of some slightly off-axis rays. It can be shown, however, that a precise correction for this latter effect[28] is given by

$$\tilde{v}_{obs} = \tilde{v}_{true}\left(1 - \frac{\Omega}{4\pi}\right) \tag{1}$$

where $\tilde{v}$ signifies wavenumber and Ω is the effective limiting solid angle of the optical system, usually determined in practice by the angular size of the detector stop subtended at the focusing mirror or lens. The scale correction factor can be determined in a preliminary experiment in which some well known and highly characterized spectrum, such as that of carbon monoxide, is observed.

The instrument described above has been used principally for the wavenumber range 5–40 cm^{-1}. It is constructed in aluminium alloy and the lead screw driving the moving mirror is of mild steel. No compensation or correction to allow for slight differential thermal expansion at these long wavelengths is required provided reasonably stable room-temperature conditions prevail. For shorter wavelength work, attention to this question becomes progressively more important and it is a basic design point in the current attempts to extend stepping-motor interferometry into the 5 μm region.

The performance currently achievable with this instrumentation is illustrated in Fig. 2. Carbon monoxide is chosen since the principal rotation lines are evenly spaced and widely separated. Moreover, they are accurately calculable in wavenumber from the rotational constants obtained by using microwave techniques and, as mentioned above, this gas has been used to check the calibration of the instrument. With sharp lines, the line centre is determined using the simple interpolation formula of Bell[29] (see Fig. 3).

$$\varepsilon = \frac{S(-1) - S(1)}{2[S(-1) + S(1) - 2S(0)]} \tag{2}$$

where ε is the fractional sampling interval (in the wavenumber domain) of the true peak absorption position, from $S(0)$, the position of the nearest sampling position to the peak. This formula is based on the assumption of a quadratic form in the vicinity of the absorption peak and is suitable only for sharp lines. For broadened lines the centre of gravity of the absorption is a more satisfactory criterion of line centre. Figure 2 gives an indication of the noise level which

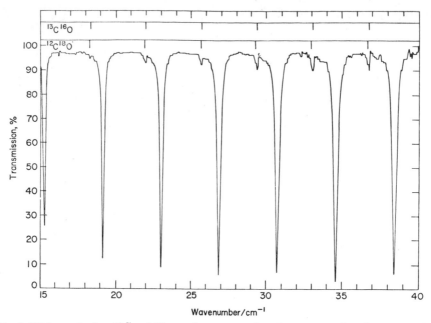

Fig. 2. High resolution ($\Delta \tilde{\nu} \approx 0.07$ cm⁻¹) pure-rotational spectrum of carbon monoxide. The lines due to the isotopic species $^{13}C^{16}O$ and $^{12}C^{18}O$, at natural abundance, are clearly observed.

can be achieved in the transformed spectrum and shows the small features due to the rotation of carbon monoxide molecules containing the less abundant isotopic species of carbon and oxygen.

The second illustration of the quality of spectra now attainable is given by that of ozone (Fig. 4). Ozone is, of course, a critical component of the middle stratosphere where it is in equilibrium with molecular and atomic oxygen roughly in accordance with the Chapman reactions.[30] Its equilibrium could possibly be disturbed by a number of trace gases introduced either by industrial

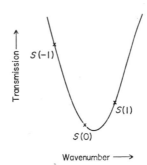

Fig. 3. Use of the Bell interpolation formula. The spectrum is only calculated, of course, at discrete points and the nearest of these to the line centre is $S(0)$.

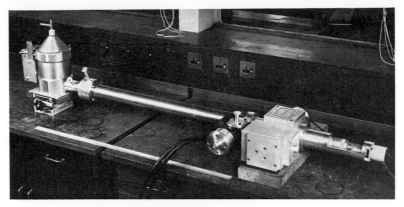

Plate 1. Practical layout of the high-resolution interferometer which is shown schematically in Fig. 1 (p. 45).

Plate 2. Balloon carrying the interferometer just prior to launch.

Plate 3. Photograph of the apparatus shown in section in Fig. 20 (p. 70).

or aircraft pollution and routine measurements on it are of general environmental importance. Ozone is an asymmetric rotor[31] and the upper curve shows its computed spectrum, based on known molecular constants. The close agreement with the lower, observed spectrum is both striking and gratifying, small divergences being attributable entirely to traces of water vapour in the sample.

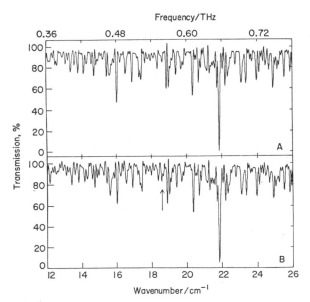

Fig. 4. High-resolution spectrum of ozone: curve A is that calculated from the microwave parameters and curve B is that observed. The weak feature marked with an arrow is the 18.6 cm⁻¹ line of water vapour.

The spectra are presented as percentage transmission against wavenumber, by ratioing specimen and background (i.e. gas-cell evacuated) spectra, a procedure which eliminates errors due to channel fringes and other background variations. The random noise in the interferograms, using a current-stabilized radiation source, is about 1 in 10^4 referred to maximum signal at zero path-difference (ZPD), and digitization of the analog signal to 1 in 2×10^4 using a phase-sensitive detector and digital voltmeter is therefore required for optimum results.

Normal practice is now to use phase modulation of the signal[32,33] in preference to amplitude modulation since this technique can be shown to give a useful improvement in signal-to-noise ratio. Not only is there a more efficient use of the signal received, since the detector receives radiation from the source continuously and not intermittently, but *all* the detected signal has been interferometrically modulated and there is no d.c. offset of the signal. Stray short-wave radiation entering the instrument is therefore unmodulated, and fluctuations due to it are eliminated. Also of course, noise due to fluctuation of the source is reduced (though not eliminated) as the mean recorded d.c. signal is zero and its contribution to the noise is removed.

In order to economize in observation and computing time, and to obtain high resolution spectra in the shortest possible time, single-sided interferograms are usually recorded. A phase-modulated interferogram is ideally a perfect antisymmetric function about ZPD but in order to record it faithfully as such, within the limits of digital recording, it is necessary for the first interferogram ordinate to be registered precisely at zero path difference. If this is not done distortion of the computed spectrum giving rise to line asymmetry and shift will occur. Since it is difficult and tedious to realize this ideal experimental situation, an alternative procedure due to Forman et al.[34] is generally used to correct for phase errors due to a displaced sampling comb. The technique requires that a small length of interferogram be recorded before ZPD is reached on the interferogram and, in addition to transforming the displaced single-sided function, a transform is also carried out over the small central section of the interferogram. From this section a phase function can be computed which is used (via digital convolution) to correct for the phase errors introduced by the displacement of the sampling comb, and also for phase errors due to other artefacts such as slight misalignment of the interferometer.

Many standard gas spectra have now been measured in the 10 to 40 cm^{-1} range and are readily available in report form[35] and in the open literature.[36] They include CO, NO, N_2O, NO_2, H_2O, HNO_3, O_3, CCl_3F, CCl_2F_2, CF_3Cl, H_2S and SO_2. A full description of the computational techniques used, including the fast Fourier transform applied to both single and double-sided interferograms, and the phase-correction method of Forman et al. is also obtainable.[37]

2.2 Fourier Techniques Applied to Stratospheric Monitoring

In 1971 it was suggested by Johnston[38] and Crutzen[39] that the oxides of nitrogen, NO and NO_2, might play a significant role in the photochemistry of the stratosphere by reducing the mean concentration of ozone from that expected according to the Chapman reactions,[30] to that actually observed. The simple catalytic cycle

$$NO + O_3 \rightarrow NO_2 + O_2$$
$$NO_2 + O \rightarrow NO + O_2$$

net $\quad O + O_3 \rightarrow 2O_2$

in which both ozone and atomic oxygen are destroyed but the concentrations of the nitrogen oxides remain unaffected was proposed. The calculations suggested that mixing ratios of the order of a few parts in 10^9 at the reduced temperature and pressure of the atmosphere at 25 km altitude, could explain the known ozone concentrations. It was subsequently pointed out that 1000 supersonic transports (SSTs) operating daily in the stratosphere could introduce as a pollutant a comparable quantity of NO_x, since these oxides are formed in, and exhausted from, turbine engines in known and significant amounts. Concern about the effect of large fleets of SSTs on the ozone layer and on its ability to attenuate the biologically harmful solar ultraviolet radiation in the 200–300 nm wavelength range, led to a major international effort to monitor trace stratospheric gases in which Fourier spectroradiometry has played, and will probably continue to play an important part. The first objective, of course, has been to measure the present levels of all trace gases which may be important, before large fleets of SSTs are launched. Nitrous oxide, N_2O, formed by bacteriological processes at the earth's surface, is thought to be a likely source material for naturally occurring NO_x in the stratosphere. More recently a new threat to our protective ozone screen has been suggested. Chlorine atoms can likewise act as effective catalysts for the breakdown of ozone, and the chlorine-containing aerosol propellants such as the freons, which are being manufactured and used in ever-increasing quantities, may add significantly to the total natural level of stratospheric chlorine when they diffuse from the lower atmosphere into the stratosphere.

The overall programme of research has been supervised in the main by three national committees, COMESA (Committee on the Meteorological Effects of Stratospheric Aircraft) in Britain, COVOS (Comité d'études des Conséquences des Vols Stratosphériques) in France, and CIAP (Climatic Impact Assessment Program) in the United States. A variety of measurement methods, including chemiluminescence and chemical sampling, has been used as well as spectrometric techniques. Fourier methods have been used in the near infrared to observe the absorption spectrum of the atmosphere using the sun as a radiation source,[40,41] and in the submillimetre-wave region[42−44] using emission methods. In the latter case, the thermal-emission spectrum of the stratosphere is recorded from a high observing platform (aircraft or balloon), and gas concentrations are estimated from the absolute measured intensities of various characteristic transitions.

Emission spectroradiometry has two significant advantages over absorption spectrometry for stratospheric measurements. Firstly, it is not necessary to focus the sun through the instrument, and no sun seeker is needed for this purpose. Secondly, it can be used at night as well as by day, so that diurnal variations can be measured, and the effect of the changing solar ultraviolet intensity monitored.

In order to obtain an overall picture of the constitution of the stratosphere, so that realistic data can be fed into the various one-, two- and three-dimensional models of its chemistry and dynamics, we require both the overall global distribution of the trace gases and their vertical profiles. In the submillimetre-wave region it is necessary to observe from high altitude in order that the recorded spectra shall not be masked by the intense rotational spectrum of water vapour which is present, of course, in the lower atmosphere in large

amounts. Observations so far have been made from high flying aircraft, prin-
cipally Concorde, and from balloons. Observation from space platforms, such
as Spacelab, may follow in the years ahead. By viewing the atmospheric emission
at an angle above the horizontal, radiation is received from all altitudes above
the platform, and this enables the observer to calculate the total amount of a
trace gas above him. In practice it is not possible to determine the distribution

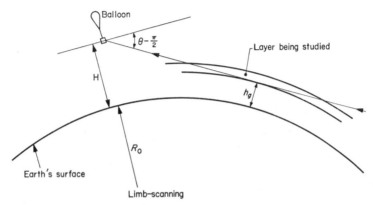

Fig. 5. The principle of the 'limb-scanning' method.

of concentration, however, from such observations, except by measuring from
a number of levels and taking the differences between the results. In order to
obtain vertical-profile information, it is necessary to view individual layers of
the atmosphere from above, using the limb-scanning method,† at different
grazing heights, h_g. The emission received then originates predominantly from
well defined layers of approximately constant altitude. This simple geometrical
fact is made clear by Fig. 5, in which it is seen that a narrow layer of gas at
grazing height, h_g, will give rise to a sharp increase in the signal received as θ,
the zenith angle, is scanned to make the observing direction pass through the
layer.

To meet the immediate requirement for measuring the existing levels an
effort was made in the early days of the international programme to carry out
a general global survey,[45] using an NPL submillimetre Fourier spectrometer
mounted in one of the prototype Concorde aircraft. As an observing platform
Concorde was unique, in that its cruise altitude was over 15 km, and it offered
adequate space and facilities for experimental work. Geographical coverage
was limited mainly by the destinations chosen for the sales tours and by the
routes selected for the flight test programme. In this way, observations were
made from the British prototype from Britain eastwards to Tokyo, and thence
south to Sydney (Australia). A further set of observations was subsequently

† The 'limb' is the edge of the Earth as viewed from a height, and limb-scanning means
scanning the atmosphere above the horizon. This is illustrated in Fig. 5.

made between Britain and Capetown (S. Africa), and many flights were made over the Bay of Biscay, the Western Approaches and the North Atlantic beyond Iceland and well into the Arctic circle. The latitude coverage was therefore roughly 70° N to 40° S. As indicated above, these observations furnished information mainly on the total amounts of several trace gases above cruise height though some limited profile information below this altitude was also obtained. In the final stages of the programme, a Fourier spectrometer was flown from Aire sur l'Adour in S.W. France to an altitude of 35 km and vertical profile information on nitric acid, nitrogen dioxide and nitrous oxide as well as water vapour and ozone was obtained by the method of limb-scanning from above the maximum of the ozone layer. We survey here the implementation of these two projects and their results.[46,47]

2.2.1 Global survey of trace gases from Concorde

Figure 6 shows a layout of the simple Fourier interferometer installed in the British prototype Concorde 002, which was used for the geographical survey mentioned above. The thermal emission from the atmosphere is restricted by the geometry of the system to an acceptance angle of about 0.5°, entering the instrument through a specially constructed window mounted in the side of the aircraft. In the earlier flights, a sandwich window consisting of two plane-parallel centimetre-thick discs of polypropylene was used but this gave rise to

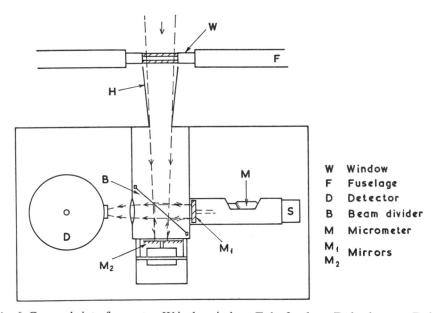

Fig. 6. Concorde interferometer. W is the window, F the fuselage, D the detector, B the beam divider, M the micrometer and M_1 and M_2 the interferometer mirrors. (Crown Copyright.)

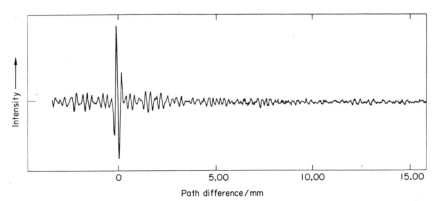

Fig. 7. Interferogram observed aboard Concorde.

some condensation problems, particularly in tropical regions, and it was subsequently replaced by a single disc of crystalline quartz. The moving mirror M_1 was driven on a carriage by an accurately ground screw and stepping motor, with the capability of a maximum displacement from ZPD of 10 cm. This gave a limiting resolution approaching 0.03 cm^{-1} in the unapodized case, though maximum resolution was not usually used because of time limitations. Spectra are normally not subjected to the apodization process since it has been shown[48] that, when a spectrum is computed which consists of lines approaching

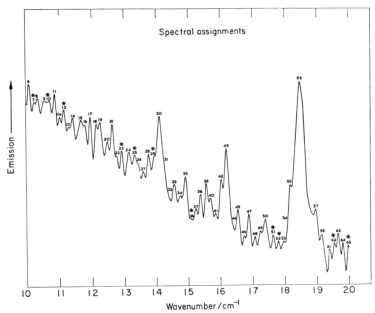

Fig. 8. Spectrum resulting from Fourier transformation of the interferogram shown in Fig. 7.

in width the theoretical resolution of the instrument, the spurious side-lobes due to the sinc form (sinc (x) is defined as $\sin(\pi x)/\pi x$) of the unapodized spectral window-function are largely suppressed, and apodization serves no useful purpose; indeed it only leads to reduced resolving power and the suppression of information. Phase modulation[32,33] of the signal was used in this instrument, the mirror M_2 being vibrated at a frequency of 180 Hz. The detector was a liquid-helium-cooled indium-antimonide Rollin bolometer with an NEP of 10^{-12} W Hz$^{-1/2}$.

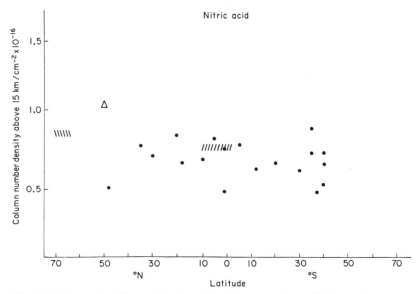

Fig. 9. Column densities of nitric acid and its variation with latitude. Key: $\triangle$ = November 1971; ● = June 1972; /// = January 1973; \\\ = May 1973.

Though recent observations have confirmed that the stratosphere is relatively dry, the mixing ratio being only of the order of two or three parts per million, water vapour has an intense rotational spectrum spanning the whole of the far-infrared and submillimetre-wave regions, so that even observing from Concorde we can only usefully compute the very long-wave end of the spectrum between 10 and 40 cm^{-1}, where the intensity of the water spectrum is falling away.

A typical interferogram recorded from Concorde is shown in Fig. 7. The noise signal in the interferograms was generally less than 1% and often approached 0.3% of the maximum phase-modulated signal in the region of zero path-difference. The interferogram transforms into a spectrum such as that shown in Fig. 8, where the main features are due to the electric-dipole rotational spectra of water and ozone, and to the magnetic-dipole rotational spectrum of oxygen.[49] The small features marked by asterisks are attributable to nitric acid, nitrogen dioxide and nitrous oxide; from a knowledge of the appropriate line intensities (see Section 2.1) estimates of average mixing-ratio or total column-density can be made for each species. Nitrous oxide and nitric acid can be identified relatively easily because both are present in sufficient amounts, but the results obtained on total amounts of nitrogen dioxide were much less reliable. Definitive measurements of NO_2 were subsequently made from much greater altitude (see below).

Figure 9 shows measured values of the mean mixing ratio of nitric acid between Fairford (England) and Sydney (Australia), recorded[45] during the 1972 sales tour of Concorde.

The sensitivity with which concentrations of a trace constituent can be measured depends upon its molecular dipole-moment and the extent to which its spectrum is masked by other species. For a number of gases of average dipole-moment, a few parts in 10^9 can be detected using submillimetre-wave Fourier methods.

2.2.2   Vertical profile measurements of trace gases from balloons

Figure 10 shows the configuration used in a balloon-borne Michelson interferometer constructed at the National Physical Laboratory for limb-scanning the atmosphere from up to 35 km altitude.[47] The angular field of the radiation received was limited by a rectangular field stop aligned so that a wide azimuthal angle but only a small angle in the zenith plane were accepted. For vertical

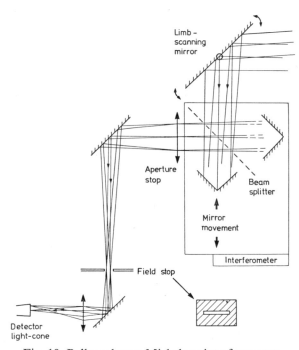

Fig. 10. Balloon-borne Michelson interferometer.

limb-scanning this gives increased signal in the horizontal plane whilst limiting the vertical angle to give adequate height resolution. The azimuthal angle was 5° while the vertical angle of acceptance was limited to 0.5°. At grazing height this gives a vertical resolution, Δh, of about 5 km. The interferometer mirrors were aluminized corner-cube reflectors, which are less sensitive to misalignment than plane mirrors, and the beam divider was a stretched film of 400 gauge (i.e. 100 μm) melinex (ICI trade name for their make of polyethylene tereph-thalate). The detector was once again a Rollin type. The thermal radiation

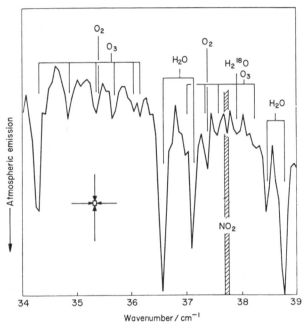

Fig. 11. Atmospheric emission spectrum recorded from the balloon at 35 km. The NO_2 Q-branch near 37.8 cm^{-1} is clearly resolved (Harries *et al.*, Ref. 47).

from the atmosphere was received through a rectangular aperture in the mount-ing plate and was reflected vertically downwards into the interferometer by the limb-scanning mirror. This mirror controlled the direction of viewing and its mean position could be set via a motor by tele-command from the ground. It was also servo-controlled to correct for the swing of the balloon gondola, as described later.

Since the balloon platform is operated at so great an altitude, masking of the spectrum by water vapour is less of a problem than in the aircraft-borne case, and computation of the spectrum can usefully be carried out to 50 cm^{-1}. This is a significant advantage, for the strong Q-branch of NO_2 at 37.8 cm^{-1} can be clearly resolved from the neighbouring water lines and a far more re-liable estimate of concentration can be made.

Two other features of this instrument should be mentioned. First, it is necessary for the interferometer to view away from the sun to avoid signal errors due to stray solar radiation entering the aperture. Two out-of-balance photocells on the reverse side of the mounting therefore search for the sun in azimuth, rotating the gondola via a servo-controlled flywheel until the instrument is turned away from the sun. Second, a zenith sun-seeker[50] with both a coarse and a fine sensor, locks itself on to the sun and feeds a continuous correction to the angular setting of the limb-scanning mirror, to compensate for the swing of the gondola in the zenith plane.

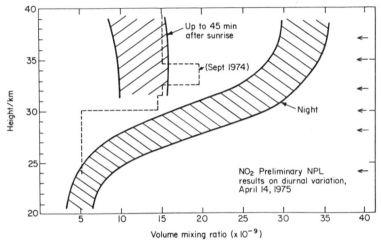

Fig. 12. Computed vertical profile of NO_2 and its diurnal variation.

The photograph (Plate 2) shows the apparatus just prior to launch. The main payload is suspended on a small subsidiary balloon, so that when the large balloon is released, a smooth, jolt-free take-off is achieved. Figure 11 shows a section of a recorded spectrum in which the NO_2 Q-branch near $37.8 cm^{-1}$ is clearly resolved, and Fig. 12 shows the computed vertical profile of NO_2 from a complete limb-scanning experiment.

2.2.3 Calculation of gas concentrations from stratospheric spectra

High resolution spectra are required to resolve particular lines and bands in order that their intensities can be measured accurately. It is therefore necessary to use a large capacity digital computer combined with the fast Fourier-transform to invert the interferogram function into the spectrum. The form of the spectrum is influenced by the transmission function of the instrument and this in turn depends upon the beam divider, the method of modulation and other factors. It is therefore necessary to estimate envelopes of zero intensity and maximum intensity (i.e. black-body emission intensity corresponding to the temperature of the atmosphere) for each spectrum. Hence the emission intensity of each line can be measured from the spectrum and corrected for the instrumental function. The zero-intensity baseline is estimated from the spectra in the so-called atmospheric-window regions where atmospheric lines are known to be weak, while the black-body envelope is located by the extremities of a few strong water lines, known to be saturated. The intensities, I_e, of individual spectral features can then be measured directly from the recorded spectra.

The determination of vertical concentration-profiles from the measured intensities of the spectral emission requires a general radiation-transfer calculation to be carried out, in each case by digital computer. Only a brief outline of the calculation can be given here, but details have been given by Farmer.[40]

The emission intensity associated with a spectral transition is a function of zenith viewing-angle, θ, wavenumber, $\tilde{v}$, and altitude of observation, H. Then

$$I_e(\tilde{v}, \theta, H) = \int_H^\infty B[\tilde{v}, T(h)] \frac{\partial t}{\partial h} (\tilde{v}, \theta, H, h) \, \mathrm{d}h \tag{3}$$

where B is the Planck function at temperature T, and t is the monochromatic transmittance of the atmosphere between height h and the observer at H. The transmittance t is related to the optical depth σ by

$$t(\tilde{v}, \theta, H, h) = \exp\{-\sigma(\tilde{v}, \theta, h, H)\} \tag{4}$$

σ being dependent upon the molecular number density $q(h)$, the extinction coefficient† $k(\tilde{v}, h)$ and a geometrical factor $g(\theta, h)$ by the equation

$$\sigma(\tilde{v}, \theta, H, h) = \int_H^h q(h') \, g(\theta, h') \, k(\tilde{v}, h') \, \mathrm{d}h' \tag{5}$$

where h' is a dummy variable. Hence $q(h)$ can be computed digitally and averaged over a specified layer, Δh, (in practice about 5 km) by iteration.

3   DISPERSIVE FOURIER TRANSFORM SPECTROSCOPY, (DFTS)

In Section 2 we have described some typical applications of conventional FTS, in which the incoming radiation is auto-correlated by the interferometer, and the auto-correlation function is transformed to give the power spectrum of the source modified by the effective response-function of the entire receiving

---

† The extinction coefficient $k(\tilde{v}, h)$ is that used by atmospheric physicists. It means the absorption per unit length per unit atmosphere pressure as a function of height. It should not be confused with the extinction coefficient or absorption index $k(\tilde{v})$ which is generally accepted as the imaginary component of the complex refractive index of a medium and which is related to the absorption coefficient $\alpha(\tilde{v})$ by $k(\tilde{v}) = \alpha(\tilde{v})/4\pi\tilde{v}$.

system.[51] If, in addition, an absorbing specimen is placed either directly in front of the source or in front of the detector, the recorded spectrum is modified in a characteristic manner, and by ratioing the spectra recorded with and without the specimen present, the power absorption spectrum of the specimen is obtained. Apart from the peculiar advantages of Fourier transform spectroscopy, the process is formally quite similar to single-beam conventional spectroscopy and likewise there is no (or very little!) information forthcoming about the dispersion spectrum of the specimen.

If we wish to measure the dispersion of a specimen by Fourier interferometric methods, we must locate the specimen in one of the mirror arms of the interferometer, introducing thereby a wavenumber-dependent path-difference, and hence phase-dispersion into the interferogram.[52] In this case not only will the interferogram centre be displaced by a distance dependent upon the mean refractive index of the specimen, but some asymmetry, characteristic of the dispersive properties of the material, will also be introduced.[53] This interferogram, coupled with the corresponding background interferogram, contains all the information necessary to derive both the absorption and the dispersion spectra of the specimen. Since the interferogram function is no longer symmetrical, it is of course necessary to use the full complex Fourier transform, that is to compute both the sine and cosine terms of the transform. It can be shown,[54] in the general case, that the absorption spectrum, $\alpha(\tilde{\nu})$, and the refraction spectrum, $n(\tilde{\nu})$, of the specimen are given by:†

$$\alpha(\tilde{\nu}) = \frac{1}{2d} \ln \frac{\{p_0(\tilde{\nu})\}^2 + \{q_0(\tilde{\nu})\}^2}{\{P(\tilde{\nu})\}^2 + \{Q(\tilde{\nu})\}^2} \tag{6}$$

where p and q are the sine and cosine transforms respectively and the subscript zero indicates background data, and

$$n(\tilde{\nu}) = 1 + \frac{\bar{x}}{2d} - \frac{1}{4\pi \tilde{\nu} d} \left\{ \arctan \frac{Q(\tilde{\nu})}{P(\tilde{\nu})} + m\pi \right\} \tag{7}$$

where m is a small integer which ideally should not exceed zero in the computed range of $\tilde{\nu}$. Capital P and Q signify that the specimen transforms are taken with respect to the brightest fringe in the displaced pattern as origin.

The ratio of the complex transforms, with and without the specimen inserted, is known as the complex insertion-loss, $\hat{L}(\tilde{\nu})$. An analytical treatment of the relationship between $\hat{L}(\tilde{\nu})$ and $\hat{n}(\tilde{\nu})$, the complex refractive-index of the specimen, has been given to an excellent degree of approximation by Chamberlain[55] and a more rigorous treatment is to be found in the papers of Honijk et al.[56,57]

---

† This assumes, of course, that the beam traverses the specimen twice. In some variant designs of interferometer, the Mach-Zehnder for example, the beam traverses the specimen only once.

Current measurement capabilities are such that Chamberlain's formulation is sufficiently precise for all present purposes.

In implementing this method in practice, it must be borne in mind that expressions (6) and (7) present a somewhat simplified picture, in which it is assumed that the radiation traverses the specimen only twice, and takes no account of surface reflections or of multiple reflections within either the specimen or the cell windows (if a closed cell is used). The effects of multiple reflections within a parallel specimen are treated by Chamberlain,[55] and techniques of 'editing' interferograms to remove the effects of reflections at the liquid/window/vacuum interfaces can be found in Refs. 58 and 59.

3.1 Dispersive Measurements on Transparent Liquids

3.1.1 The free-layer technique

Figure 13 shows one of the earlier interferometer configurations for measuring the dispersion of relatively transparent liquids. It is usually known as the 'free-layer technique' and was developed by Chamberlain.[60] The liquid is retained by gravity, as shown, in a cup, the bottom of which constitutes the fixed interferometer mirror. The interferometer is, therefore, constructed for simplicity in the vertical position and, after optical alignment of the mirrors, the whole instrument is tilt-adjusted so that M_2 is precisely horizontal. Liquid introduced into the cup will then form an accurately plane-parallel sample. The main body

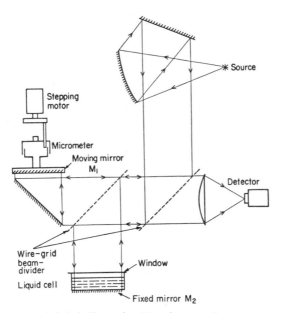

Fig. 13. Early phase-modulated dispersive Fourier-transform spectrometer based on the 'free-layer' principle. (Crown Copyright.)

of the interferometer is evacuated to remove water vapour, but the liquid sample is isolated from the rest of the instrument by a thin melinex or polyethylene film, which causes negligible distortion of the recorded interferograms. Errors introduced by the saturated vapour in the gap between liquid surface and window are generally negligible unless the vapour pressure is high and the vapour has an intense rotational spectrum. The effects can be minimized by reducing the gap to the smallest practicable size, though the window will, of course, tend to bow away from the liquid under the differential pressure.

In general, the interferogram, neglecting the small effects of the film window, will be given by the sum of contributions, usually called 'signatures',

$$V(x) = V_R(x) + V_T(x) + V_M(x). \tag{8}$$

$V_R(x)$ is due to radiation reflected from the upper surface of the liquid. Its brightest fringe is displaced from the principal signature, $V_T(x)$, the interference function due to reflection at M_2, by $2\bar{n}d$, where d is the thickness of the liquid specimen and $\bar{n}$ its average refractive index. Since sharp features are not encountered in the spectra of liquids, high resolution spectra are not usually required and the observed data can safely be terminated before this signature appears. An alternative procedure, which may be used provided the signature $V_R(x)$ is reasonably remote from the main signature, is to edit it out, replacing it with a short stretch of data from the noise-limited extreme of the interferogram. $V_M(x)$ is the overall signal due to multiple reflections within the liquid specimen, and is negligible unless the absorption is very low. Even if the effect

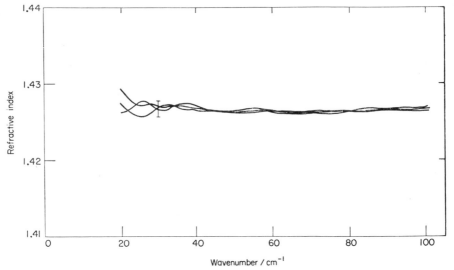

Fig. 14. Demonstration of the reproducibility achievable in liquid-phase spectroscopy. The specimen was a 2.05 M solution of p-difluorobenzene in cyclohexane and the three curves show three independent runs. (Crown Copyright.)

of $V_M(x)$ is significant, the need for making a correction may again be eliminated, either by judicious editing, or by cutting off the interferogram before this signature is reached. $V_M(x)$ gives rise to a characteristic channel-spectrum, and provided the spectral resolution is less than the spacing of the channel fringes, the fringes will be smoothed out and cause no distortion of the spectrum. The criterion used to satisfy this condition is $D < 2\bar{n}d$, where D is the maximum path difference introduced, $\bar{n}$ is the mean refractive index of the liquid and d its thickness. The problems of multiple reflections in liquids in Fourier transform spectrometry have been discussed comprehensively by Chamberlain.[55]

Figure 14 shows the measured submillimetre-wave dispersion of a solution of p-difluorobenzene in cyclohexane using the free-layer technique and illustrates the reproducibility currently obtainable. The absolute level was established at 29.7 cm^{-1} by laser measurement, to $\pm 0.1\%$, while the scatter in n over three runs was $\pm 0.02\%$.

3.1.2   The closed variable-path cell

The free-layer technique suffers not only from the problem of rotational absorption by the vapour in the free space above the liquid, but also from the difficulty of measuring the liquid thickness precisely. For more strongly absorbing liquids, the required specimen thickness becomes progressively smaller, so that not only does it become difficult to maintain the liquid film and to measure its thickness, but the signature $V_R(x)$ overlaps $V_T(x)$, and simple editing procedures on the interferogram become impracticable. An effective solution to the last of these problems is to record two specimen interferograms, one on the thickness of liquid required to determine its phase and modulus spectrum, and a second with a large liquid thickness in the cell, so that any reflection from the back interface is suppressed, and data are only recorded of reflection from the upper liquid surface. Two transforms are carried out and the effects of front-surface reflection are eliminated by subtraction in the spectral domain.[61] However, most of the experimental problems of the free-layer technique, when used for absorbing liquids, are eased by using a variable path-length cell in which the liquid is held between the reflecting surface M_2 and a front window. There is, in this case, no problem due to vapour absorption, no difficulty due to vibration-induced ripples on the liquid surface and, provided the refractive index of the window material is closely matched to that of the liquid specimen, there is little reflection from the liquid/window interface to complicate the transmitted signal. Windows, however, introduce their own problems. They must be chemically and physically inert as far as the specimen liquid is concerned, highly transparent in the spectral region of interest, thick enough to reject the signature due to the front-window surface from the recorded interferogram, adequately rigid, and suitable for optical working. Moreover, ideally we require materials with a range of refractive indices to match those of a variety of liquids. These criteria can never be met fully and compromise is always necessary. Germanium and silicon have suitable mechanical properties

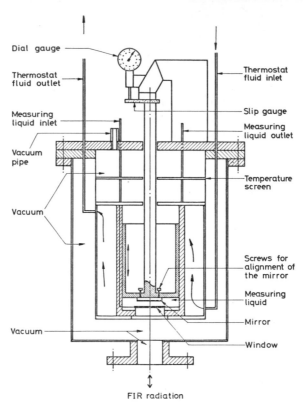

Fig. 15. Cell designed and constructed at the University of Leiden by Honijk et al.[64] for determining the complex refractive-index spectra of liquids.

and are highly transparent when pure, but both have a high refractive index, and reflective losses are normally serious at both surfaces. Crystalline quartz suffers from a narrower band pass, but its refractive index is lower and it also has the merit of transparency in the visible which eases problems of alignment. In cases where very short cell lengths are not required, TPX† may sometimes be used in spite of its relatively low rigidity, and it has the advantage of matching quite closely the refractive index of a number of organic liquids.

The experimental procedure in transmission DFTS is quite straightforward, as long as the liquid is not too heavily absorbing and the cell length too small for editing procedures to be practicable. The computation of the complex refractive index $\hat{n}(\tilde{\nu})$ from the complex insertion loss $\hat{L}(\tilde{\nu})$ is complicated, however, and the iterative procedures for doing this have been described by Honijk et al.[62] and Afsar.[63]

Figure 15 is a diagram of a variable-path liquid cell of the type described,

† TPX is a polymeric material based on poly-4-methyl-pentene-1. Its far-infrared properties have been described by G. W. Chantry, H. M. Evans, J. W. Fleming and H. A. Gebbie, *Infrared Phys.* **9**, 31 (1969).

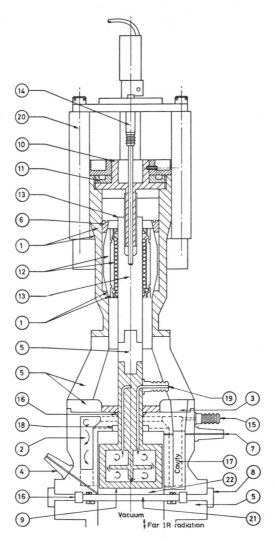

Fig. 16. Cell designed and constructed at the University of Nancy by Goulon *et al.*[65] for determining the complex refractive-index spectra of liquids. 1 = Alignment by conical sections; 2 = Thermostatting fluid; 3 = Conical hole for the ground glass stopper of thermometer; 4 = Injection of the liquid to be studied; 5 = Nylon spacer; 6 = Ball-bushing adjustment ring; 7 = Output of air or N_2 when filling the cell with the liquid to be studied; 8 = Alignment ring; 9 = Nickel-gold plated and thermostatted reflecting surface; 10 = Rotating screw; 11 = Locking ring; 12 = Recirculating ball bushing; 13 = Stainless steel nut for moving the plunger; 14 = Transducer; 15 = Input or output of the thermostatting fluid for the cell; 16 = Teflon ring for making the cell vacuum tight; 17 = Cavity for the thermometer (partially filled with the liquid under test); 18 = Teflon wiping ring; 19 = Input or output of the thermostatting fluid for the plunger; 20 = Transducer support; 21 = Germanium or TPX window (5 mm thick); 22 = specimen.

due to Honijk *et al.*[64] An important feature of such a cell is that its temperature can be controlled and measured; this is, of course, critical for many chemical applications. Figure 16 shows an alternative design due to Goulon *et al.*[65] which has proved to be extremely useful for studying liquid-phase critical phenomena.

3.1.3   The variable-path fixed-length absorption cell for liquid samples

Although DFTS yields both the real and the imaginary terms of the complex permittivity or refractive index, it is generally true that the imaginary part can be determined more precisely by a direct power transmission measurement. This is particularly true when α is very small and therefore sensitive to what would otherwise be very minor sources of error.

A parallel-window absorption cell placed directly in front of the detector of a conventional Fourier spectrometer is normally in a convergent beam, and the absorbing paths of all off-axis rays exceed the geometrical length of the cell, giving rise to errors[66] in the determined values of α. This problem can be minimized by the use of a concave lens in front of the cell to render the convergent radiation near-parallel, and a convex lens on the exit side to focus on to the detector. In extreme cases, however, this is still unsatisfactory, since the radiation source is necessarily of finite size, particularly in the far infrared where sources are weak, and off-axis radiation always contributes to the signal received. When a conventional variable-path liquid cell is used, therefore, the lateral movement of one of the windows gives rise to small changes in the signal received, particularly at the periphery of the field, due to the slight impressed changes in the optical configuration.

An ingenious solution to this problem has been devised by Kilp,[67] whose design for a far-infrared cell, used in the power transmission interferometer configuration, is shown in Fig. 17 (top and bottom). The plano-surfaces of the negative and positive PTFE lenses (2) and (3) (see Fig. 17 (bottom)) define the fixed limits of the cell, which is divided into two sections by a PTFE diaphragm (4). This diaphragm is supported in a stainless steel, flexible annular mount, and its position is controlled through stainless steel bellows by a thrust micrometer. The two cell sections are thus completely isolated from one another. The front section of the cell contains a low-loss, low-dispersion liquid such as cyclohexane, and the back section contains the specimen liquid. Since cyclohexane, PTFE, and most non-polar liquids have refractive indices which are fairly closely matched, reflection at the interfaces is minimal and the signal received is dependent almost entirely on changes in absorption as the path through the specimen is varied. For liquids with α-values in the range 0.1–1.0 neper† cm^{-1},

---

† The unit neper is used to signify that the logarithms used in Lambert's Law

$$\alpha(\bar{\nu}) = 1^{-1} \ln (I_0/I)$$

are natural logarithms, that is to base e. The term comes from the Latin version of the name Napier, the discoverer of natural logarithms.

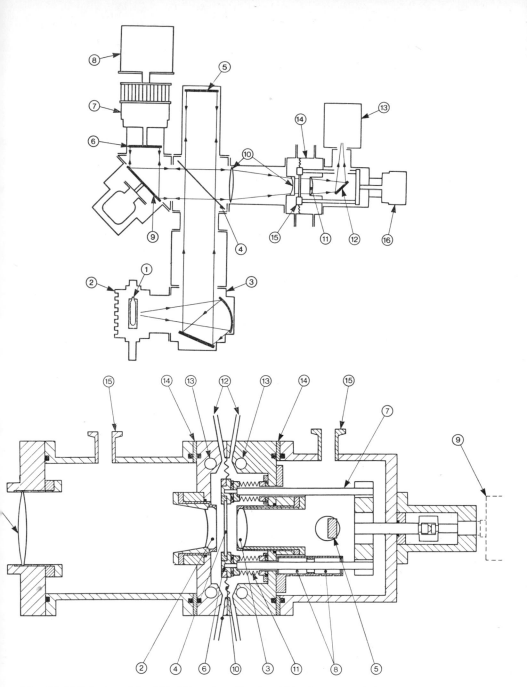

Fig. 17. Cell designed by Kilp [67] and realized at NPL for determining the absorption spectra of low-loss liquids. Top 1 = Mercury lamp; 2 = Water-cooled lamp house; 3 = Two mirror collimator; 4 = Mylar beam splitter; 5 = Fixed mirror; 6 = Scanning mirror; 7 = Micrometer; 8 = Stepping motor; 9 = 45° vibrating mirror; 10 = Beam condensing lenses; 11 = Focusing lens; 12 = 45° mirror; 13 = Detector; 14 = Two-chamber liquid cell; 15 = Movable window; 16 = Window drive micrometer. Bottom 1, 2, 3 = Lenses; 4 = Separating vane window; 5 = 45° mirror assembly; 6 = Adjustment plate; 7 = Guide rod; 8 = Ball bush; 9 = Barrel micrometer; 10 = Flexible PTFE diaphragm; 11 = Bellows; 12 = Inlet and outlet tubes to cell; 13 = Water-cooling channel; 14 = Insulating ring; 15 = Pipe connector.

this cell[68] has been found to give excellent performance, greatly reducing measurement errors as compared with more conventional types of cell. It has been particularly useful, for example, in measuring the changes of absorption of dilute solutions with varying concentration, in which case the high-transmission solvent (e.g. cyclohexane) is introduced into one part of the cell and the solutions of different concentrations are located in the other part. It is not, of course, a dispersive technique but, in the case of low absorption, it provides a valuable complementary facility.

3.2 DFTS of Heavily Absorbing Specimens

3.2.1 DFTS of near-opaque liquids

For extremely absorbing liquids, the transmission method becomes impracticable. For example, a 20 μm-thick film of a liquid having a power absorption coefficient of 1000 neper cm^{-1} absorbs, in the double-transmission arrangement, 99% of the incident energy. Not only does the reduced intensity give rise to a poor signal-to-noise ratio in the interferogram, but the mean thickness of the layer becomes progressively more difficult both to maintain and to measure with adequate precision. Also, the interferogram signature due to reflection at the window/specimen interface closely overlaps that from the rear mirror and the editing procedures become impossible. The limiting film thickness which it is practicable to use is probably about 20 μm. The method of DFTS using

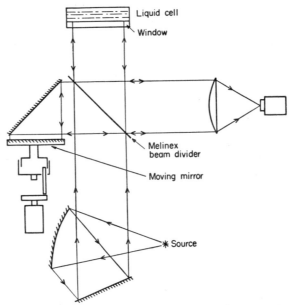

Fig. 18. Apparatus for determining the complex reflection-spectra of heavily absorbing liquids. (Crown Copyright.)

dispersion due to reflection at a window/liquid surface has therefore been evolved as a solution to these problems.

A suitable interferometer configuration is shown diagrammatically in Fig. 18. The instrument is again constructed in the vertical position, the liquid being retained by gravity above a rigid transparent window. The polymer TPX has been used as a material for this purpose, but again the choice of window will depend upon chemical considerations and on the physical nature of the specimen, since in this case it is essential for the refractive index of the window to differ significantly from that of the liquid. If it does not, very little power will be reflected from the solid/liquid interface. The liquid thickness must simply

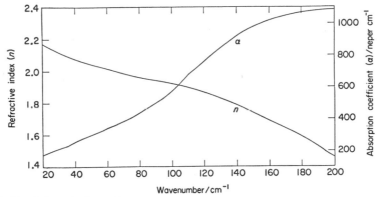

Fig. 19. Far infrared dispersion and absorption spectra of liquid water (Chamberlain *et al.*, Ref. 69(b)).

be great enough to ensure that all radiation which penetrates the boundary is absorbed, and cannot be reflected back from the upper liquid surface into the system. The instrument, of course, must be evacuated, for flushing with dry gas is seldom adequate in the submillimetre-wave region. The interferogram is then recorded and stored and a second, reference interferogram, is taken after replacing the specimen liquid with an equal weight of clean mercury, which acts as a near-perfect reflector in the far infrared. Since we are concerned with measuring a phase shift on reflection from the specimen surface, which may be the equivalent of only a few micrometres of optical path, it is most important to use identical weights of specimen and mercury, to ensure equal mechanical deformation of the window for each interferogram. This is particularly true of TPX, which is a much less rigid material than, for instance, silicon. The precision with which the refractive index is determined is directly proportional to the mechanical stability (that is, the reproducibility of the sampling comb) of the interferometer, but it may be possible to locate the absolute refractive-index levels by independent laser-transmission measurements at the fixed wavenumbers provided by the HCN and H_2O lasers. The intrinsic spectral brightness of these lasers makes this feasible for all but the most opaque liquids.

The complex positional insertion loss, $\mathscr{L}(\tilde{v})$, which is the ratio of the two transforms, is then related to the complex amplitude-reflectivity of the liquid/ window interface, and hence to the complex refractive indices by the relation

$$\mathscr{L}(\tilde{v}) = \hat{r}_{WL}(\tilde{v})\, e^{i\pi} = \frac{\hat{n}(\tilde{v}) - \hat{n}_W(\tilde{v})}{\hat{n}(\tilde{v}) + \hat{n}_W(\tilde{v})} \tag{9}$$

Since both the real and imaginary parts of $\hat{n}_W(\tilde{v})$ are assumed known, the optical constants of the liquid may be obtained directly using this equation. Figure 19 shows results[69] obtained by this method up to a wavenumber of 200 cm^{-1} for liquid water for which α rises above 1000 neper cm^{-1}.

3.2.2   Measurements on heavily absorbing solids

The technique used in determining the submillimetre-wave optical constants of strongly absorbing solids is closely analogous to that described for liquids in Section 3.2.1. This technique was pioneered by Bell et al.[70] and instrumental variants and developments have been produced by Gast and Genzel,[71] Chamberlain et al.[72] and Parker et al.[73] Figure 20 shows the vertical layout employed at NPL, with phase modulation introduced by the vibrating 45° reflector in the variable-path arm.

We are concerned critically in this case, as in the previous case, with the dispersive phase-change on reflection at the specimen surface, and this phase must be related to the phase at a reference mirror located precisely in the plane of the specimen. This is far more difficult to arrange than one might

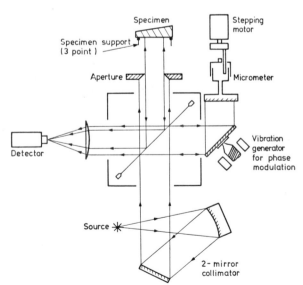

Fig. 20. Dispersive Fourier-transform spectrometer for determining the complex refractive-index spectra of absorbing solids.

imagine. The specimen must be optically worked, so that its surface defines a plane to better than 0.1 μm, and must be thick enough not to deform significantly under its own weight. Even light specimens of many materials of interest may suffer sufficient indentation, elastic or non-elastic, when supported on a three-ball support, to introduce phase errors which will invalidate the results. The reflective phase-changes are usually equivalent to only a few micrometres of effective path, and replacement of the specimen by the reference

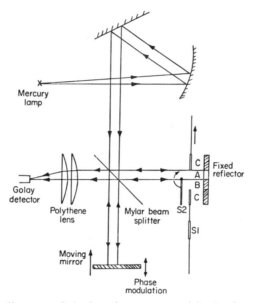

Fig. 21. Schematic diagram of the interferometer used by Parker *et al.* at Westfield College [73b]. Shown are the two movable screens S1 and S2 in front of the fixed reflector and the paths of the coherent beams of radiation using Part A.

mirror must be achieved to a fraction of a micrometre. A sophisticated mount is used therefore, in which the specimen or mirror is supported on three balls, defining a reference plane, but the major part of the weight is balanced out by three ball supports each mounted on the end of a light beam balance. Plate 3 is a picture of the instrument at present in use and gives an idea of the complex design of the specimen mount. It must be remembered that in these amplitude-reflectivity measurements very high thermal and mechanical stability is required, and good room-temperature control is essential. Since the radiation source necessarily generates considerable heat, it must be water-cooled and a prolonged warming-up period is required after switching on to achieve thermal equilibrium in the system. In the instrument described it is not possible to vary the specimen temperature, except to the limited extent allowed by varying the controlled ambient temperature.

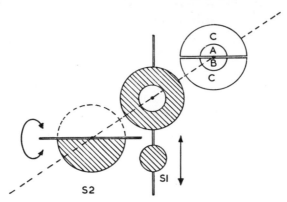

Fig. 22. The geometry of the two screens and the divisions of the field of view at the fixed reflector. A is the free specimen surface, B and C are surface aluminized (Parker and Chambers, Ref. 73(a)).

Chamberlain's method suffers from the mechanical disadvantages outlined above, but has the considerable merit of being non-destructive as far as the specimen is concerned. A powerful variant of his method has, however, been developed by Parker et al.[73a] at Westfield College, London. This is illustrated in Fig. 21. Phase modulation is used, which leads to a rather simpler optical layout, the fixed reflector being the specimen under examination. This is rigidly mounted in the interferometer and does not need to be replaced by a reference reflector, so that mechanical errors due to this procedure are eliminated. The specimen is partly aluminized as shown in Fig. 22, and areas A, B and C can be exposed separately by a system of opaque shutters, carefully designed to

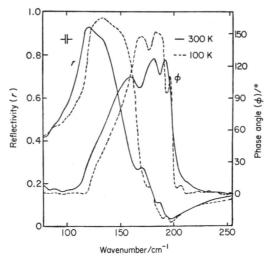

Fig. 23. Amplitude (r) and phase (ϕ) reflection-spectra of KBr at 300 and 100 K (Parker and Chambers, Ref. 73(b)).

prevent cross-talk between the three. The outer annular ring is only exposed for alignment purposes. Exposing areas A and B in turn, interferograms are recorded from the two coplanar surfaces. There is thus no requirement for the mirror to be exactly replaced by the specimen but the price paid is the loss of reflecting surface, and hence signal, and also the effective destruction of the specimen. The complex power-spectrum, $\hat{S}(\tilde{v})$, is computed from each interferogram, giving the amplitude, ρ, and the phase, ϕ. The amplitude reflectivity, r is then given by

$$r(\tilde{v}) = \frac{\rho(\tilde{v})}{\rho_0(\tilde{v})} \tag{10}$$

and the phase of the reflectivity by

$$\Phi(\tilde{v}) = \phi(\tilde{v}) - \phi_0(\tilde{v}) + \pi. \tag{11}$$

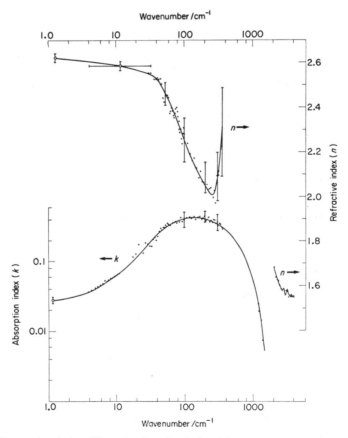

Fig. 24. Absorption-index (k) and refractive-index (n) spectra for ordinary soda glass at room temperature. The absorption index is the imaginary part of the complex refractive index $\hat{n} = n - ik$.

We can then determine the complex refraction spectrum from the relation

$$n(\tilde{v}) - ik(\tilde{v}) = \frac{1 + r(\tilde{v})\,e^{i\Phi(\tilde{v})}}{1 - r(\tilde{v})\,e^{i\Phi(\tilde{v})}} \tag{12}$$

Figure 23 shows the amplitude and phase spectra of KBr determined by Parker et al.[73b] using this method and excellent agreement has been achieved with results of other workers.

The complementary techniques of FTS and DFTS in reflection have also been applied to the measurement of the properties of ordinary soda glass,[74] in which the power-absorption coefficient peaks at about 350 cm^{-1} at a value of about 1500 neper cm^{-1}. The results for absorption index k and refractive index n are shown in Fig. 24. To measure the properties of materials with such high absorption using transmission techniques would require specimens too thin to be practicable.

4   FOURIER SPECTRORADIOMETRY OF PULSED PLASMAS

The Fellgett advantage, which is central to Fourier transform spectroscopy, only applies strictly in the detector-noise-limited case. If the principal source of noise is the random fluctuation of the source, i.e. if one is in the photon-noise-limited condition, then the advantage is lost and may even become a disadvantage. Great attention is therefore usually paid to maintaining the source emission as steady as possible in conventional Fourier-transform spectroscopy. If the source intensity is varying slowly in time, as for instance is often the case when atmospheric emission is being measured, the problem can then be overcome by recording the interferogram in a time short in relation to any significant change in intensity. But if we need to measure the time-varying emission of a pulsed source, such as a high-density pulsed plasma, during the lifetime of the pulse, then significantly different techniques are required. Two lines of attack have been developed. The first is designed to measure the time-varying emission from short pulses (lasting a few microseconds) and the second is to deal with the less demanding problem of measuring the emission spectrum when the pulses are up to 500 ms long, such as those from the Tokamak type of magnetically contained plasma.

4.1   The Time-varying Emission from Short-duration Pulses

The limitations imposed by detector sensitivity, detector speed of response and available speed of mirror scan make it impracticable at the moment to obtain useful spectral information from a single pulse. It is therefore necessary to make measurements on many pulses which must be reproducible in total energy, shape and spectral content if the results are to be meaningful. Essentially one is averaging several pulses so, if random pulse-to-pulse variations in emission much exceed detector noise, we shall be source-noise-limited and the Fellgett advantage will be lost.

The following procedure was developed at NPL[75,76] for measuring the short pulses from the linear-pinch discharge source at Imperial College, London. The emission pulses were received by a Michelson interferometer based upon the NPL modular-cube design, and featuring a boron-doped germanium photoconductive detector operating at liquid helium temperature. The response time of this detector is about 0.1 μs and its NEP 10^{-12} W Hz$^{-1/2}$. The interferometer was set at ZPD, the discharge fired and the signal intensity recorded as

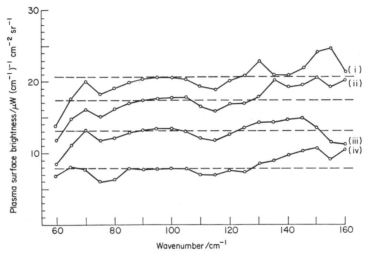

Fig. 25. Submillimetre-wave bremsstrahlung emission from a linear-pinch plasma during the collapse phase.

a time-function on an oscilloscope. The intensity was then measured from the recorded photographic trace at microsecond intervals following the initiation of the pulse. Repeated measurements were averaged and showed that reproducibility to $\pm 5\%$ was normally achieved. This procedure was then repeated on succeeding pulses, at path steps Δx, until adequate spectral resolution was achieved. A series of interferograms was thus constructed, corresponding to sequential moments in the life of the pulse. The pulses can only be generated at half-minute intervals, and so the whole operation is very time-consuming. However, the tedious procedure of measuring intensities from the oscillographs was subsequently superceded by the development of an automatic data-acquisition system.[77]

Figure 25 shows some results obtained by this method, illustrating the submillimetre-wave bremsstrahlung emission from a linear-pinch plasma during the collapse phase immediately prior to t_{pri} (time of peak radiation intensity). The spectral resolution was 10 cm^{-1} and the time-resolution about 0.5 μs.

4.2 The Measurement of Millimetre and Submillimetre-wave Power from Tokamak Machines

The recently developed Tokamak is one of the most successful magnetic containment devices currently used in the field of thermonuclear fusion research. The vessel in which the plasma is generated is toroidal, and a number of viewing ports are provided for diagnostic purposes. Plasma temperatures in the 10^7 K region are currently being produced in the research machines and this is only one order of magnitude less than the 10^8 K which will be necessary for a future working reactor. In such a device it will be important, of course, to restrict energy losses from the plasma to a minimum, and one possibly serious source of loss is electron cyclotron emission in the millimetre/submillimetre waveband.

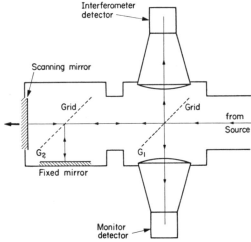

Fig. 26. Rapid-scan polarization interferometer developed for measurement of electron cyclotron emission from a Tokamak plasma.

Fourier spectrometric methods of measuring this loss have been recently developed at NPL and applied to Tokamak machines in Britain, France and the United States.

Figure 26 shows the basic configuration used.[78] It is not the simple form of Michelson interferometer but, instead, a polarizing interferometer incorporating two wire-grid beam-dividers, and working on the principle developed by Martin and Puplett.[79] The way this device operates is outlined in Section 5, and it is sufficient here to remark that the system has a flat spectral response from the long (millimetre) wave region into the infrared, its frequency performance being limited only by the quality and spacing of the wires. In the region in which we are interested here, it is significantly superior to a conventional Michelson interferometer with plastic-film beam division. Moreover, the first grid, G_1, acts not only as a polarizer, but transmits the perpendicular radiation component directly on to a second detector in order to monitor the power of the source. The interferometric modulation is produced by a rapidly vibrating mirror, scanning the path-difference through 20 mm at 50 Hz. The instrument therefore has a wavenumber resolution of 0.5 cm^{-1} and a time resolution of 10 ms. Since the duration of a Tokamak pulse is typically 0.2 s, 20 measurements are recorded during a single pulse. For the wavelength region of interest ($\lambda = 0.05$–0.5 cm) the audio-frequencies, corresponding to the range of spectral elements, extend up to 4000 Hz and the detector should therefore have a

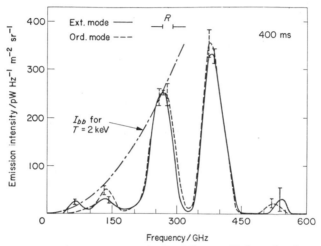

Fig. 27. Cyclotron emission spectrum obtained from a Tokamak plasma. I_{bb}—black body intensity at temperature T. Tokamak field 5.0 Tesla.

response time less than 10^{-4} s. It also needs to be relatively insensitive to electrical pick-up, which is intense in the vicinity of the large pulsed source, and to have a low NEP since fairly low power levels need to be measured in the research phase of the programme. The indium-antimonide photoconductive-detector of Putley[21] has been found to be the most suitable to date.

Figure 27 shows the cyclotron emission spectrum measured on the French TFR (Tokamak à Fontenay-aux-Roses) in the radial direction from the torus and in two perpendicular polarizations. The two curves are seen to be similar. This is an unexpected result, since on theoretical grounds the extraordinary emission was expected to be dominant. It is thought that multiple reflection at the torus walls is largely responsible for this discrepancy.

The power calibration of the instrument was carried out using a high-pressure mercury-arc discharge lamp, which is equivalent to a black body at about 3000 K in this spectral region, and also using a 2 mm Klystron of known power. The total uncertainty of the absolute intensity levels in the emission lines is ±40%, but the relative intensities and frequency positions can be relied on to ±10%.

Though the goal of economic power generation from high-temperature plasmas is yet a long way off, the two techniques described give us not only measurements of power loss, which can assist in extrapolating into the still-higher temperature regime of the future reactor, but also provide diagnostic information, for example on the number densities and temperatures of the plasma electrons.

5   INSTRUMENTAL INNOVATIONS

5.1   The Polarizing Interferometer

The Michelson interferometer with a single-film dielectric beam-divider is conceptually the simplest two-beam instrument. Its transmissivity is, however, strongly wavenumber-dependent because of multiple-beam interference in the film,[51] this dependence taking the form of a sequence of lobes, the widths of which are determined by the film thickness. Absorption in the beam divider, which is invariably encountered in the far infrared, also influences the spectral transmission and the higher wavenumber lobes may become too attenuated to be useful. Moreover, since the lobe pattern has a zero at zero wavenumber, the transmissivity always falls towards zero at long wavelengths. Another way of looking at this is to say that as the wavelength becomes long in relation to the optical thickness of the film, the reflectivity falls to zero and the efficiency of the beam divider falls with it. This deficiency is not present in the operation of the lamellar grating interferometer,[51] but on the other hand this device suffers from other severe limitations. Thus its resolution is limited because radiation 'shadowing' occurs as the groove depth is increased and its operational pass-band has to be a compromise between low and high frequency performance. Additionally it does not lend itself readily to the application of such powerful techniques as phase-modulation or fast scanning.

An ingenious solution to the problem of providing a broad spectral response, without a superimposed pattern of lobes, has been provided by Martin and Puplett.[79] This is the polarizing interferometer referred to in the earlier sections. The performance of the polarizing interferometer has been established in many experiments at NPL and elsewhere, but a particularly spectacular confirmation comes from the work of Carli et al.[80] who have obtained spectra of the atmosphere from an aircraft at an altitude of about 10 km, with a resolution of 0.02 cm^{-1} from linearly apodized interferograms. The instrumental performance showed the expected flat response but the spectra could only be observed from 3–40 cm^{-1} because, at higher wavenumbers, water-vapour emission is so intense that the black-body continuum limit is reached. Operation up to 200 cm^{-1} is now quite feasible—especially for dielectric spectroscopy —and there is no *a priori* reason why performance up to 500 cm^{-1} should not be achieved. It is really just a technical problem of grid construction and this development is currently proceeding at Queen Mary College, London, and at NPL by Costley *et al.* The wire used for the grid is always tungsten, despite its brittleness. Commercial grids are available (wound with tungsten) from the Spectroscopic Accessory Company of London.

The principle of operation of the polarizing interferometer is best understood from the explanation given by Martin and Puplett which we follow closely here. For simplicity they consider a hypothetical instrument with a beam dividing grid, D_1, and a beam uniting grid, D_2 (see Fig. 28). In the normal Michelson

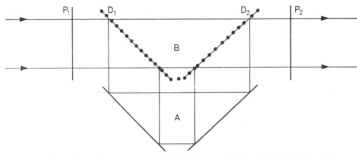

Fig. 28. Polarization interferometer of Martin and Puplett.[79] P_1, P_2—polarizers; D_1, D_2—grid beam-dividers; A, B—interfering beams.

interferometer, of course, the functions of these two grids are combined in a single optical element. As indicated in the figure, the wire grids are located with the stretched wires perpendicular to the plane of the paper, which we will refer to as the horizontal plane. The wires are therefore vertical. The incoming unpolarized radiation is plane polarized by P_1 in a direction 45° to the vertical, so that at D_1 half of the incident radiation is transmitted with its electric vector polarized in the horizontal plane and half is reflected polarized in the vertical plane. At D_2 the two beams are recombined into a single beam which, due to the path difference between beams A and B, is elliptically polarized. This resultant beam is then again plane polarized by P_2, which has its axis either parallel with or perpendicular to P_1.

The signal detected can be shown to vary with path difference in the same way as with a conventional Michelson interferometer. If polarizers P_1 and P_2 are parallel then, for radiation of wavenumber $\tilde{\nu}$, the intensity is given by

$$I_{\parallel} = \frac{I_0}{2}(1 + \cos 2\pi\tilde{\nu}x) \tag{13}$$

where I_0 is the plane polarized intensity incident on D_1 and x is the path difference between the beams.

Similarly,

$$I_{\perp} = \frac{I_0}{2}(1 - \cos 2\pi\tilde{\nu}x) \tag{14}$$

The interferogram, $I(x)$, for a broad-band source will be the sum of all components, $I_\parallel$ or $I_\perp$, and the power spectrum is again obtained from the Fourier transform of the interferogram. By subtracting $I_\perp$ from $I_\parallel$ one can get an interferogram which oscillates about a true zero and this would have, as remarked earlier, the advantage of improving signal-to-noise ratio by eliminating variations in the d.c. term, $I_0/2$. An elegant way of achieving this is to replace P_1 or P_2 with a polarizing chopper, the sectors of which are themselves

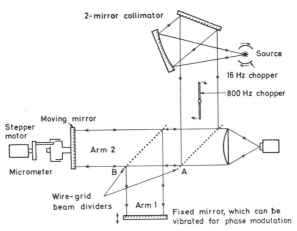

Fig. 29. Typical polarization interferometer as used at NPL.

wire grid polarizers aligned alternately at right angles in the plane of rotation. Instrumentation based on this idea is currently being developed at Queen Mary College, London.

The flat spectral range of the polarizing interferometer is limited by the spacing of the wires, by the flatness of the grid and, to a lesser extent, by the optical constants of the metal. The high-wavenumber performance begins to deteriorate significantly above $\tilde{v} = (4d)^{-1}$ where d is the wire spacing, so to get mid-infrared performance, d has to be small. Free-standing grids are the preferred form but, when one is thinking of the 500 cm^{-1}-and-above region, they become rather impractical. The manufacture of free-standing grids made from 5 μm diameter wire and with $d = 10$ μm is currently being undertaken by Costley at NPL but, for finer spacing, one must resort to grids produced on plastic film by lithographic methods. Development of this technique is going ahead at Queen Mary College, London. Polarizers and beam dividers up to 10 cm (or more) in diameter will be produced by a simple replication procedure on a plastic-film substrate only 2 μm thick. The effect of such a thin substrate on the performance of the grids is expected to be negligible. If these grids prove to work well, the polarizing interferometer will become usable up to the mid-infrared region, but in the meantime spectroscopists are well served by a combination of free-standing grids for the region up to 200 cm^{-1} and film beam-dividers for the region 200–600 cm^{-1}.

The grids are generally more fragile and subject to damage than the plastic film beam-dividers and, of course, once broken they cannot be replaced at the trivial cost of replacing a plastic film; however, the considerable advantage of

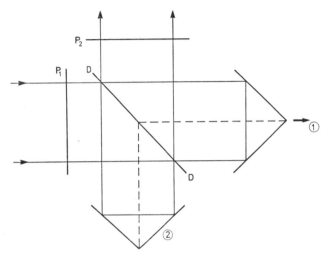

Fig. 30. Polarizing interferometer of Martin and Puplett,[79] using roof-top reflectors. P$_1$, P$_2$—polarizers; D—beam divider; 1,2—roof-top reflectors.

flat response has led to their being the preferred divider for the submillimetre region and the polarizing interferometer is found to be just as flexible in application as the conventional instrument. Figure 29 shows a practical configuration which can be used either with phase or amplitude modulation, whilst Fig. 30 shows an interferometer using two 'roof-top' retro-reflectors which rotate the plane of polarization of each beam through 90° and make possible a configuration similar to that of the conventional Michelson interferometer.

5.2   Power Reflection Measurements using FTS

The dispersive Fourier methods described in Section 3 provide the means for determining the complex refractive indices of a wide range of materials from the very transparent to the near opaque. Moreover, using a variety of editing/ computing procedures, coupled with a range of experimental techniques, the effects of surface reflections and multiple interference can now be readily accounted for. DFTS equipment, however, particularly for measurements in reflection on strongly absorbing solid specimens, is expensive and sophisticated and its operation usually requires skilled and experienced workers. In many cases, only the power reflectivity of the specimen (that is, the square of the

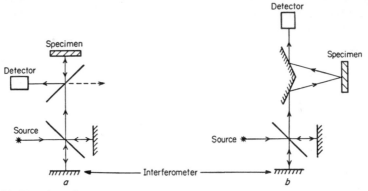

Fig. 31. Two interferometer configurations for power-reflection measurements.

modulus of the complex reflectivity) may be required, and this can be measured by simpler means. Two interferometer configurations for making power-reflectivity measurements are shown in Fig. 31. As is well known, the reflectivities of an interface between two isotropic media differ for radiation polarized parallel with, and perpendicular to, the plane of incidence for all except normal rays. It is necessary, therefore, to define the angle of incidence if meaningful results are to be obtained. For convenience, and to obtain maximum signal, the arrangement shown in Fig. 31 (b) may be used at an average angle of incidence of about 10°, in which case the effect of polarization will be small. However, the normal-incidence configuration shown in Fig. 31 (a) is used at NPL;[81] in this arrangement half the signal is lost, but use is made of phase modulation and highly sensitive helium-cooled detectors to compensate as far as possible for this loss. Figure 32 shows the power reflection spectra of two

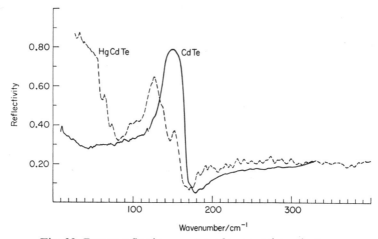

Fig. 32. Power-reflection spectra of two semi-conductors.

semi-conductor specimens recorded with the NPL equipment. A measurement is made with the specimen in position, and then again with the specimen replaced by a reference mirror. The resulting power reflectivity will then be given by

$$|\hat{r}(\tilde{\nu})|^2 = \frac{(n-1)^2 + k^2}{(n+1)^2 + k^2} \tag{15}$$

provided the effects of internal reflections are negligible.

The optical constants n and k themselves cannot be determined very easily from these data, as a Kramers-Kronig analysis involves uncertainties arising from the use of a truncated integral, and the alternative procedures, involving the recording of data in two polarizations and at varying angles of incidence, lack sensitivity. If the full complex permittivity is required it is best to resort to DFTS.

5.3 Multiple Specimen Holders

Fourier transform spectroscopy is still, despite several ingenious attempts to circumvent it, a single-beam technique in which spectra obtained with and without the specimen in the beam are ratioed to produce the transmission spectrum of the specimen. For measurement in the far-infrared region the instrument is evacuated and the process of breaking the vacuum to remove or replace the specimen can introduce undesirable complications. Most users have therefore devised means by which specimen and blank can be interchanged without otherwise disturbing the interferometer. One solution, used by the commercial instrument manufacturers, is to have a large sample chamber containing a system of mirrors which can be controlled from outside. The beam can be switched readily and it is even possible with some designs to determine the reflection spectrum as well as the transmission spectrum. This experimental facility is gained however at the cost of reduced étendue or 'light-grasp' and, when this cannot be tolerated, variant designs are necessary. Nicol has developed at NPL a rotatable cold finger assembly which permits specimens and blanks, both at liquid-nitrogen temperature, to be rotated into and out of the beam. This can be used with the small sample chambers of the modular-cube system thus ensuring the largest possible étendue. Fleming has developed an ingenious device which rotates specimens and blanks into the optical path of the liquid-helium-filled light-pipe of the Putley detector. Birch[81] has developed a similar device which permits power-reflection spectra to be obtained from specimen and reference at liquid helium temperature.

6 CONCLUSION

A few years ago, the rapid development of tunable coherent emission devices for the far infrared seemed to threaten the continued development of inter-ferometry. However, it has proved unexpectedly difficult to make these sources give out much power at a reasonably narrow linewidth and additionally they are still very expensive and capricious in their operation. These facts have restricted their use to some very special experiments and the vast majority of far-infrared experiments are still done by interferometry. Of course, the limi-tation of interferometry is still the low emission from the black-body sources, which are all we have, but nevertheless there are very few experiments which have proved beyond the capabilities of the modern interferometers and their associated equipment.

ACKNOWLEDGMENTS

We are glad to acknowledge the assistance given by our colleagues M. N. Afsar, J. R. Birch, A. E. Costley and J. W. Fleming in reading and commenting on the typescript. Professor D. H. Martin of Queen Mary College and Dr T. J. Parker of Westfield College, London, kindly supplied information and figures.

REFERENCES

(1) A. A. Michelson, *Light Waves and their Uses*, University of Chicago Press, 1902; *Studies in Optics*, University of Chicago Press, Phoenix Edition, 1962.
(2) P. B. Fellgett, Ohio State Symposium on Molecular Spectroscopy (1952).
(3) P. Jacquinot, *J. Opt. Soc. Am.* **44**, 761 (1954).
(4) P. Jacquinot, *Rep. Prog. Phys.* **23**, 267 (1960).
(5) J. Connes and P. Connes, *J. Opt. Soc. Am.* **56**, 896 (1966); J. Connes, P. Connes and J. P. Maillard, *Atlas des Spectres dans le Proche Infrarouge de Venus, Mars, Jupiter et Saturne*, Centre National de la Récherche Scientifique, Paris, 1969.
(6) J. W. Fleming, *IEEE Trans. Microwave Theory Tech.* **MTT-22** Pt. 1, 1023 (1974); J. W. Fleming and G. W. Chantry, *IEEE Trans. Instrum. Meas.* **IM-23**, 473 (1974).
(7) J. Chamberlain, *Principles of Interferometric Spectroscopy*, Completed, Revised and Edited by G. W. Chantry and N. W. B. Stone, Wiley, 1977.
(8) *Proceedings of the Aspen Conference on Fourier Spectroscopy*, AFCRL-71-0019, Special Report No. 114.
(9) H. A. Gebbie, N. W. B. Stone, G. Topping, E. K. Gora, S. A. Clough and F. X. Kneizys, *J. Mol. Spectrosc.* **19**, 7 (1966).
(10) H. A. Gebbie and N. W. B. Stone, *Proc. Phys. Soc.* **82**, 309 (1963).
(11) J. W. Fleming and M. J. Gibson, *J. Mol. Spectrosc.* **62**, 326 (1976).
(12) G. R. Bird, G. R. Hunt, H. A. Gebbie and N. W. B. Stone, *J. Mol. Spectrosc.* **33**, 244 (1970).
(13) J. E. Harries, *Nature* **241**, 515 (1973).
(14) J. E. Harries, D. G. Moss and N. R. W. Swann, *Nature* **250**, 475 (1974).
(15) J. W. Fleming, *Chem. Phys. Lett.* **25**, 553 (1974).
(16) J. W. Fleming and R. P. Wayne, *Chem. Phys. Lett.* **32**, 135 (1975).
(17) J. W. Fleming and G. F. Neill, *J. Mol. Spectrosc.* **59**, 493 (1976).
(18) G. W. Chantry, H. M. Evans, J. Chamberlain and H. A. Gebbie, *Infrared Phys.* **9**, 85 (1969).

(19) D. G. Moss, *J. Phys. E.*, to be published.
(20) M. A. Kinch and B. V. Rollin, *Br. J. Appl. Phys.* **14**, 672 (1963).
(21) E. H. Putley, *Phys. Technol.* **4**, 202 (1973); *J. Sci. Instrum.* **43**, 857 (1966).
(22) E. H. Putley, *Appl. Opt.* **4**, 649 (1965).
(23) T. G. Blaney, *Rev. Phys. Appl.* **9**, 279 (1974).
(24) H. D. Drew and A. J. Sievers, *Appl. Opt.* **8**, 2067 (1969).
(25) J. U. White, *J. Opt. Soc. Am.* **32**, 285 (1942); E. R. Stephens, *Infrared Phys.* **1**, 187 (1961).
(26) G. W. Chantry and J. W. Fleming, *Infrared Phys.* **16**, 655 (1976).
(27) J. W. Fleming and J. Chamberlain, *Infrared Phys.* **14**, 277 (1974).
(28) J. Connes, *J. Phys. Radium* **19**, 197 (1958).
(29) R. J. Bell, *Introductory Fourier Transform Spectroscopy*, Academic Press, New York, 1972, p. 261.
(30) S. Chapman, *Rep. Prog. Phys.* **9**, 92 (1943).
(31) E. K. Gora, *J. Mol. Spectrosc.* **3**, 78 (1959).
(32) J. Chamberlain, *Infrared Phys.* **11**, 25 (1971).
(33) J. Chamberlain and H. A. Gebbie, *Infrared Phys.* **11**, 57 (1971).
(34) M. L. Forman, W. H. Steel and G. A. Vanasse, *J. Opt. Soc. Am.* **56**, 59 (1966).
(35) J. W. Fleming, *High-Resolution Far Infrared Studies of the Absorption Spectra of Gases*, NPL Report Mat. App. 34 (1974).
(36) References (15), (16) and (17) and also J. W. Fleming, *Spectrochim. Acta* **32A**, 787 (1976).
(37) J. W. Fleming, *Application of the Fast-Fourier-Transform Technique in Submillimetre-Wave Spectrometry*, NPL Report Mat. App. 27 (1973).
(38) H. Johnston, *Science* **173**, 517 (1971).
(39) P. J. Crutzen, *J. Geophys. Res.* **76**, 7311 (1971).
(40) C. B. Farmer, IAGA Conference, Kyoto, Japan (1973).
(41) M. Ackerman, J. C. Fontanella, D. Frimout, A. Girard, N. Louisnard, C. Muller and D. Nevejans, *C.R. Acad. Sci. Paris E.* **277**, Série B, 33(1973).
(42) J. P. Baluteau, E. Bussoletti, P. Lena and A. Marten, *Proc. 2nd CIAP Conf.* (A. J. Broderick, ed.), Transportation Systems Centre, Cambridge, Mass., 1972, p. 99.
(43) J. E. Harries and N. W. B. Stone, *ibid.* p. 78.
(44) J. E. Harries, J. R. Birch, J. W. Fleming, N. W. B. Stone, D. G. Moss, N. R. W. Swann and G. F. Neill, *Proc. 3rd CIAP Conf.* (A. J. Broderick and T. M. Hard, eds.), 1974, p. 197.
(45) J. E. Harries, NPL Reports DES16 (1972), DES21 (1973), Dept. of Trade and Industry, Crown Copyright.
(46) J. E. Harries, NPL Report DES24 (1973), Dept. of Trade and Industry, Crown Copyright.
(47) J. E. Harries, D. G. Moss, N. R. W. Swann and G. F. Neill, *Nature* **259**, 300 (1976).
(48) W. J. Burroughs and J. E. Harries, *Infrared Phys.* **11**, 99 (1971).
(49) H. A. Gebbie, W. J. Burroughs and G. R. Bird, *Proc. Roy. Soc. London A* **310**, 579 (1969).
(50) J. Blamont of CNRS Service d'Aéronomie, Verrieres du Buisson Paris, kindly supplied this equipment.
(51) G. W. Chantry, *Submillimetre Spectroscopy*, Academic Press, London and New York, 1971.
(52) J. Chamberlain, Submillimetre-Wave Techniques in *High-Frequency Dielectric Measurement* (J. Chamberlain and G. W. Chantry, eds.), IPC Science and Technology Press Ltd., Guildford, 1973.
(53) J. Chamberlain, J. E. Gibbs and H. A. Gebbie, *Infrared Phys.* **9**, 185 (1969).
(54) J. Chamberlain, J. E. Gibbs and H. A. Gebbie, *Nature* **198**, 874 (1963).

(55) J. Chamberlain, *Infrared Phys.* **12**, 145 (1972).
(56) D. D. Honijk, W. F. Passchier, M. Mandel and M. N. Afsar, *Infrared Phys.* **16**, 257 (1976).
(57) D. D. Honijk, W. F. Passchier and M. Mandel, *Physica* **64**, 171 (1973); **68**, 457 (1973): W. F. Passchier, D. D. Honijk and M. Mandel, *Infrared Phys.* **15**, 95 (1975); **16**, 389 (1976).
(58) J. Chamberlain, M. N. Afsar, D. K. Murray, G. D. Price and M. S. Zafar, *IEEE Trans. Instrum. Meas.* **IM-23** (4), 483 (1974).
(59) J. Chamberlain, M. N. Afsar and J. B. Hasted, *Nature (London) Phys. Sci.* **245**, 28 (1973).
(60) N. W. B. Stone, J. E. Harries, D. W. E. Fuller, J. G. Edwards, A. E. Costley, J. Chamberlain, T. G. Blaney, J. R. Birch and A. E. Bailey, *Proc. IEEE.* **122**, 10R (1975).
(61) M. N. Afsar, J. B. Hasted and J. Chamberlain, *Infrared Phys.* **16**, 301 (1976).
(62) D. D. Honijk, W. F. Passchier, M. Mandel and M. N. Afsar, *Infrared Phys.* (in press).
(63) M. N. Afsar, *Physica*, to be published.
(64) D. D. Honijk, W. F. Passchier, P. J. Doorschodt, W. C. Bauer and M. Mandel, to be published.
(65) J. Goulon, J. L. Rivail, M. N. Afsar and G. W. Chantry, to be published.
(66) J. W. Fleming, *Infrared Phys.* **10**, 57 (1970).
(67) H. Kilp, D. C. Barnes, F. W. J. Clutterbuck, M. N. Afsar and G. W. Chantry, *J. Phys. E.*, to be published.
(68) H. Kilp, M. N. Afsar and G. W. Chantry, *Infrared Phys.*, to be published.
(69) (a) J. Chamberlain, M. S. Zafar and J. B. Hasted, *Nature (Lond.) Phys. Sci.* **243**, 116 (1973).
     (b) J. Chamberlain, M. N. Afsar, J. B. Hasted, M. S. Zafar and G. J. Davies, *Nature*, **255**, 319 (1975).
(70) E. E. Bell, *Proc. Aspen Intern. Conf. Fourier Spectrosc.*, 1970, p. 71; *AFCRL-71-0019 Special Report* 114 (1971); *Infrared Phys*, **6**, 57 (1966); K. W. Johnston and E. E. Bell, *Phys. Rev.* **187**, 1044 (1969).
(71) J. Gast and L. Genzel, *Opt. Commun.* **8**, 26 (1973).
(72) J. R. Birch, G. D. Price and J. Chamberlain, *Infrared Phys.* **16**, 311 (1976).
(73) (a) T. J. Parker and W. G. Chambers, *IEEE Trans.* **MTT-22**, No. 12 (1974).
     (b) T. J. Parker and W. G. Chambers, *Infrared Phys.* **16**, 349 (1976).
(74) J. R. Birch and N. W. B. Stone, *J. Phys. E.* **6**, 1101 (1973); J. R. Birch, R. J. Cook, A. F. Harding, R. G. Jones and G. D. Price, *J. Phys. D.* **8**, 1353 (1975).
(75) J. Chamberlain, A. E. Costley and D. D. Burgess, *Proc. Symposium on Submillimetre Waves*, Polytechnic Institute of Brooklyn, New York, 1970, p. 573.
(76) A. E. Costley, J. Chamberlain and D. D. Burgess, *IERE Conf. Proc.* **22**, 197 (1971).
(77) A. E. Costley, T. J. Bonney, P. Garnett and J. E. G. Wheaton, *IERE Conf. Proc.* **20**, 173 (1970).
(78) A. E Costley, J. Chamberlain, K. Muruoka and D. D. Burgess, 1st Intern. Conf. on Submillimetre Waves and their Applications, Atlanta, Georgia (1974), Digest of technical papers, IEEE Cat. No. 74, CHO 856-5MTT, p. 147; A. E. Costley and J. Chamberlain, *IERE Conf. Publ.* **113**, 210 (1974); A. E. Costley, R. J. Hastie, J. W. M. Paul and J. Chamberlain, *Phys. Rev. Lett.* **33**, 758 (1974).
(79) D. H. Martin and E. Puplett, *Infrared Phys.* **10**, 105 (1969).
(80) B. Carli, D. H. Martin and E. Puplett, *Nature* **257**, 649 (1975).
(81) J. R. Birch, *Infrared Phys.* **12**, 29 (1972).

Chapter 3

FORCE-CONSTANT CALCULATIONS—THE STATE OF THE ART

Peter Gans

Department of Inorganic and Structural Chemistry, The University, Leeds LS2 9JT, U.K.

1 INTRODUCTION

The computation of force constants has proved to be an almost intractable problem. The principal reason for this is that, diatomic molecules apart, the amount of information required to make the force-constants determinate in a mathematical sense is usually greater than can be obtained experimentally.

To determine n parameters, a minimum of n independent observations is required. However, if the observations are subject to experimental error the relationships between parameters and observables will be partly inconsistent, so usually more observables than parameters are needed. This situation is treated by the principle of least squares. But there are certain assumptions concerning the distribution of errors underlying the principle of least squares[1] which are not normally met in force-constant calculations. In particular, estimates of the errors in parameters will not be very meaningful if the degree of over-determination is small. So, although the principle of least squares is usually applied in force-constant calculations, it is usually not fully justified.

This review is concerned with the tactics that have been employed to obtain meaningful results from force-constant calculations and concentrates on attempts to overcome the mathematical difficulties that are the direct result of their indeterminate nature. The treatment is somewhat selective, following the author's interests, but the literature has been scanned to the end of 1975, some two years later than the last reviews to appear on this subject.[2,3]

The basic theory is laid out in the classic book entitled *Molecular Vibrations*,[4] and a number of simplified texts have since appeared.[5-9] Most recently a rigorous up-to-date and comprehensive text has appeared which covers all aspects of the theory of vibrations.[10] The only major new development, the calculation of anharmonic force constants, is discussed below as is the extension of the theory to crystal lattices, which is gaining impetus at the present time.

Implicit in all that follows is the Born-Oppenheimer approximation. Bunker[11] has considered the breakdown of this approximation for diatomic molecules. He showed that while the Dunham expansion, eqn. (1), is still valid the Dunham coefficients Y_{ij} are now dependent on the quantities k_i and l_i.

$$F(v, J) = \sum_{ij} Y_{ij}(v+\tfrac{1}{2})^i[J(J+1)]^j \tag{1}$$

However the necessary corrections to force constants are less than 0.1% for all diatomics. Hence, for most purposes the error introduced by making the Born-Oppenheimer approximation is smaller than the experimental errors.[12] The main consequence of the Born-Oppenheimer approximation is that force constants are invariant to isotopic substitution.[13]

Few developments have taken place in the application of group theory. Molecules with internal rotation have been considered within the Longuet-Higgins framework. For example Y_2X-XY_2 molecules such as ethene[14] are treated in the double group $G_{16}^{(2)}$ and $M(CH_3)_2$ molecules[15] in the double group $G_{36}{}^\dagger$. Edgell[16] has made an important suggestion. Considering the molecule $Mn(CO)_5Br$, whose Raman spectrum does not obey the C_{4v} selection rules, he has pointed out that a molecule may contain chemically equivalent atoms or groups which are symmetrically non-equivalent—the axial and equatorial carbonyl groups in this case. Thus, the molecule has the dual symmetry of a point group and a permutation group, and the selection rules calculated on that basis for $Mn(CO)_5Br$ are in agreement with experiment. Tables for factor group analysis of crystal spectra have been published.[17]

Model force fields such as Urey-Bradley (UBFF and MUBFF) and Orbital Valence Force Field (OVFF and MOVFF) will not be considered here; these have been reviewed.[2] Examples of the comparison of UBFF, MUBFF, OVFF and MOVFF with the general quadratic valence force field have been given for hexahalides[18] and hexahalide complexes of lanthanide ions.[19]

1.1   Definitions

The potential function V is expanded as a Taylor series in displacement co-ordinates from an equilibrium configuration (2, 3).

$$V = \tfrac{1}{2}\sum_{ij} F_{ij}r_i r_j + \frac{1}{3!}\sum_{ijk} F_{ijk}r_i r_j r_k + \frac{1}{4!}\sum_{ijkl} F_{ijkl}r_i r_j r_k r_l + \ldots \tag{2}$$

$$V_e = 0; \quad \frac{\partial V}{\partial r_i} = 0; \quad F_{ij} = \frac{\partial^2 V}{\partial r_i \partial r_j}; \quad F_{ijk} = \frac{\partial^3 V}{\partial r_i \partial r_j \partial r_k}; \quad F_{ijkl} = \frac{\partial^4 V}{\partial r_i \partial r_j \partial r_k \partial r_l} \tag{3}$$

The displacement coordinates may refer to atomic positions (cartesian co-ordinates, r), inter-atomic parameters (internal coordinates, R) or symmetry-adapted combinations (symmetry coordinates, S). The normal coordinates are represented by Q.

The conditions that the molecule does not undergo translational or rotational

motions are known as the Eckart conditions, eqn. (4). Now, if an isotopic substitution is made, the displacements r_k in eqn. (4)

$$\sum_k \beta_{ik} r_k = 0 \quad i = 1 \ldots 6 \tag{4}$$

will change. This has an important consequence for the internal coordinates, R,
which are said to be **rectilinear** if they are related by a linear transformation, eqn.
(5), to the cartesian coordinates.

$$R_i = \sum_k B_{ik} r_k \tag{5}$$

Because of the mass dependence of the Eckart conditions, rectilinear coordinates
are also mass dependent. When the expansion given as eqn. (2) is truncated at the
quadratic term the mass dependence of the force constants disappears; when the
expansion is carried to cubic and higher terms, **curvilinear** coordinates, which are
related to cartesians by a non-linear transformation, must be used, as for
example in eqn. (6).

$$R_i = \sum_k B_{ik} r_k + \sum_j \sum_k B_{ijk} r_j r_k + \ldots \tag{6}$$

Thus, a **harmonic** force-constant calculation in which the F_{ij} are obtained may
be performed in rectilinear coordinates. An **anharmonic** calculation, where the
cubic force constants F_{ijk} and/or quartic force constants F_{ijkl} are calculated,
must be performed in curvilinear coordinates. Only for the molecule CO_2 has
the calculation been carried beyond the quartic terms.[20,21] The discussion of
anharmonic force-constant calculations is thus conveniently considered
separately.

1.2 Anharmonic Force Constants

Two excellent reviews on anharmonic calculations have appeared
recently,[22,23] and the reader is referred to these for more details. Some indication of the difficulties involved is given by counting the number of force constants involved. Following Watson,[24] the number of independent structural
parameters required to specify a force field is given by the number of times (n_p)
the totally symmetric representation appears in $[\Gamma^n_{\text{vib}}]$, where Γ_{vib} is the direct
sum of the irreducible representations for which the molecular vibrations are a
basis. $[\Gamma^2_{\text{vib}}]$ gives the number of quadratic force constants, $[\Gamma^3_{\text{vib}}]$ the number of
cubic ones, and so forth. $[\Gamma^n_{\text{vib}}]$ is the nth symmetric power of Γ_{vib}, as in eqns.
(7–10).

$$n_p = \frac{1}{g} \sum_R \chi^i(R) \tag{7}$$

$$\chi^2(R) = \tfrac{1}{2}[\chi(R)^2 + \chi(R^2)] \tag{8}$$

$$\chi^3(R) = \tfrac{1}{6}[\chi(R)^3 + 3\chi(R)\chi(R^2) + 2\chi(R^3)] \tag{9}$$

$$\chi^4(R) = \tfrac{1}{24}[\chi(R)^4 + 6\chi(R^2)\chi(R)^2 + 8\chi(R)\chi(R^3) + 3\chi(R^2)^2 + 6\chi(R^4)] \tag{10}$$

$\chi''(R)$ is the character in $[\Gamma''_{vib}]$ under the symmetry operation R. The number of force constants for some small molecules is given in Table 1. Recalling the earlier comment regarding the number of observables required, it is clear that a quartic force field for a molecule such as NOCl is virtually unobtainable. Mills[22] gives the quartic force field for 54 diatomic species and lists 25 triatomic species for which anharmonic force field calculations have been reported; only eight of these are well-determined quartic fields.

TABLE 1
Number of force constants in small molecules

Molecule	quadratic	cubic	quartic	total
XY	1	1	1	3
YXY linear	3	3	6	12
YXZ linear	4	6	9	19
YXXY linear	6	11	23	40
YXY bent	4	6	9	19
YXZ bent	6	10	15	40
Y_3XZ	12	38	102	152

The situation is far from gloomy however. Various model potential functions have been described,[23] which, by giving relationships amongst the cubic and quartic constants, permit more accurate determination of the quadratic constants. Thus molecules as complex as ethene may be analysed.[25] In any case, using a model function greatly reduces the number of parameters and hence the number of experimental data required. For example, for SO_2 and NO_2 a 19 parameter function was reduced to one of nine parameters.[26]

Another approach involves the acquisition of more and better data by unconventional spectroscopic means. These chiefly involve the use of lasers. Emission lines from a $^{13}C^{16}O$ laser in the region 1500–1900 cm^{-1} were measured to an accuracy of ± 0.003 cm^{-1}.[27] Another laser study of carbon monoxide extended measurements from $J = 28$ to $J = 37$ ($P_{36} \approx 1218$ cm^{-1}) so that Dunham coefficients up to the sixth degree could be obtained.[28] In fact this has forced the theoreticians to take centrifugal distortion theory to higher[29] and higher[30] (12th) order approximation. With so much data forthcoming it is not surprising that a computer program has been written to deal with it.[31]

Another class of experiments which provides precise and extensive data involves double resonance,[32] of which there are now numerous varieties. For example, infrared/microwave double resonance permitted the vibration-rotation spectrum of methane to be measured with a precision customarily associated with microwave spectra.[33] The 3.39 μm line of a He/Ne laser was used. Further advances will undoubtedly come with the use of tunable lasers, such as the spin-flip Raman laser.[32]

The technique of anharmonic force-constant calculation obviously is complex.

The experimental quantities are the frequencies of rotational and vibrational-rotational lines. From these may be calculated the 'spectroscopic constants' such as harmonic frequency, anharmonicity constant, rotational constant, Coriolis coupling constant, centrifugal distortion constant and others (Ref. 22, Table 3). The relationship between these quantities and the force constants is then determined and, if necessary, the Jacobian elements ($\partial c / \partial F_{ij}$), etc., are calculated. The object of a least squares refinement is thus to reproduce the spectroscopic constants. A difficulty with this technique is that the precision of each spectroscopic constant is different, so that the degree of over-determination varies for various force constants.[34]

The alternative method, which is to iterate directly on the observed frequencies, suffers from the opposite defect; data which could make evaluation of higher-order constants possible are ignored, but it does allow individual measurements to be weighted correctly,[35] and it obviates the need to calculate the spectroscopic constants.

Approximate quartic force-constant calculations have been performed on species in the solid state such as the cyanate[36] and thiocyanate[37] ions.

1.3 *Ab initio* Calculation of Force Constants

Force constants can be calculated by *ab initio* quantum-mechanical methods. In a recent review[38] impressive results were quoted for some diatomic species such as CH, CH^+ and BeH. There seem to be two main difficulties. Firstly, the potential energy curve must be calculated to high accuracy because it has to be differentiated twice to yield force constants and hence vibrational frequencies. Hartree-Fock calculations do not usually give sufficient accuracy unless considerable Configurational Interaction (CI) is allowed.

The second difficulty concerns the fitting of the calculated potential energy values by model functions such as polynomials. Too few data points will result in a fit whose curvature at the minimum (and hence force constant) will be incorrect.

Yet despite these difficulties, some clear progress is being made. An SCF/CI calculation on the triatomic molecule HCN gave force constants that were no more than 15% in error.[39] In this calculation both cubic and quartic force constants were calculated. In other calculations approximate methods such as MINDO/2[40] or extended Hückel molecular orbitals[41,42] have been used. When applied to diatomic molecules such as C_2, Si_2, Ge_2 and Sn_2 the latter method did not give particularly striking agreement with experiment.[43] Indeed, when one sees even the most sophisticated calculations giving rather poor answers, one must seriously question the value of results obtained by approximate methods.

The definition of model potential functions can be very useful; for example a Morse function yields accurate predictions of the vibrational-rotational structure for the bending vibration in H_2O.[44] The approximate prediction of complex spectra is even more valuable. For example, an *ab initio* study of the water dimer $(H_2O)_2$, though rather dependent on the basis set, gave results in the low frequency region which are in qualitative agreement with the interpretation of the observed spectra.[45] Similarly, *ab initio* calculations corroborated the empirical assignment for methylamine (CH_3NH_2), except for the uncertain *a''* vibrations.[46] At the present state of development, then, good *ab initio* calculations may serve to confirm qualitatively the band assignments in spectra of medium complexity.[47]

Very little work has been done recently to define model force fields in the light of quantum-mechanical calculations.[48] An occasional attempt is made to find an empirical correlation between force constants and bond covalency,[49] and this can be of predictive value.

1.4   Anharmonicity Corrections

A quadratic force field calculation is one in which all the quadratic force constants, F_{ij} in eqn. (2) are calculated. If the cubic and other force constants are implicitly taken into account, the force field is said to be harmonic, and the force constants derived from a harmonic quadratic force-field calculation are the same as the quadratic force constants derived from an anharmonic force-field calculation. This equality is achieved[4] by correcting the observed frequencies for the effects of anharmonicity, and thus obtaining the so-called harmonic frequencies, ω_k, which are usually different from the observed frequencies. If sufficient frequencies of overtone and combination bands are not available for the direct calculation of anharmonicity corrections,[4] empirical methods such as Dennison's Rules[50] may be used. Additionally, the known anharmonicity constants of related molecules are frequently used as a guide,[51] and moreover it is common practice, where isotopically substituted molecules are available, to correct the harmonic frequencies so that the product rule (q.v.) is more nearly observed.

Another approach is applicable in highly symmetrical molecules. When there are only two vibrational frequencies of the same symmetry, Dennison's rules and the product rule determine all the first-order anharmonicity constants bar one; this can be estimated from Coriolis coupling constants and centrifugal distortion constants.[52] Recently the concept of group anharmonicity has been advanced.[53]

Another correction that is needed more often than not is for anharmonic resonances. The reader is probably familiar with Fermi resonance, but there are many other possible types, and they are amply discussed by Suzuki.[23]

2   FORCE-CONSTANTS AND OBSERVABLES

The computation of quadratic force constants is performed using the techniques of linear algebra, because in this approximation there is a linear transformation between the starting coordinates (cartesian, internal, symmetry) and the normal coordinates. Although the relationship between force constants and observables is not linear, as the true force field is approached the linear approximation becomes increasingly valid. There are several different observables in addition to the vibrational frequencies, though most of them apply only in the gas phase. Hence, for solids, the problems due to under-determination of the force field are almost always present and the approximate methods of Section 5 will be in demand.

2.1 The GF Method

It is customary to treat the quadratic force constants in the **GF** matrix convention.[4] Briefly, the salient relationships are these. A linear transformation, eqn. (11), between internal coordinates R and the cartesian coordinates r is established.

$$\mathbf{R} = \mathbf{Br} \tag{11}$$

The **B** matrix may be rectangular $(3N \times 3N - 6)$ or square $(3N \times 3N)$ if the six Eckart coordinates are included in **R**. The kinetic energy of vibration is then given by eqn. (12).

$$2T = \tilde{\dot{\mathbf{R}}}\,\mathbf{G}^{-1}\,\dot{\mathbf{R}} \tag{12}$$

The inverse kinetic energy matrix **G** may be obtained from **B** by equation (13), in which $\mathbf{M}^{-1}$ is a diagonal matrix of inverse masses.

$$\mathbf{G} = \mathbf{B}\,\mathbf{M}^{-1}\,\tilde{\mathbf{B}} \tag{13}$$

Alternatively, the **G** matrix may be constructed by a vectorial method expressed in eqn. (14), element by element.

$$G_{tt'} = \sum_{k=1}^{N} \frac{1}{m_k}\, s_{tk}\, s_{t'k} \tag{14}$$

This formula clearly shows how each element of **G** is a function of only two coordinates, R_t and $R_{t'}$, so that $G_{tt'}$ will be unaffected by the choice of other coordinates.

The potential energy of vibration is given by eqn. (15), and the secular eqns. (16) define the normal coordinates by eqn. (17).

$$2V = \tilde{\mathbf{R}}\,\mathbf{F}\,\mathbf{R} \tag{15}$$

$$\mathbf{GFL} = \mathbf{L}\,\Lambda \tag{16}$$

$$\mathbf{R} = \mathbf{L}\,\mathbf{Q} \tag{17}$$

F contains the quadratic force constants F_{ij}, the columns of **L** are the eigenvectors of **GF**, and Λ is a diagonal matrix of eigenvalues of **GF**. These eigenvalues may be related to the observed frequencies by (18).

$$\lambda_k = 4\pi^2 c^2 \nu_k^2 \tag{18}$$

It is not convenient to diagonalize the unsymmetrical **GF** matrix, but since **G** is Hermitian (this follows directly from the definition in eqn. (13)) **GF** may be transformed to an equivalent matrix **H**, whose eigenvalues are Λ. First, **G** is factorized into the non-singular matrix **A**, eqn. (19). The factorized **G** matrix

$$\mathbf{G} = \mathbf{A}\,\tilde{\mathbf{A}} \tag{19}$$

is substituted into the secular eqn. (16) to yield eqn. (20), whence (21) is obtained.

$$\mathbf{A}\,\tilde{\mathbf{A}}\,\mathbf{F} = \mathbf{L}\,\Lambda\,\mathbf{L}^{-1} \tag{20}$$

$$\mathbf{A}^{-1}\mathbf{A}\,\tilde{\mathbf{A}}\,\mathbf{F}\,\mathbf{A} = \tilde{\mathbf{A}}\,\mathbf{F}\,\mathbf{A} = \mathbf{H} = \mathbf{A}^{-1}\mathbf{L}\,\Lambda\,\mathbf{L}^{-1}\,\mathbf{A} \tag{21}$$

The eigenvectors, **C**, of the Hermitian matrix **H** are related to **L** by eqn. (22).

$$\tilde{\mathbf{C}}\,\mathbf{H}\,\mathbf{C} = \Lambda; \quad \mathbf{L} = \mathbf{A}\,\mathbf{C} \tag{22}$$

It is easy also to verify the relations (23) and (24).

$$\tilde{\mathbf{L}}\,\mathbf{F}\,\mathbf{L} = \Lambda \tag{23}$$

$$\mathbf{L}\,\tilde{\mathbf{L}} = \mathbf{G} \tag{24}$$

2.2   Coriolis Coupling Constants

Equation (23) defines the relationship between the force constants and the observed frequencies. The relationship with Coriolis coupling constants was given by Meal and Polo,[54] and is shown in eqn. (25),

$$\zeta^\alpha = \mathbf{L}^{-1}\,\mathbf{C}^\alpha\,\tilde{\mathbf{L}}^{-1} \tag{25}$$

where **L** is the eigenvector matrix of **GF**, ζ^α is a zeta matrix of Coriolis constants and $\mathbf{C}^\alpha$ is a matrix, dependent upon molecular geometry, as is the **G** matrix; indeed it can also be computed by the s vector method, eqn. (26).

$$C_{tt'}^\alpha = \sum_{k=1}^{N} \frac{1}{m_k} (s_{tk} \times s_{t'k}) \cdot e_\alpha \tag{26}$$

A direct relationship between ζ^α and **F** is in eqn. (27).

$$\zeta^\alpha = \Lambda^{-1}\,\tilde{\mathbf{L}}\,\mathbf{F}\,\mathbf{C}^\alpha\,\tilde{\mathbf{L}}^{-1} \tag{27}$$

2.3   Centrifugal Distortion Constants

For centrifugal distortion constants, τ, a direct relationship with force constants is not possible. In fact, the centrifugal distortion constants are linearly related to the elements of the inverse of $\mathbf{F}$, the compliance constants $(F^{-1})_{uv}$, through the expression of Kivelson and Wilson, eqn. (28),

$$\tau_{\alpha\beta,\gamma\delta} = -\tfrac{1}{2} \sum_{u,v} \mu^u_{\alpha\beta} \, \mu^v_{\gamma\delta} \, (F^{-1})_{uv} \qquad (28)$$

in which the μs are elements of the inverse instantaneous inertia tensor.[55] Alternative formulae which use the inertia tensor rather than its inverse have been given by a number of authors.[2] The more common centrifugal distortion constants, D, are simply linear combinations of the τs.

2.4   Mean-Square Amplitudes and Inertia Defects

There are other observables which occasionally may help to determine the force field, though it is more usual that a known force field is used to interpret the observed data. For example, mean-square amplitudes of vibration, if known, greatly improve the precision of a structure determination by electron diffraction.[56] Only in the case of very symmetrical molecules will the diffraction data be sufficiently good to determine mean-square amplitudes.

Mean-square amplitudes have been exhaustively discussed by Cyvin and co-workers.[5,57] The defining equations are in eqn. (29),

$$\Sigma = \mathbf{L} \, \delta \, \tilde{\mathbf{L}} \qquad (29)$$

where δ is a diagonal matrix of periodic amplitudes. Substitution of eqn. (23) into eqn. (29) reveals that the mean-square amplitudes, Σ, are linear functions of the compliance constants, eqn. (30).

$$\Sigma = \mathbf{L} \, \delta \, \Lambda \, \mathbf{L}^{-1} \, \mathbf{F}^{-1} \qquad (30)$$

The inertia defect, Δ_r, is determinable only in planar molecules and so is of limited applicability.[51,58] Δ_r is directly related to zeta constants and harmonic frequencies and tends to be a useful check on the computed force field rather than of direct value in its determination.

2.5   Infrared Intensities

Intensity data are related to the force field through the usually unknown dipole and polarizability derivatives. Hence, the latter are the quantities usually determined by this analysis. Steele[7] has outlined the relationship between the intensity of a normal vibration I_k and the dipole derivatives with respect to the internal coordinates $\partial p / \partial R_i$, eqn. (31).

$$I_k = \frac{N\pi}{3c^2 \, \omega_k} \sum_{ij} L_{jk} L_{ik} \frac{\partial p}{\partial R_i} \frac{\partial p}{\partial R_j} \qquad (31)$$

Mohan and Müller[59] extended this treatment to include the effects of isotopic substitution and suggested that the requisite dipole moment derivatives could be obtained by quantum mechanical calculation. Equation (31) can be put in matrix form, eqn. (32),

$$I = K \tilde{L} p L \tag{32}$$

by writing $p_{ij} = (\partial p / \partial R_i)(\partial p / \partial R_j)$. Comprehensive reviews of infrared intensities have been presented by Person and Steele,[60] and independently by Steele.[60]

2.6 Raman Intensities

A similar approach is possible with Raman intensities, using Wolkenstein's bond polarizability approach. The requisite expressions were given by Long,[61] and a contemporary review of Raman intensities has been presented by Hester.[62]

Clark and Mitchell compared force constants of group IV tetrahalides derived with the aid of Raman intensities with those of the GHQFF. They concluded that the Wolkenstein assumptions are not wholly adequate for those molecules[63,64] (see also Ref. 65).

To summarize, the observables which can be used to determine force constants include the vibrational frequencies, Coriolis coupling constants, centrifugal distortion constants, mean-square amplitudes, inertia defects, and infrared and Raman band intensities. Each of these quantities may be determined for one or more isotopic species, though the resulting data are not all independent. The isotopic substitution may conserve molecular symmetry or only partially conserve it. In some cases the isotopic frequency shifts are more precisely determined than the absolute frequencies. This is particularly true for molecules subject to partial isotopic substitution, where the vibrational frequencies of all the species are measured simultaneously; it also is true for matrix-isolation studies for the same reason.[66] At all events, the force field should reproduce all the experimentally observed quantities. In the next section the individual stages in this process are discussed, and this is followed by a discussion of the refinement process.

3 QUADRATIC FORCE-FIELD CALCULATION

3.1 Choice of Coordinates

The set of internal coordinates defined by Decius is sufficient to classify all internal vibrations. They include stretching, bending, rocking, wagging and out-of-plane coordinates. Additionally there is the torsional coordinate, but this is different from the others in that barriers to rotation are often small and so torsional vibrations usually have large amplitudes. The Taylor-series expansion of potential energy, eqn. (2), is thus only slowly convergent. The torsional energy is therefore often expanded as a function of r in a Fourier series rather than in a Taylor series.

The treatment by Wilson, Decius and Cross[4] is incomplete in regard to torsional coordinates. A note by Hildebrand[67] clears up the ambiguities and gives the s vectors appropriate to molecules such as ethane. An alternative set of torsional coordinates has been proposed.[68]

Cyvin and Brunvoll suggested a 'whirling' coordinate as an alternative to a torsional one in sandwich compounds, and gave s vectors and G matrix elements.[69] Unfortunately these s vectors only eliminate overall rotation in special cases, and it is proved impossible to construct s vectors for a generally applicable whirling coordinate.[70]

Ring puckering also presents problems of definition. A set of independent puckering coordinates for four-membered rings serves as an example of the kind of coordinates that have been proposed.[71]

Although there are no agreed conventions, Cyvin, in a series of 16 papers, has proposed 'tentatively standardized symmetry coordinates' for 102 molecular types containing up to 7 atoms. A summary of this work, together with all references is in pp. 366–375 of Ref. 57. There is good reason to accept these conventions, though it would be preferable if they were more widely recognized. As an example of the confusion that can exist, see McNaught's discussion of the five different G matrices proposed for Y_3XZW molecules.[72]

3.2 The G Matrix

The G matrix can be constructed element by element using the formulae given by Decius,[73] which use the results of eqn. (14), and which apply to pairwise combinations of internal coordinates. Whitmer has had the audacity to announce a computer program that embodies FORTRAN code for these formulae.[74]

For large molecules the use of the Decius formulae is tedious and subject to error. Also there may be advantages in having the B matrix available. With these considerations in mind Henshall and Freeman have shown how the s vectors may be derived from a geometrical definition of the molecule.[75] Freeman has made a valuable contribution by showing how they could be refined iteratively from approximate values.[76] This is useful because the molecular geometry so calculated must be self consistent, particularly if redundancies are present. The iterative refinement and G matrix calculation are embodied in an ALGOL program.[77] Gans has extended this program to cope with 'linear bonds' such as occur in metal carbonyl complexes.[78] The program's main defect is that it deals only with stretching and bending coordinates, though it could easily be extended to deal with the others. G matrix elements have been given for two molecular types containing linear bonds—Y_3XZW (e.g. borine carbonyl)[72] and $Y_2X(ZW)_2$ (e.g. propanedinitrile).[79] It has been pointed out that the G matrix elements relating to the bending of a 'linear bond' have an arbitrary sign, and that consequently the corresponding force constants also have an arbitrary sign.[78]

3.3 Treatment of Redundancies

Redundant symmetry coordinates arise from the use of symmetrically equivalent internal coordinates which are not linearly independent. The two most common types are local ones, where a number of bonds meet at a common atom, and cyclic ones, where the molecule contains a ring structure. The G matrix elements corresponding to redundant coordinates are zero, and therefore the corresponding eigenvalues are zero and the corresponding force constants are indeterminate in the secular eqns. (16). This means that these force constants cannot be determined.

To clarify these points consider the a_1 vibrations of a tetrahedral molecule (e.g. CH_4).[52] The redundant coordinate is the one for which all six angles increase by the same amount. The symmetry-adapted G and F matrices for the a_1 symmetry block are given in eqn. (33)

$$\mathbf{G} = \begin{pmatrix} G_r + 3G_{rr} & 0 \\ 0 & 0 \end{pmatrix} \quad \mathbf{F} = \begin{pmatrix} f_r + 3f_{rr} & f_{r\alpha} + f'_{r\alpha} \\ f_{r\alpha} + f'_{r\alpha} & f_\alpha + 4f_{\alpha\alpha} + f'_{\alpha\alpha} \end{pmatrix} \tag{33}$$

so that $(f_{r\alpha} + f'_{r\alpha})$ and $(f_\alpha + 4f_{\alpha\alpha} + f'_{\alpha\alpha})$ are indeterminate. Since the t_2 symmetry block yields $(f_{r\alpha} - f'_{r\alpha})$ and $(f_\alpha - f'_{\alpha\alpha})$ and the e block yields $(f_\alpha - 2f_{\alpha\alpha})$ is is clear that all the internal force constants which relate to angle bending are indeterminate! Thus the force field is not determinate in internal coordinates; only certain symmetry-adapted combinations, the symmetry force constants, are determinate. This can be confirmed by using Watson's formula, eqn. (8).

In large molecules the redundant coordinates are not easily determined in advance. However, if rectilinear coordinates are being used the redundancy relations are always linear.[80] In anharmonic calculations and in quadratic calculations in certain model force fields (such as UBFF) which imply curvilinear coordinates each redundancy condition causes a linear term to appear in the potential energy when it is expressed in rectilinear coordinates.[81]

A linear redundancy condition will result in the G matrix being singular. The eigenvalues of GF can nevertheless be determined as discussed below and will contain one zero for each redundancy. The redundancy condition can be determined numerically, but it must be stressed that removal of redundancy should be done by an orthogonal coordinate transformation which leaves the redundant coordinates and corresponding G matrix elements equal to zero. Only when the elimination is performed in this way will the symmetry force constants be invariant to isotopic substitution, as should be clear by looking at eqn. (33), because only in this way are the determinate and indeterminate parts of the symmetry force constants separated. In Ref. (6), pp. 120–122, a method is described based on the eigenvectors of G, and Schmidt's orthogonalization process. This procedure is incorporated in the ALGOL **G** matrix program quoted above.[78] Alternatively, a Schmidt orthogonalization of the **B** matrix may be performed. This procedure is also available in an ALGOL program.[82] Other methods have been suggested for the elimination of redundant coordinates, but they do not give symmetry coordinates which are related to the internal ones by an orthogonal change.[83,84]

Bertie *et al.*[85] stressed the need for orthogonal symmetry coordinates when using the Schachtschneider program,[86] because of its construction. Incorrect elimination of redundancies[87] leads to incorrect force-constant solutions. Inversion of the **B** matrix when redundancies are present is also possible.[88]

3.4 Symmetrizing the Secular Equations

There are three ways in which **GF** may be transformed into a similar but symmetric matrix **H**, eqn. (21), corresponding to the factorization of **G** as in eqn. (19). The definition of **G** in eqn. (13) gives the first method, eqn. (34).

$$\mathbf{A} = \mathbf{B}\,\mathbf{M}^{-\frac{1}{2}}, \quad \mathbf{A}\,\tilde{\mathbf{A}} = \mathbf{B}\,\mathbf{M}^{-1}\,\tilde{\mathbf{B}} = \mathbf{G} \tag{34}$$

Although this **A** matrix may be rectangular, an 'inverse' exists,[88] so eqn. (21) is valid. The method is equivalent to posing the secular equations in mass-weighted cartesian coordinates. If the Eckart conditions are included then **B** is square and the secular equations will have six zero eigenvalues (five if the molecule is linear). The main disadvantage of this method is that the symmetrization is difficult to apply. Its main advantage is that there are no redundancies to eliminate, since internal coordinates are not used. This method was first proposed by Long *et al.*[89] and has been incorporated into computer programs by others.[90,91]

The second factorization of **G** involves its diagonalization, eqn. (35).

$$\mathbf{A} = \mathbf{P}\,\Gamma^{\frac{1}{2}}, \quad \tilde{\mathbf{P}}\,\mathbf{G}\,\mathbf{P} = \Gamma, \quad \mathbf{A}\,\tilde{\mathbf{A}} = \mathbf{P}\,\Gamma\,\tilde{\mathbf{P}} = \mathbf{G} \tag{35}$$

This was first proposed by Miyazawa,[92] and has been used extensively.[86] If redundancy is present, one or more eigenvalues Γ_i will be zero, and so **H** = $\tilde{\mathbf{A}}\,\mathbf{F}\,\mathbf{A}$ will have corresponding rows of zeros. Thus the eigenvalues of **GF** are not affected, but the redundancy should not be eliminated by dropping zero rows of **A**.[83]

The Choleski factorization of **G**, eqn. (36),

$$\mathbf{G} = \mathbf{A}\,\tilde{\mathbf{A}}, \quad A_{ij} = 0, \quad i < j \tag{36}$$

is simple and involves the minimum amount of computation. Its use in this context was first proposed by Aldous and Mills.[93] The method cannot be used if **G** is singular, though Sørenson has claimed that this difficulty can be circumvented.[84]

Choleski factorization is the simplest procedure and ALGOL codings have been given for solving this and the related problems, eqn. (37).[94]

$$|\mathbf{FG} - \lambda\mathbf{E}| = |\mathbf{F} - \lambda\mathbf{G}^{-1}| = |\mathbf{G} - \lambda\mathbf{F}^{-1}| = |\mathbf{E} - \lambda\mathbf{G}^{-1}\,\mathbf{F}^{-1}| = 0 \qquad (37)$$

The application of molecular symmetry presents no difficulties as the symmetry coordinates are related to internal coordinates by an orthogonal transformation, eqn. (38).

$$\mathbf{S} = \mathbf{U}\,\mathbf{R}, \quad \mathscr{F} = \mathbf{U}\,\mathbf{F}\,\tilde{\mathbf{U}}. \qquad (38)$$

Adams and Churchill suggested that the $\mathbf{U}$ matrix need not be stored, but only $\tilde{\mathbf{A}}\mathbf{U}$ which transforms $\mathbf{F}$ to $\mathbf{H}$.[83]

3.5   Sum and Product Rules

It is well known that the frequencies of isotopically related molecules are related through a product rule, and that sum rules also exist, as discussed in Ref. 4, Section 8-5. Zeta sum rules are less familiar, and all the relevant references are given by Duncan.[2] These rules apply to single isotopic species. There are also isotopic product rules for centrifugal distortion constants, τ, and intensities.[3] More recently, an inverse sum rule for isotopic frequencies has been proposed,[95] and Aliev has derived some non-linear relationships between τ and ζ.[96]

These relationships can serve as important checks on the data used in a harmonic calculation; the adjustment of anharmonicity corrections to conform to the product rule has been mentioned. The greater significance of these relationships is that they reduce the number of independent observables, and hence the over-determination of the force field is reduced. For example, in a symmetry species containing two normal vibrations a totally symmetric isotopic substitution gives only one new independent frequency. There are nevertheless four equations relating the three symmetry force constants; accordingly, this gives the appearance of an over-determined system. The reason for the apparent paradox is that all the relationships are non-linear, so that the 'fourth equation' gives no additional information about force constants.

3.6   Analogue Methods

Analogue computing techniques have not been in vogue recently, though one dedicated analogue computer has been described.[97] This technique is almost ideal for exploring under-determined force fields.[98]

3.7   Atomic Force Constants

Another unconventional approach is the computation of 'atomic' force constants.[99] These refer to cartesian displacements and it is easy to derive the sum rule, eqn. (39),

$$\sum_i \lambda_i = \sum_\alpha (1/m_\alpha) \nabla^2_\alpha U \tag{39}$$

relating the eigenvalues λ_i to the sum over all atoms of the atomic force constants $\nabla^2_\alpha U$. Thus the eigenvalue sum is independent of the molecular geometry. There is one atomic force constant for each symmetrically equivalent set of atoms so, for example, there are only two parameters for ethene, $\nabla^2_H U$ and $\nabla^2_C U$. The remarkable feature of atomic force constants is that they represent an atomic property which is virtually independent of molecular geometry or bond multiplicity![100] Atomic force constants for C (23.77$\pm$0.45), N (22.67$\pm$2.12), O (17.74$\pm$0.94) and F (11.12$\pm$0.63 mdyn Å^{-1}) fitted a range of 70 hydrocarbons, fluorocarbons, alcohols, ethers, ketones, acids, amines and nitriles with an average error of ca. 1% on $\sum \lambda_i^2$. A similar invariance was noted for the sulphur constant in S_6, S_8 and S_{12}.[101] The results have been rationalized by molecular orbital calculations.[102] Atomic force constants will predict only the sum of eigenvalues, and so they are not very useful for the chemist. Equation (39) can be easily understood by recalling that in cartesian coordinates the **G** matrix is diagonal and consists of the inverse masses.

3.8 Potential Energy Distribution

The distribution of vibrational potential energy in the normal coordinate Q_k is given by eqn. (40),

$$V^{(k)}_{ij} = L_{ik}L_{jk}F_{ij} \tag{40}$$

and this is usually simplified by omitting all off-diagonal force constants as in eqn. (41).

$$V_{ki} = L^2_{ik}F_{ii} \tag{41}$$

Rytter[103] has suggested that the total vibrational energy is worth considering, but Adamek has shown that this does not represent any improvement on the normal expression, eqn. (41).[104] Alix and Müller reached a similar conclusion.[105] The potential energy distribution gives a method for fixing the vibrational assignment,[106] and can be used as a criterion for deciding whether an assignment is acceptable.[107]

3.9 Units

Finally, we must discuss force-constant units. Because different coordinates in eqn. (2) have different dimensions, the corresponding force-constants also have different dimensions. The fact that quantities of different dimensions may appear in the same equations is commonly ignored, an unusual situation in science. The problem is that there is no obviously acceptable scaling convention. Some workers scale the angle change coordinates by dividing by a bond length, though the choice is not always clearly stated. Mills[22] has made the interesting alternative suggestion that the bond stretching coordinates should be de-scaled by division by the equilibrium bond length, which makes bond stretching co-ordinates dimensionless. Such a scaling gives all force constants the dimension of energy, with attojoule (aJ) as a convenient unit. It has the side-effect of 're-moving' from stretching force constants that part which is linearly dependent upon bond length. Thus the quadratic force constants for the hydrogen halides are: HF 8.116, HCl 8.388, HBr 8.234, HI 8.130 aJ. These values show the trends which are independent of bond length changes, though many chemists would prefer values that are explicitly length-dependent.

Another area of disagreement is over the appropriate SI units to use. Many authors now quote a stretching force constant in the unit Newton per metre (1 mdyn Å^{-1} = 100 N m^{-1}). The corresponding stretch-bend unit is the nano-newton (1 mdyn = 10 nN), while the bending unit is the attojoule (1 mdyn Å = 1 aJ). Equation (42) will yield force constants in these SI units, when $\tilde{v}$ is expressed in wavenumber per centimetre (cm^{-1}) and masses are given in atomic mass units (^{12}C = 12.0000).

$$\lambda = \frac{4\pi^2 c^2 \tilde{v}^2}{N} = 0.589146 \left(\frac{\tilde{v}}{100}\right)^2 = \left(\frac{\tilde{v}}{130.28}\right)^2 \tag{42}$$

From a didactic point of view the aJ unit is a useful energy unit for electronic and vibrational spectroscopy since $1\text{aJ} \equiv 50340 \text{ cm}^{-1}$, but again there is no agreement over the appropriate power of ten. However, the SI system does not even have a suitable prefix for 10^{-24} or 10^{-21}.

4 FORCE-CONSTANT REFINEMENT

Since force constants are related to observables by a set of non-linear equations they must be calculated by an iterative process. Whether or not the parameters are over-determined a least-squares method is used. A brief resumé of this method will be given first, in order to underline the assumptions and approxi-mations involved.

4.1 The Theory of Least-Squares Methods

It is convenient at the outset to rearrange the force constants $\mathbf{F}$ into a para-meter vector $\mathbf{f}$, and to denote the observables by ϕ_k, each with an associated weight w_k. Writing $\varepsilon_k = (\phi_k^{\text{obs}} - \phi_k^{\text{calc}})$, the sum of squares, σ, is given by eqn. (43)

$$\sigma = \sum_k (\phi_k^{\text{obs}} - \phi_k^{\text{calc}})^2 w_k = \tilde{\varepsilon} \mathbf{W} \varepsilon. \tag{43}$$

It can be expanded as a Taylor series, involving the Hessian, $\mathbf{H}$, as in eqn. (44),

$$\sigma = a + \tilde{\mathbf{b}} \, \mathbf{f} + \tfrac{1}{2} \tilde{\mathbf{f}} \mathbf{H} \, \mathbf{f} + \dots \tag{44}$$

the first assumption being that the higher terms can be ignored. This is equivalent to assuming that there is a linear relationship between ϕ and $\mathbf{f}$, such as eqn. (45),

$$\phi^{\text{calc}} = \mathbf{A}\,\mathbf{f} + \mathbf{B} \tag{45}$$

as will be readily seen if this relation is substituted into eqn. (43). Differentiation of the quadratic part of eqn. (44) yields the gradient $\mathbf{g}$, eqn. (46).

$$\mathbf{g} = \frac{\partial \sigma}{\partial \mathbf{f}} = \breve{\mathbf{b}} + \mathbf{H}\,\mathbf{f} \tag{46}$$

When σ is a minimum, $\mathbf{g} = 0$ so that $\breve{\mathbf{b}} = -\mathbf{H}\,\mathbf{f}^{\min}$. This value of $\breve{\mathbf{b}}$ is substituted back into eqn. (46) to yield eqn. (47).

$$(-\mathbf{H}\,\mathbf{f}^{\min} + \mathbf{H}\,\mathbf{f}) = -\mathbf{H}\,\Delta \mathbf{f} = \mathbf{g} \tag{47}$$

The correction term $\Delta \mathbf{f}$ which is obtained by solving (47) is added to $\mathbf{f}$ and gives $\mathbf{f}^{\min}$, the value of $\mathbf{f}$ for minimum σ. This is the required parameter set.

The gradient $\mathbf{g}$ and Hessian $\mathbf{H}$ can be obtained by differentiation of eqn. (43). The results are eqns. (48) and (49):

$$\mathbf{g} = -2\,\tilde{\mathbf{J}}\,\mathbf{W}\,\boldsymbol{\varepsilon}, \quad J_{kj} = \frac{\partial \phi_k}{\partial f_j}, \tag{48}$$

$$\mathbf{H} = 2\,\tilde{\mathbf{J}}\,\mathbf{W}\,\mathbf{J} + 2\,\mathbf{B}\,\mathbf{W}\,\boldsymbol{\varepsilon}, \quad B_{kij} = \frac{\partial^2 \phi_k}{\partial f_i\,\partial f_j}, \tag{49}$$

where J_{kj} are the Jacobian elements, The next approximation usually made is that $\mathbf{B}\,\mathbf{W}\,\boldsymbol{\varepsilon}$ is negligible, i.e. $\mathbf{H} = 2\,\tilde{\mathbf{J}}\,\mathbf{W}\,\mathbf{J}$. Substituting this expression and that for the gradient into eqn. (47), and we obtain eqn. (50),

$$(\tilde{\mathbf{J}}\,\mathbf{W}\,\mathbf{J})\,\Delta \mathbf{f} = \tilde{\mathbf{J}}\,\mathbf{W}\,\boldsymbol{\varepsilon} \tag{50}$$

the normal **equations** of least squares. The assumptions concerning eqns. (44) and (49) should be noted; each will subsequently cause difficulties with the refinement.

The relationships between observables and parameters are given in eqns. (23), (25), (28), (29) and (32) and none is linear, hence the need for an iterative procedure to find $\mathbf{f}^{\min}$. However, it is clearly advantageous that the relationship should be linear to first order. This is true for the expressions for eigenvalues, eqn. (23), zetas, eqn. (27) and intensities, eqn. (32), but centrifugal distortion constants and mean-square amplitudes are linear to first order in the compliance-constants $(F^{-1})_{ij}$. This has led some authors to formulate the refinement wholly in compliants, as discussed in Section 4.3. If data of both sorts are included in the refinement, clearly the linear approximation of eqn. (44) will be good for some observables and bad for others.

It can be shown that when $\mathbf{f} \approx \mathbf{f}^{\min}$, eqn. (47) is a good approximation. Thus, the value of $\Delta \mathbf{f}$ calculated from this equation will be more subject to error the further $\mathbf{f}$ is from its optimum value.

The approximation to **H**, eqn. (49), that puts **B W** $\varepsilon = 0$ is more serious, since this is only valid in general when $\varepsilon = 0$.

The combined effect of these approximations is to make the refinement ill-conditioned, with σ often oscillating rather than converging to its minimum value. This is illustrated in Fig. 1, which relates to a particularly ill-conditioned problem.[108] The points are those generated by solving eqn. (50) successively, starting from an arbitrary initial point. If σ were quadratic, the contours would be ellipses. Thus, the values of Δf calculated at points 3 and 8 are in error because the function is not quadratic in that region. (Note how the contours become elliptical near the minimum). The divergence from points 4, 9, 6 and 7 is even more marked, and this is due to the approximation **B W** $\varepsilon = 0$. There is a zone, which these points are near, where $(\tilde{\mathbf{J}} \mathbf{W} \mathbf{J})$ is singular, so that the absence of the **B W** ε term makes **H** singular also. When **H** is singular there is no unique solution to eqn. (47).

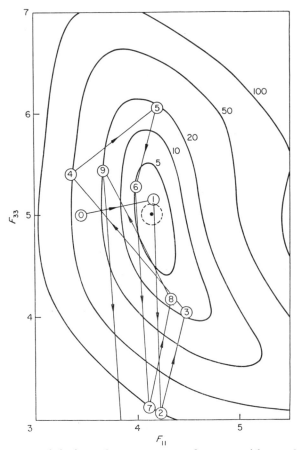

Fig. 1. Points generated during a force-constant refinement with $n = 3$. The contours are of the sum of squares, σ, [eqn. (43), $w_k = 1/\lambda_k$]. For further details see Ref. 108.

In general, the normal equations matrix ($\mathbf{\tilde{J}\,W\,J}$) will be singular at the minimum if the force field is under-determined (and *vice versa*). This can be understood in terms of correlation between parameters. If the parameters f_i and f_j are under-determined, equal values of σ can be obtained for various combined values of f_i and f_j so that the correlation coefficient ρ_{ij} is equal to one. ρ_{ij} is derived from ($\mathbf{\tilde{J}\,W\,J}$)$^{-1}$ by eqn. (51),

$$\rho_{ij} = \frac{P_{ij}}{\sqrt{(P_{ii}\,P_{jj})}}, \quad \mathbf{P} = (\mathbf{\tilde{J}\,W\,J})^{-1} \tag{51}$$

so when $\rho_{ij} = 1$, ($\mathbf{\tilde{J}\,W\,J}$)$^{-1}$ is singular,[109] which implies that ($\mathbf{\tilde{J}\,W\,J}$) is also singular; they cannot, however, be obtained from each other by inversion, because both matrices are less than full rank.

The force field may be determinate, but the standard deviation on some force constants may exceed the constant's value. In this situation there will be a correlation coefficient whose value approaches one. ($\mathbf{\tilde{J}\,W\,J}$) will not be singular at the minimum, but will be ill-conditioned with respect to inversion.

With this introduction we can analyse the various procedures that have been proposed to deal with ill-conditioned refinements.

4.2 Ill-Conditioned Refinement

The simplest strategy is to apply a fraction of the calculated correction $\Delta\mathbf{f}$.[110] The fraction may be chosen so as to obtain the largest decrease in σ. The method can be proved to be convergent (σ is reduced at each iteration)[111] but convergence may be extremely slow: consider the effect of applying this procedure to the $\Delta\mathbf{f}$ calculated at point 9 in Fig. 1.

A second method is to apply a damping factor ξ, as in eqn. (52).

$$(\mathbf{\tilde{J}\,W\,J} + \xi\mathbf{D})\,\Delta\mathbf{f} = \mathbf{\tilde{J}\,W}\,\varepsilon \tag{52}$$

$\mathbf{D}$ is a diagonal matrix. This was first applied by Papoušek *et al.*[112] who attributed the method to Levenberg.[113] A computer program based on these ideas was developed by Freeman and Henshall.[114] Gellai and Janscó showed that the damped least-squares procedure was a special case of the application of the generalized inverse.[115] Adams and Churchill also developed a damping technique.[83] The damped least-squares method has been used with great success in over-determined systems.[111] The chief difficulty with the method lies in the strategy for choosing ξ. $\mathbf{D}$ is usually taken as the diagonal elements of ($\mathbf{\tilde{J}\,W\,J}$), and ξ should be zero, ideally, at convergence. A very efficient algorithm has been given by Fletcher[116] in which ξ is chosen and varied automatically (FORTRAN sub-routine).

Whether or not the damped least-squares method will lead to a satisfactory solution for the force-constants depends on the condition of ($\mathbf{\tilde{J}\,W\,J}$) at the minimum. If the value of ξ on 'convergence' is not zero, then the normal-equations matrix must be ill-conditioned, and the solution must be regarded with suspicion. In this case it would be as well to compute the correlation coefficients from the inverse of the undamped normal-equations matrix ($\xi = 0$), if that is possible.

Another approach was suggested by Bruton and Woodward.[117] Recognizing that a singular normal-equations matrix implies indeterminate force constants, they used the eigenvectors associated with the zero eigenvalues of ($\mathbf{\tilde{J} W J}$) to remove these force constants from the refinement in the initial stages, when ill-conditioning is worst. Nemes[118] made the comment that the computed standard deviations could be used as a criterion for rejecting force constants rather than the eigenvalues of ($\mathbf{\tilde{J} W J}$), but the two criteria are really equivalent. Curtis[119] has extended the method so that the 'weak' or under-determined force constants are eliminated by an orthogonal transformation.

This approach is one which has been used extensively in X-ray structure refinement[120] to eliminate parameters not fully determined at that stage (Bruton and Woodward acknowledge discussions with Rollett). Its use in vibrational refinement, however, is questionable unless the final force constants are the full set. Removal of one force constant from a correlated pair will give the remaining parameter an illusory appearance of determinacy.

A completely different approach is to eschew the use of derivatives and to minimize σ by direct variation of parameters.[121] Unfortunately, the 'axial iteration' method used by Shimanouchi and Suzuki is one of the least efficient of the direct search methods,[111] and convergence may be very slow.[122] For this reason, and because an effective derivative method is known, the direct search technique cannot be recommended.

The inclusion of the $\mathbf{B W} \varepsilon$ term in eqn. (49) was shown to improve convergence considerably,[108] but the second derivatives were not obtained in closed form. A much more efficient way of introducing the second term to $\mathbf{H}$ is to use an updating formula which utilizes the gradient changes during iteration to derive the second derivatives of σ, $(\partial^2 \sigma / \partial f_i \, \partial f_j)$ which are the elements of $\mathbf{H}$. This is possible because in the approximation that σ is a quadratic function of $\mathbf{f}$, $\mathbf{H}$ is constant. The original updating formula, due to Fletcher and Powell,[123] was used by Gans.[124] Subsequently the method was explored in some model calculations[108,125] and it was shown that putting $\mathbf{H} = 2 \mathbf{\tilde{J} W J}$ initially gave rapid convergence. This minimization procedure was incorporated in Schachtschneider's program and used to good effect in computing force constants for some carbohydrate derivatives.[126] Further improvements have been effected by introducing improved updating formulae and techniques.[107]

The Fletcher-Powell method has been evaluated mainly on under-determined systems. In these systems one is effectively solving a set of implicit non-linear equations. If the force field has been constrained the equations may be inconsistent; if they are self-consistent the solution should be exact, $\varepsilon = 0$. Either way, one solves the equations by minimizing σ, though this is not a least-squares system in the usual sense of there being more equations than parameters. The Fletcher-Powell method seems to be as ideally suited to under-determined systems as the damped method is to over-determined systems. Is there an optimal choice for all calculations? I believe that the Fletcher-Powell method is the best because it will always converge satisfactorily, whereas the damped method may not do so on under-determined systems. The determinancy of the solution is not known in advance.

Some final comments concerning the weights, $\mathbf{W}$, used in eqn. (43). These weights should be inversely proportional to the uncertainty (variance) of the measurements and herein lies the difficulty, particularly when measurements of different kinds like infrared and microwave are involved. Aldous and Mills[93] discuss the question of weights most carefully. They identify the largest error in frequencies as due to the uncertain anharmonicity correction, but the choice of weights $w_k = 1/\lambda_k^2$ is hardly sound, since it is not based on statistical argument. The equal-weights hypothesis has been advanced by Overend and Scherer,[127] but this is also open to criticism. Perhaps the best compromise is to try various weighting schemes and if the force field is well-determined the computed force constants should not depend upon the choice of weight.

4.3   Compliance Constants

The matrix of compliance constants, $\mathbf{C}$, is simply the inverse of the force-constants' matrix, $\mathbf{F}$. The transformation, however trivial seeming, is not so in fact because $\mathbf{C}$ possesses an important property that $\mathbf{F}$ does not possess. Each compliance constant C_{ij} is a function of the two coordinates R_i and R_j (or S_i and S_j) alone, in the same way that G_{ij} is a function of these two coordinates alone. This means that compliance constants are independent of the choice of other coordinates and are therefore much easier to transfer from one molecule to another, or from one model force field to another. Cyvin gives a particularly clear exposition of these facts.[5] The compliance constant C_{ij} is invariant to a coordinate transformation that leaves R_i and R_j unchanged. Decius has also shown that $\mathbf{C}$ is determinate even when $\mathbf{G}$ is singular, i.e. when redundancy is present.[128] Let A be a rectangular matrix defining a transformation from symmetry coordinates S to a set from which the redundant coordinates are eliminated, eqn. (53).

$$\mathcal{S} = \mathbf{A\,S} \tag{53}$$

The force constants and compliance constants are then given by eqn. (54)

$$\mathcal{F} = \tilde{\mathbf{A}}\,\mathbf{F\,A}, \quad \mathcal{C} = \mathbf{A\,C\,\tilde{A}} \tag{54}$$

so that $\mathcal{C}$ is fully determined, though its elements are not all independent.

The illustration given by Jones and Ryan[129] is persuasive. Three force fields for the water molecule are given in Table 2. In all three fields the stretching coordinates are r_1 and r_2 yet f_r and f_{rr} come out with different values. C_r and C_{rr} on the other hand, are the same in all three cases, showing the transferability of compliance constants among different kinds of force field.

The fact that centrifugal distortion constants are linear functions of compliance constants (cf. eqn. (28)) and mean-square amplitudes are linear to first order (cf. eqn. (30)) has encouraged some authors to calculate compliance constants by iteration. The secular equations are easily obtained by inverting eqn. (16) to get eqn. (55), or the alternative form eqn. (56).

$$\mathbf{F}^{-1}\,\mathbf{G}^{-1}\,\mathbf{L} = \mathbf{L}\,\mathbf{\Lambda}^{-1} \tag{55}$$

$$\mathbf{L}^{-1}\,\mathbf{F}^{-1}\,\tilde{\mathbf{L}}^{-1} = \mathbf{\Lambda}^{-1} \tag{56}$$

There is no real advantage in using this procedure since inevitably some parameters are related linearly to the observables (e.g. eigenvalues) while others have the inverse relationship (e.g. τs). This does not mean that there is no advantage in quoting results as compliance constants, though this simply duplicates the information contained in the force constants; hence there is no need to give both sets of values.

TABLE 2
Force constants/N m^{-1} and compliance
constants $\times 10^3$/m N^{-1} for the water
molecule in three force fields.[129]

Valence		Central		Urey-Bradley	
f_r	845	k_r	913	k_r	826
f_{rr}	-10.1	k_{rr}	57.9	H_α/r_e^2	98
f_α/r_e^2	76.1	k_q	203	F	8
$f_{r\alpha}/r_e$	22.8	k_{rq}	-123	F'	40
C_r	1.19	C_r	1.19	C_r	1.19
C_{rr}	0.024	C_{rr}	0.024	C_{rr}	0.024
C_α/r_e^2	13.38	C_q	5.82	$C_\alpha r_e^2$	13.38
$C_{r\alpha}/r_e$	-0.369	C_{rq}	0.737	$C_q r_e$	7.61

There is a product rule relating the inverse eigenvalues, but no corresponding sum rule. However, it cannot be true, as claimed by Wright and Rao,[130] that the force field is more clearly defined in compliants, because the number of observables and parameters is unchanged. In place of the sum rule there must be some non-linear relationship amongst observables (see also Cummings and Wood[95]).

4.4   Expressions for the Jacobian Elements

The computation of the Jacobian elements, J_{kj} of eqn. (48), is usually performed by using first-order perturbation theory, following the classic paper by Mills.[131] There are two main assumptions involved. One is that the eigenvalues are not close together, and the other is the harmonic approximation. The latter is a subtle point since not only the frequencies but also the zetas and taus should be the 'harmonic' values; this is rarely the case, but in anharmonic calculations it cannot be assumed that ζs and τs are independent of vibrational quantum number.

The starting point is the secular equations in the form of eqn. (23), with $\mathbf{L}$ normalized as in eqn. (24), viz. $\mathbf{L}\tilde{\mathbf{L}} = \mathbf{G}$. In the perturbed form this becomes eqn. (57),

$$(\tilde{\mathbf{L}}^0 + \tilde{\mathbf{L}}^1)\,(\mathbf{F}^0 + \mathbf{F}^1)\,(\mathbf{L}^0 + \mathbf{L}^1) = \Lambda^0 + \Lambda^1 \tag{57}$$

where the quantities $\mathbf{F}^1$, $\mathbf{L}^1$ and Λ^1 are the small changes resulting from the perturbation. Mills showed that the eigenvector perturbation could be expressed by eqn. (58), where the $\mathbf{B}$ matrix elements are given by eqn. (59).

$$\mathbf{L}^1 = \mathbf{L}^0\,\mathbf{B} \tag{58}$$

$$B_{ii} = 0, \quad B_{ij} = \sum_u \sum_v \frac{L^0_{ui}L^0_{vj}F^1_{uv}}{\lambda_j - \lambda_i} \tag{59}$$

and that the Jacobian elements for the eigenvalues that are consistent with this are as given in eqn. (60),

$$J_{i,uv} = (\partial\lambda_i/\partial F_{uv}) = (2 - \delta_{uv})\,L^0_{ui}L^0_{vi} \tag{60}$$

where δ_{uv} is the Kronecker delta; $\delta_{uv} = 0$ unless $u = v$. For zeta constants, a similar perturbation applied to eqn. (25) results in eqn. (61).

$$\zeta^1 = \tilde{\mathbf{B}}\,\zeta^0 + \zeta^0\,\mathbf{B} \tag{61}$$

From this the Jacobian elements are easily derived, and in the case of symmetric top molecules these simplify to the form of eqn. (62).

$$(\partial\zeta_{ii}/\partial F_{uv}) = \frac{2}{(1 + \delta_{uv})} \sum_j^{(j \neq i)} \zeta_{ij} \frac{(L^0_{ui}L^0_{vj} + L^0_{vi}L^0_{uj})}{(\lambda_i - \lambda_j)} \tag{62}$$

For the τs we begin with eqn. (28). The perturbation in $\mathbf{F}^{-1}$ is given by eqn. (63)

$$(\mathbf{F}^{-1})^1 = -(\mathbf{F}^{-1})^0\,\mathbf{F}^1(\mathbf{F}^{-1})^0 \tag{63}$$

and the derivatives follow from this, eqn. (64).

$$(\partial\tau_{\alpha\beta,\gamma\delta}/\partial F_{uv}) = \left(\frac{-1}{1 + \delta_{uv}}\right) \sum_{t,w} \mu^t_{\alpha\beta}[(F^{-1})^0_{tu}\,(F^{-1})^0_{vw} + (F^{-1})^0_{tv}\,(F^{-1})^0_{uw}]\,\mu^w_{\gamma\delta} \tag{64}$$

When isotopic frequency shifts are being refined rather than the frequencies themselves, the Jacobian elements are obtained by direct differentiation, eqn. (65).[132]

$$\left(\frac{\partial(\lambda_i - \lambda_i^*)}{\partial F_{uv}}\right) = \left(\frac{\partial\lambda_i}{\partial F_{uv}}\right) - \left(\frac{\partial\lambda_i^*}{\partial F_{uv}}\right) \tag{65}$$

Alternatively, if the shift is small it may be treated as a small perturbation.[133]

If redundancies are present Mills' procedure cannot be applied, but Strey has shown that the expressions for $(\partial\zeta/\partial F)$ are unchanged. There are small differences in the expressions for τ and $(\partial\tau/\partial F)$.[134] The Jacobian elements for mean-square amplitudes are also given. Sørenson[135] obtained the same expressions as Strey, but based his analysis on the Choleski factorization of the singular $\mathbf{G}$.[84]

The Jacobian for compliance constants is derived from eqn. (56) by an analogous perturbation treatment.[136] For the inverse eigenvalues this results in eqn. (66).

$$(\partial\lambda_i^{-1}/\partial C_{uv}) = (2-\delta_{uv})\,(\tilde{L}^{-1})_{ui}\,(\tilde{L}^{-1})_{vi}\,C_{uv} \tag{66}$$

Equation (28) is particularly easy to differentiate and gives eqn. (67).

$$(\partial\tau_{\alpha\beta,\gamma\delta}/\partial C_{uv}) = \frac{-1}{2+2\delta_{uv}}\,(\mu_{\alpha\beta}^u\,\mu_{\gamma\delta}^v + \mu_{\alpha\beta}^v\,\mu_{\gamma\delta}^u) \tag{67}$$

Derivatives for the mean-square amplitudes in the approximate form due to Morino are also given.

TABLE 3
Jacobian matrix for methyl fluoride

	a_1						e					
	F_{11}	F_{12}	F_{13}	F_{22}	F_{23}	F_{33}	F_{44}	F_{45}	F_{46}	F_{55}	F_{56}	F_{66}
λ_1	×	×	×	×	×	×						
λ_2	×	×	×	×	×	×						
λ_3	×	×	×	×	×	×						
λ_1^*	×	×	×	×	×	×						
λ_2^*	×	×	×	×	×	×						
λ_3^*	×	×	×	×	×	×						
λ_4							×	×	×	×	×	×
λ_5							×	×	×	×	×	×
λ_6							×	×	×	×	×	×
λ_4^*							×	×	×	×	×	×
λ_5^*							×	×	×	×	×	×
λ_6^*							×	×	×	×	×	×
ζ_4							×	×	×	×	×	×
ζ_5							×	×	×	×	×	×
ζ_6							×	×	×	×	×	×
ζ_4^*							×	×	×	×	×	×
ζ_5^*							×	×	×	×	×	×
ζ_6^*							×	×	×	×	×	×
D_J	×	×	×	×	×	×	×	×	×	×	×	×
D_{JK}	×	×	×	×	×	×	×	×	×	×	×	×
D_J^*	×	×	×	×	×	×	×	×	×	×	×	×
D_{JK}^*	×	×	×	×	×	×	×	×	×	×	×	×

Rao[137] has extended this treatment to include expressions relating to Coriolis coupling constants. The expression for the degenerate vibrations of a symmetric top, analogous to eqn. (62), are given in eqn. (68), writing $N = \tilde{L}^{-1}$.

$$\left(\frac{\partial \zeta_{ii}}{\partial C_{uv}}\right) = \frac{2}{(1+\delta_{uv})} \sum_{j}^{(j \neq i)} \zeta_{ij} \frac{(N_{ui} N_{vj} + N_{vi} N_{uj})}{(\lambda_i^{-1} - \lambda_j^{-1})} \tag{68}$$

Expressions for the 'inverse' isotopic shifts, Δ_{ii}^{-1}, are exactly analogous to eqn. (68) with Δ_{ii}^{-1} in place of ζ_{ii}. Both sets of expressions are of the same form as the corresponding expressions for force constants[131,133] but replacing L, λ and Δ by N, λ^{-1} and Δ^{-1}. Approximate formulae for the mean-square amplitudes were also given. Rao also discusses each set of derivatives in the case that redundant coordinates are present.

This section is concluded by describing how the Jacobian is set up in a moderately complicated situation.[93] The observed data are the frequencies λ_1 to λ_6, Coriolis constants ζ_4 to ζ_6 and centrifugal constants D_J and D_{JK} for the molecules CH_3F and CD_3F. The Jacobian is given in Table 3 in outline form. The secular equations are symmetry factored into a_1 and e blocks. The zetas refer only to the e block whereas the Ds refer to both. Data for the deutero compounds are starred.

4.5   Multiple Solutions

It is well known that more than one force-constant solution may be found for a molecular species.[93,138] The existence of more than one reasonable force-constant solution is tantamount to the force field being indeterminate. The key word here is 'reasonable'. There is a deplorable tendency amongst spectroscopists to consider only spectroscopic information. The chemist often has much more information—structural, thermodynamic, etc.—and any solution should be consistent with these data also. This means that more attention should be given to structure/force-constant correlations.

For harmonic quadratic calculations the $n!$ solutions may be found by simple permutations of the observed frequencies, but if more than frequency data are used then the Monte-Carlo approach may be preferred.[139] In this approach the initial force-constant values are varied randomly within probable limits and a refinement is performed for each set of initial values. After sufficient trials (25 to 100 for $n = 3$) all solutions will be found. The Monte Carlo approach has been extended to the consideration of anharmonic force fields with model potential functions. With NOCl, NOF and NOBr six solutions were found which reproduce the anharmonicity data equally well (the quadratic constants were fixed).[140] In a subsequent paper on non-linear symmetric triatomic molecules[141] the quadratic constants were also allowed to vary (see also Bezverkhnaya et al.[142]).

4.6   Force Constants for Molecules in the Solid-state

The **GF** method may be extended to the spectra of crystals. A simple theory of the linear lattice was applied to the hydrogen cyanide polymer.[143] A generalization to three-dimensional lattices has been made by Piseri and Zerbi,[144] and by Beattie *et al.*[145] Both sets of workers used mass-weighted cartesian coordinates in order to avoid problems of redundancy. An example of the application of this method is the determination of a valence force field for crystalline tellurium, in which there are helical chains of Te atoms. A 20-parameter force field was successfully determined.[146]

The main problem, of course, is to define a model for inter-molecular forces. A start has been made in this direction. Lattice frequencies in benzene and naphthalene were calculated in good agreement with the observed frequencies,[147] using an empirical atom-atom pairwise potential function. That is only one example of calculations in the area of solid-state chemistry, an area which is currently of considerable promise.

5   APPROXIMATE FORCE-CONSTANT SOLUTIONS

In the preceding sections it was assumed that sufficient information could be obtained to determine a general quadratic force field. Unfortunately this is not the case for the vast majority of compounds, as they do not exist in the gaseous state. The only experimental data for these molecules are the vibrational frequencies of one or more isotopic species. These data are normally insufficient to determine the quadratic force field when $n > 2$, that is, when any symmetry species contains more than two normal vibrations.

In these circumstances the whole emphasis of the force-constant calculation must change. Its purpose must be more to justify the vibrational assignment than to determine the extent of mixing between coordinates. The use of a model potential function (e.g. UBFF) only masks the true uncertainty, though with restricted classes of molecule some degree of transferability of force constants is to be expected. It cannot be expected, on the other hand, that any one set of approximations will be valid for all molecules. Such a hope would be as futile as to expect a correlation between force constants and bond dissociation energies to be widely applicable, and for much the same reason: there is too much variation in the nature of the covalent bond. Therefore all approximate methods must be treated with caution. One must always ask what information is produced by a force-constant calculation that is not already implicit in the vibrational frequencies. The stock answer to this question, that the mass dependence implicit in the normal frequencies has been removed, will only be satisfactory if the approximations involved do not introduce other serious errors.

These considerations lead one inexorably to the unsurprising view that as much experimental data as possible should be collected so as to reduce the number of approximations involved in the calculation. The converse is also true. For example, it is absolutely pointless to calculate Coriolis coupling constants for species such as $InCl_6^{3-}$ and $RhBr_6^{3-}$ which will never give gas-phase spectra.[148,149]

The problem can be stated simply. There are $n(n+1)/2$ unique force constants for each symmetry block containing n normal vibrations, but only n frequencies for each isotopic species. Furthermore, additional isotopic species do not add data *pro rata* because of the product rule in the first place, and because of the way isotopic substitution may not affect all frequencies.[150] Thus, for $n = 2$, two isotopic species yield three independent frequencies which just determine the field. For $n = 3$ three isotopic species are required[151] to define the six force constants. The situation obviously gets worse as n increases.

There are three approaches to the calculation of approximate force fields. Firstly the eigenvectors can be derived by some unique factorization of the **G** matrix such that the normalization conditions of eqn. (24) apply. Such solutions, which are wholly determined by the kinetic energy matrix, give 'kinematically defined' force constants. Secondly, in the 'step-wise coupling' methods, coupling between vibrations is introduced step by step while the force constants always reproduce the observed frequencies. Thirdly, reference may be made to extremal properties of the force constants. These categories are not mutually exclusive. A review on approximate methods has appeared recently.[152]

Underlying many approximate methods is the simple idea that if eqn. (23) holds, the 'inverse relationship' eqn. (69) is also valid.

$$\mathbf{F} = \tilde{\mathbf{L}}^{-1} \mathbf{\Lambda} \mathbf{L}^{-1} \tag{69}$$

This relationship was first given by Taylor.[153] Thus if **L** is an eigenvector matrix of **GF** and $\mathbf{\Lambda}$ is a matrix of the observed eigenvalues, **F** will be an 'exact' solution. **L** need only obey the normalization conditions, eqn. (24), and these can be written in the form of eqn. (70).

$$\mathbf{L}\tilde{\mathbf{L}} = \mathbf{L}^0 \mathbf{A}\tilde{\mathbf{A}}\tilde{\mathbf{L}}^0 = \mathbf{G} \tag{70}$$

A is an orthogonal matrix and $\mathbf{L}^0$ is some arbitrary matrix which satisfies eqn. (24). The matrix **A** can be regarded as a parametric device through which all possible eigenvectors can be generated. Substitution of eqn. (70) into eqn. (69) yields eqn. (71)

$$\mathbf{F} = (\tilde{\mathbf{L}}^0)^{-1} \mathbf{A}\mathbf{\Lambda}\tilde{\mathbf{A}} (\mathbf{L}^0)^{-1} \tag{71}$$

which is a general parametric representation of the force-constants' matrix. The orthogonal matrix **A** is defined by $n(n-1)/2$ parameters, the same number as the number of undetermined force constants, so this provides a means of investigating the totality of 'exact' solutions by systematic variation of parameters which define **A**.

It must be added that there are two motives for using these approximate methods. One is to produce a solution that conforms to some predetermined criterion: a criterion concerning vibrational mixing, for example. The other is to avoid the computational difficulties of ill-conditioned refinements. This last should no longer apply, since it has been shown that refinement with the Fletcher-Powell method of function minimization is not ill-conditioned.[107,126] This means that the simplest hypothesis, the force-constant solution in which only diagonal symmetry force constants are non-zero, is always computationally feasible. Such a computation, of course, has n parameters corresponding to n frequencies (considering only one isotopic molecule) so an 'exact' solution should exist. Such a solution can be obtained by applying the inverse relationship, eqn. (69).

5.1 Kinematically Defined Solutions

Any factorization of the **G** matrix which conforms to eqn. (70) gives an eigenvector matrix which can be used in the inverse relationship, eqn. (69). The number of possible factorizations is limitless, as implied in eqn. (70), though few are of direct value in vibrational analysis. Taylor first suggested[153] that the diagonalization of **G**, eqn. (35), could be used to provide an eigenvector matrix, eqn. (72) and a force-constant matrix (73).

$$(\mathbf{P}\,\mathbf{\Gamma}^{\frac{1}{2}})\,(\mathbf{\tilde{\Gamma}}^{\frac{1}{2}}\,\mathbf{\tilde{P}}) = \mathbf{G}, \quad \mathbf{L} = \mathbf{P}\,\mathbf{\Gamma}^{\frac{1}{2}} \tag{72}$$

$$\mathbf{F} = \mathbf{P}\,\mathbf{\Gamma}^{-\frac{1}{2}}\,\mathbf{\Lambda}\,\mathbf{\Gamma}^{-\frac{1}{2}}\,\mathbf{\tilde{P}} \tag{73}$$

Billes rediscovered this method,[154] noting that it was equivalent to allowing **G** and **F** to be simultaneously diagonalized by **P**, eqn. (74).

$$\mathbf{\tilde{P}}\,\mathbf{G}\,\mathbf{P} = \mathbf{\Gamma}, \quad \mathbf{\tilde{P}}\,\mathbf{F}\,\mathbf{P} = \mathbf{\Lambda}\,\mathbf{\Gamma}^{-1} \tag{74}$$

An essentially identical point was made by Gussoni and Zerbi.[155]

Several properties result from these relationships. **GF** is symmetric and is also diagonalized by **P**, as can be verified from eqns. (72) and (73). Freeman has proved that, if the eigenvalues are listed in descending order, the trace of **F**, tr(**F**), is a maximum.[156]

Some problems arise with this, as with all approximate methods, when considering two or more isotopic species. There is no *a priori* reason why any approximate force-constant solution for one isotopic species should predict accurately the frequencies of another isotopic species. In an over-determined situation there is only one solution, the force field, which is adequate for all isotopic species. Therefore it is entirely fortuitous if an approximate solution also serves to provide the isotopic shifts.

For the Taylor-Billes method the invariance of force constants to isotopic substitution requires eqn. (75) to hold.

$$\mathbf{P}\,\mathbf{\Gamma}^{-\frac{1}{2}}\,\mathbf{\Lambda}\,\mathbf{\Gamma}^{-\frac{1}{2}}\,\mathbf{\tilde{P}} = \mathbf{P}^*\,\mathbf{\Gamma}^{*-\frac{1}{2}}\,\mathbf{\Lambda}^*\,\mathbf{\Gamma}^{*-\frac{1}{2}}\,\mathbf{\tilde{P}}^* \tag{75}$$

The starred matrices refer to a second isotopic species. It follows that if $\mathbf{P} = \mathbf{P}^*$, that is, if $\mathbf{G}$ and $\mathbf{G}^*$ are diagonalized by the same matrix $\mathbf{P}$, then $\mathbf{G}$ and $\mathbf{G}^*$ commute.[157] However, it is incorrect to suggest that $\mathbf{G}$ and $\mathbf{G}^*$ will be simultaneously diagonalized by the same $\mathbf{P}$ in the Taylor-Billes method.[158,159] Equation (75) requires only that eqn. (76) holds if the Taylor-Billes method is applied to two isotopic species.

$$\mathbf{\Gamma}^{-1} \mathbf{\Lambda} \tilde{\mathbf{P}} \mathbf{P}^* = \tilde{\mathbf{P}} \mathbf{P}^* \mathbf{\Gamma}^{-1*} \mathbf{\Lambda}^* \tag{76}$$

As already suggested, there is no reason why this relationship should hold. However, it only requires $\tilde{\mathbf{P}} \mathbf{P}^*$ to be diagonal; it does not require $\mathbf{P}^* = \mathbf{P}$.

Equation (72) represents one of a class of factorizations of $\mathbf{G}$ as shown in eqn. (77),

$$(\mathbf{P} \mathbf{\Gamma}^{\frac{1}{2}} \mathbf{A}) (\tilde{\mathbf{A}} \tilde{\mathbf{\Gamma}}^{\frac{1}{2}} \tilde{\mathbf{P}}) = \mathbf{G} \tag{77}$$

where $\mathbf{A}$ is an arbitrary orthogonal matrix. Herranz and Castaño,[160] using the method of undetermined multipliers, showed that $\mathrm{tr}(\mathbf{L})$ was maximized by the choice $\mathbf{A} = \tilde{\mathbf{P}}$. Hence the eigenvectors are defined by eqn. (78)

$$(\mathbf{P} \mathbf{\Gamma}^{\frac{1}{2}} \tilde{\mathbf{P}}) (\mathbf{P} \tilde{\mathbf{\Gamma}}^{\frac{1}{2}} \tilde{\mathbf{P}}) = \mathbf{G}, \quad \mathbf{L} = \mathbf{P} \mathbf{\Gamma}^{\frac{1}{2}} \tilde{\mathbf{P}} \tag{78}$$

and $\mathbf{L}$ is symmetric; in fact $\mathbf{G}$ and $\mathbf{L}$ are simultaneously diagonalized by $\mathbf{P}$, so $\mathbf{G}$ and $\mathbf{L}$ commute.

The criterion that $\mathrm{tr}(\mathbf{L})$ be a maximum was chosen on the basis that this would ensure that the diagonal elements of $\mathbf{L}$ were the largest, corresponding to a hazily defined idea of minimal mixing between vibrations. The fact that the idea is not clearly defined need not concern us, as its validity is clear in general terms,[161] and the factorization, eqn. (78), is simple to apply. It was suggested independently by Pulay and Török,[162] though the reasons for it were not as clearly stated.

Another factorization of $\mathbf{G}$ is shown by eqn. (36), the Choleski factorization. This is re-written as eqn. (79)

$$\mathbf{G} = \mathbf{T} \tilde{\mathbf{T}}, \quad T_{ij} = 0, \quad i < j, \quad \mathbf{L} = \mathbf{T}. \tag{79}$$

The eigenvector matrix is lower triangular and so can be inverted easily; its inverse, $\mathbf{T}^{-1}$, is also lower triangular, and consequently $\mathbf{GF}$ is lower triangular, too. Furthermore, the diagonal elements of $\mathbf{GF}$ are equal to the eigenvalues, $(GF)_{ii} = \lambda_i$. These properties are easily verified if $\mathbf{T}$ is substituted into the inverse relationship in eqn. (69).

This choice of eigenvector was first suggested by Larnaudie.[163] He suggested that a range of solutions could be obtained by putting $\mathbf{L} = \mathbf{TA}$, where $\mathbf{A}$ is a two-dimensional rotational matrix. The choice $\mathbf{L} = \mathbf{T}$ does predicate minimum mixing in a precise sense. That is, many elements of the potential energy distribution, eqn. (40), will be zero, and the principal potential energy matrix, $\mathbf{V}$, eqn. (41), will be upper triangular, $V_{ki} = 0$ for $k > i$. The effect of the rotational matrix $\mathbf{A}$ is to increase coupling progressively, so Larnaudie called his procedure a method of progressive rigidity.

More recently other authors have concentrated on the use of $L = T$, as in eqn. (79). Peacock and Müller showed that for $n = 2$ and $\lambda_1 > \lambda_2$, F_{22} is minimum with respect to F_{12} and gave explicit expressions for all force constants.[164] Σ_{11} is also a minimum with respect to Σ_{12}. This condition was equated[164] to the one proposed by Becher and Ballein,[165] in which one normal coordinate was taken to be equal to a symmetry coordinate without any contributions from the others. Another constraint,[166-169] namely that $F_{12}/F_{22} = G_{12}^{-1}/G_{22}^{-1}$, turns out to be exactly the same as specifying $L_{12} = 0$.[170]

Müller and co-workers have extended the treatment to the case $n = 3$, again giving explicit formulae for all the force constants and mean-square amplitude elements Σ_{ij},[171] and Freeman has pointed out that, with $L = T$ and eigenvalues in descending order, F_{nn} has a stationary value.[172]

One point that must always be borne in mind is that when using the inverse relationship of eqn. (69), the result depends on the ordering of eigenvalues in Λ. If the ordering is incorrect then nonsense results; the frequencies are effectively assigned to the wrong symmetry coordinates. The results for NOF[171] obtained using the method of (progressive) rigidity were incorrect because it was falsely assumed that $\nu(NF) > \delta(ONF)$.[173]

Another class of factorizations[174] of G combine partial diagonalization of G with Choleski factorization of the result as in eqn. (80)

$$\tilde{P}\, G\, P = H = T\, \tilde{T}, \quad L = P\, T. \tag{80}$$

The matrix P is, for example, a Householder transformation matrix and T has zeros in the lower triangle wherever they appear in H. The result is an eigenvector matrix whose last row and column are zero except for $L_{n,n-1}$ and L_{nn}. For example with $n = 3$ we have $L_{13} = L_{23} = L_{31} = 0$, compared to $L_{13} = L_{23} = L_{12} = 0$ in the method of progressive rigidity. The Householder transformations can be continued until G has been reduced to tri-diagonal form, in which case the Choleski factorization is particularly easy, T_{ij} being zero except on the leading diagonal and sub-diagonal.

5.2 Stepwise Coupling

The idea behind the stepwise coupling schemes is to start with a simplified, diagonal G matrix and a corresponding diagonal F matrix and to introduce the off-diagonal part of G step by step so as to permit the computation of an 'exact' F matrix at each step, including the last step when the true G matrix is used. Naturally, the scheme applies when only n frequencies are available; because 'exact' solutions can always be constructed then, and the 'exact' solution must contain some arbitrary assumptions concerning the undetermined parameters.

The stepwise coupling methods certainly avoid the problems of ill-conditioned refinement and indeed this seems to be their main purpose. The force-constant solution is not defined by any physical or mathematical constraint, but derives from the initial F matrix in a somewhat unpredictable manner. However, these clear and inherent defects have not stopped the method from gaining popularity, presumably because of the ease with which 'exact' force-constant solutions are obtained.

The first approach was suggested by Fadini.[175] This was based on the direct expansion of the secular determinant and involved a somewhat laborious procedure. Becher and Mattes[176] introduced a much simpler procedure in which the F matrix is produced by the 'inverse relationship' eqn. (69). Initially G is approximated by its diagonal elements and F is given by $F_0 = \Lambda G_0^{-1}$. The off-diagonal part of G is added in increasing fractions in a (predetermined) number of steps, according to eqn. (81).

$$G_m = \left[1 - \left(1 - \frac{m}{m_0}\right)^2\right] (G - G_0) \tag{81}$$

m increases monotonically and m_0 determines the number of steps. After each addition the eigenvectors of GF are computed and a new F matrix is formed via the inverse relationship.

Although the method seems to converge, different values might be obtained according to the path and the number of steps involved. Originally a minimum of five steps was recommended, but as many as fifty might be needed before F becomes constant.[177] A logarithmic progression is said to have advantages over the quadratic one in eqn. (81).[178] An even more bizarre suggestion is that some off-diagonal force constants can be constrained to zero; eqn. (23) is then treated as a system of $n(n+1)/2$ equations in fewer unknowns and is solved by a least-squares method.[179] The Becher-Mattes approach has also been used to compute mean-square amplitudes directly, without calculating F, through the inverse of eqn. (29).[180]

It has been claimed that the Becher-Mattes method gives good predictions for isotopic shifts.[181] If it does so in that instance the result is entirely fortuitous and equivalent to claiming that the Becher-Mattes solution is close to the force field.[182]

Rae has proposed a 'hierarchy scheme' for normal coordinate analysis, which is a stepwise coupling scheme by another name.[183] He prefers to work in mass-weighted cartesian coordinates (in which G is diagonal), but also uses the 'inverse relationship' eqn. (69) to obtain F. Coupling is introduced on an empirical basis, in a manner reminiscent of the method of progressive rigidity.

Let us compare the solutions obtained from stepwise coupling and direct refinement, as applied to the system where there are n frequencies observed. Refinement of the n diagonal symmetry force constants proceeds smoothly if the off-diagonal, constant, force constants have values such that an 'exact' solution is possible. Ill-conditioned refinements only occur when the assumptions concerning the off-diagonal force constants are physically inconsistent.[107] Stepwise coupling ensures that physically self-consistent off-diagonal constants are generated, but this coupling can only start from one initial (diagonal) F matrix. The Fletcher-Powell refinement method, however, will converge smoothly whatever the assumptions;[107] the closer these are to being physically acceptable, the closer will be the 'exact' solution obtained by the 'inverse relationship', eqn. (69), to the original assumptions. In summary, direct refinement using the Fletcher-Powell technique will do everything that stepwise coupling does, and leaves the chemist much greater freedom to make the most appropriate assumptions.

5.3 Extremal Force Constants

Torkington[184] was the first to show that plots of F_{11} and F_{22} against F_{12} ($n = 2$) are ellipses and to derive expressions for the force constants at the extrema defined by $\partial F_{ii}/\partial F_{12} = 0$ or ∞. The extrema $\partial F_{ii}/\partial F_{12} = 0$ correspond to a minimal amount of mixing between symmetry coordinates, which has led Strey to suggest that they can be used to determine approximate force constants.[185] Freeman extended Strey's expressions to include the case $n = 3$.[186]

When $n = 2$ the force-constant solution is fully determinate and is the same as that given by the method of progressive rigidity, that is, $L_{12} = 0$. For $n = 3$, however, only one row of L^{-1} (and hence L) is fully determined, with $L_{12} = L_{13} = 0$, say. So, while the stationary values of the diagonal force constants may be tabulated,[186] the force-constant solution is not fully determined. Full determinism is achieved when the $n(n-1)/2$ strict upper triangular elements of L are zero, e.g. when $n = 3$, $L_{12} = L_{13} = L_{23} = 0$. In this solution each diagonal force constant, F_{ii}, is stationary in the (partial) system comprising only i normal modes.[186]

Extremal values for diagonal compliance constants were obtained in an analogous manner[187] and, because of the formal similarity of eqn. (29) to the inverse of eqn. (56), the stationary values of the mean-square amplitudes are obtained from the same expression for the eigenvectors.[187] The choice of a triangular L matrix means that L^{-1} is also triangular, and so the method of progressive rigidity yields stationary, diagonal, compliance constants. The treatment has been extended, and particular stress laid on the fact that when a compliance constant is stationary there are zero elements in L and so minimum mixing in the sense that many elements of the potential energy distribution are zero.[168]

Off-diagonal force constants may also take stationary values.[189]

Extremal values of the diagonal force constants with respect to one off-diagonal constant are given when $\partial F_{ii}/\partial F_{jk} = \infty$. When $n = 2$, these correspond to the points at which the slope of the force-constant ellipses becomes vertical. Gans has suggested that these extrema are obtained in general whenever the Jacobian given by $J_{ij} = L_{ji}^2$ is singular.[190] This condition was shown to be necessary, but not sufficient,[191] though the alleged counter-example was not accepted[192] and further counter-examples were claimed.[193]

To put the issue in its correct perspective, the singular Jacobian was originally observed at the convergence of refinements of diagonal force constants.[108]

In fact, it was shown that there are a number of continuous zones in which $\mathbf{J}$ is singular, one of which passes through the refinement minimum.[108] The existence of these zones was held to result from the secular equations being inconsistent through one or more choices of off-diagonal, constant, force constants with values outside the value for which $\partial F_{ii}/\partial F_{jk} = \infty$. Thus, if a singular Jacobian is found by force-constant refinement, and the corresponding eigenvectors are used in the inverse relationship eqn. (69), the resulting force constants, denoted by $\mathbf{F}^{\ddagger}$ will be extremal both in the mathematical sense and also in the sense that the values are at the limits within which 'exact' solutions may be found.

The existence of curves similar to ellipses has been demonstrated for $n = 6$.[107] It should also be pointed out that an $\mathbf{F}^{\ddagger}$ matrix corresponds to complete mixing, so that it is not suitable as an approximate force-constant solution.

5.4   Parametric Representations

The orthogonal matrix $\mathbf{A}$ in eqn. (71) is a function of only one parameter when $n = 2$, so all force constant solutions can be expressed in terms of this parameter.[153,194,195] Parametric expressions have been given for compliance constants and mean-square amplitudes,[196] for the potential energy distribution[197] and for Coriolis coupling constants.[198,199] The effects of isotopic substitution have been examined parametrically.[200–202]

When $n = 3$ there are three floating parameters and so parametric representations become difficult. In specific cases additional observed data can be introduced to reduce the number of parameters. A case in point is the e' vibrations of PF_5 for which two Coriolis constants and three frequencies are available; the force-constant solutions can then be expressed as functions of a single parameter.[203]

There is very little point in these parametric methods, since the solution could equally well be mapped in terms of force constants; when $n = 2$ that is precisely what the force-constant ellipses map. There is no evidence to suggest that the correct force constants will always have similar parameter values, and no reason to expect it.

5.5   Comparison of Methods

A few attempts have been made to evaluate the efficacy of approximate methods of calculating force constants by comparing their results with those obtained from the quadratic force constants. The main problem with this procedure is that the quadratic force field is only known for a few small molecules which are not typical, often, of the kind of larger molecule for which an approximate method cannot but be employed. So it is hardly possible to test the methods in the kind of situation where they are most needed.

Sawodny has shown that an extremal, diagonal, force field gives a solution close to the quadratic force field only in special cases.[204] Mayants and co-workers[205] gave a theoretical critique of the approximate methods and came to the conclusion that they are 'mathematically incorrect'.

Pfeiffer has made a most useful and thorough comparison.[206] Restricting consideration to the simplest case, $n = 2$, he considers all the approximate methods in the parametric representation. His results show that methods deriving from diagonalized $\mathbf{G}$ matrices[154,160,162] rarely give good results. The best results are obtained, surprisingly, with the Becher-Mattes approach, but because it is not based on any theoretical precept, the reason for this success remains a mystery. A similar conclusion was reached by Isotani.[207]

A general criticism of this work is that too often the potential energy distribution is not quoted. The potential energy distribution is just as important as the force-constant values since it gives meaning and significance to the vibrational assignment. Indeed, in an under-determined force field it can be argued that the force-constant solutions must have limited meaning, and it is more useful to know if a clear-cut assignment is possible. The use of force-constant calculations to help make assignments is a long established procedure, and probably the only justification for making approximate calculations. Recently the procedure was placed on a more formal basis by using the potential energy distribution as a criterion for deciding between possible assignments.[107]

5.6   Miscellaneous

Müller and co-workers have developed the concept of 'pseudo-exact' force constants.[208,209] The term is an unhappy neologism which is meant to imply an exact solution to a problem which is formulated in an approximate way. In this case, the approximation involved is the high (or low) frequency separation, by which means the order of the problem can be reduced. If one frequency is separated, the corresponding row and column of $\mathbf{F}$ and $\mathbf{G}^{-1}$ (or $\mathbf{G}$) are dropped from the calculation, and n is reduced by one. Thus the procedure is based on a mechanical decoupling of vibrations and the use of an approximate $\mathbf{G}$ matrix. It can be expected to yield good results if the approximation is valid, but equally, the results must be subject to the error inherent in the approximation.

The method was applied to molecules of C_{3v} (ZXY_3), C_{2v} (ZXY_2) and C_s (ZXY) symmetry, using data from isotopic species.[208] Each case originally was under-determined, with $n = 3$, and was transformed into a case for which $n = 2$. Subsequently the method was extended to allow Coriolis data to be included in the calculation.[209] The main virtue of this method is that vibrations are selectively decoupled, and the isotopic and Coriolis data can be included naturally, something which is not possible in the methods that rely on $\mathbf{G}$ matrix factorizations. The appearance of a determinate solution is nevertheless illusory, since sufficient data with which to calculate the force field are lacking.

In this review the term 'exact' has been used only to refer to force-constant solutions which reproduce the observed frequencies exactly, because they are designed to do so by using the 'inverse relationship' eqn. (69). Otherwise the term 'exact' has no meaning for force-constant solutions; even the force field is subject to uncertainty.

Redington and Aljibury have proposed an approximate method based on the maximization of parameterized restoring forces.[210] Naturally, the compliance constants are intimately involved in this method. Comparison of the results from this method with the quadratic force field are encouraging and suggest that it may be useful where partial isotopic data are available. One drawback is that the computed force constants are not invariant to light-atom substitution.

Attempts to devise approximate methods that can apply to data from two isotopic species have already been commented upon. Johansen proposed applying the 'inverse relationship' eqn. (69) separately to both molecules, and taking the mean values of the resulting force constants.[211]

Incredibly complicated parametric expressions have been given by Jordanov and Nikolova. For $n = 2$[212-214] there is little point in them, since the force-constant solution can be obtained by direct refinement. For $n > 2$, more than two isotopic species are clearly required; the claim that it is otherwise[214] has been shown to rest on a fallacious argument.[215] Fallacies were also shown to exist in other papers from the same stable.[216,217] These criticisms have been accepted.[218]

REFERENCES

(1) W. C. Hamilton, *Statistics in Physical Science*, Ronald Press, New York, 1964.
(2) J. L. Duncan, *Mol. Spectrosc.* **3**, 104 (1975).
(3) D. M. Minkin, *Vopr. Mol. Spektrosk.* 45 (1974).
(4) E. B. Wilson, J. C. Decius and P. C. Cross, *Molecular Vibrations*, McGraw-Hill, New York, 1955.
(5) S. J. Cyvin, *Molecular Vibrations and Mean Square Amplitudes*, Amsterdam, 1968.
(6) P. Gans, *Vibrating Molecules*, Chapman and Hall, London, 1971.
(7) D. Steele, *Theory of Vibrational Spectroscopy*, W. B. Saunders, Philadelphia, 1971.
(8) L. H. Jones, *Inorganic Vibrational Spectroscopy*, Dekker, New York, 1971.
(9) L. A. Woodward, *Introduction to the Theory of Molecular Vibrations and Vibrational Spectroscopy*, Oxford University Press, Oxford, 1972.
(10) S. Califano, *Vibrational States*, Wiley, London, 1976.
(11) P. R. Bunker, *J. Mol. Spectrosc.* **42**, 478 (1972).
(12) P. R. Bunker, *J. Mol. Spectrosc.* **45**, 151 (1973); *ibid.* **46**, 119, 154 (1973).
(13) A. D. Buckingham and W. Urland, *Chem. Rev.* **75**, 113 (1975).
(14) A. J. Merer and J. K. G. Watson, *J. Mol. Spectrosc.* **47**, 499 (1973).
(15) J. R. Durig and S. C. Brown, *J. Mol. Spectrosc.* **45**, 338 (1973).
(16) W. F. Edgell, *Spectrochim. Acta* **31A**, 1623 (1975).
(17) D. M. Adams and D. C. Newton, *J. Chem. Soc.* (*A*) 2822 (1970).
(18) P. Labonville, J. R. Ferraro, M. C. Wall and L. J. Basile, *Coord. Chem. Rev.* **7**, 257 (1972).

(19) M. Choca, J. R. Ferraro and K. Nakamoto, *Coord. Chem. Rev.* **12**, 295 (1974).
(20) Z. Cihla and A. Chedin, *J. Mol. Spectrosc.* **40**, 337 (1971).
(21) A. Chedin and Z. Cihla, *J. Mol. Spectrosc.* **45**, 475 (1973).
(22) I. M. Mills, *Theor. Chem.* **1**, 110 (1974).
(23) I. Suzuki, *Appl. Spectrosc. Rev.* **9**, 249 (1975).
(24) J. K. G. Watson, *J. Mol. Spectrosc.* **41**, 229 (1972).
(25) M. Katsunosuke and Y. Tanaka, *J. Chem. Phys.* **61**, 5040 (1974).
(26) D. F. Smith and J. Overend, *Spectrochim. Acta* **28A**, 2387 (1972).
(27) J. W. C. Johns, A. R. W. McKellar and D. Weitz, *J. Mol. Spectrosc.* **51**, 539 (1974).
(28) W. B. Roh and K. N. Rao, *J. Mol. Spectrosc.* **49**, 317 (1974).
(29) S. M. Kirschner and J. K. G. Watson, *J. Mol. Spectrosc.* **47**, 347 (1973).
(30) J. K. G. Watson, *J. Mol. Spectrosc.* **55**, 498 (1975).
(31) T. Nakagawa and J. Overend, *J. Mol. Spectrosc.* **50**, 333 (1974).
(32) E. Weitz and G. Flynn, *Ann. Rev. Phys. Chem.* **25**, 275 (1974).
(33) R. F. Curl, T. Oka and D. S. Smith, *J. Mol. Spectrosc.* **46**, 518 (1973).
(34) W. H. Kirchoff, *J. Mol. Spectrosc.* **41**, 333 (1972).
(35) A. Foord, J. G. Smith and D. H. Whiffen, *Mol. Phys.* **29**, 1685 (1975).
(36) D. F. Smith, *J. Chem. Phys.* **63**, 2256 (1975).
(37) D. J. Gordon and D. F. Smith, *Spectrochim. Acta* **30A**, 1953 (1974).
(38) W. G. Richards, J. Raftery and R. K. Hinkley, *Theor. Chem.* **1**, 1 (1974).
(39) U. Wahlgren, J. Pacansky and P. S. Bagus, *J. Chem. Phys.* **63**, 2874 (1975).
(40) J. T. Gleghorn and F. W. McConkey, *J. Mol. Struct.* **29**, 133 (1975).
(41) W. L. Bloemer and B. L. Bruner, *J. Mol. Spectrosc.* **43**, 452 (1972).
(42) K. B. Hathaway and J. A. Krumhansl, *J. Chem. Phys.* **63**, 4313 (1975).
(43) A. B. Anderson, *J. Chem. Phys.* **63**, 4430 (1975).
(44) D. Rogovin, H. Tigelaar and M. Sargent, *Chem. Phys. Lett.* **31**, 147 (1975).
(45) L. A. Curtiss and J. A. Pople, *J. Mol. Spectrosc.* **55**, 1 (1975).
(46) P. Pulay and F. Török, *J. Mol. Struct.* **29**, 239 (1975).
(47) W. Sawodny and P. Pulay, *J. Mol. Spectrosc.* **51**, 135 (1974).
(48) A. S. Kozlov, T. S. Pivina and V. A. Shlyapochnikov, *J. Mol. Struct.* **29**, 277 (1975).
(49) R. Becher and W. Sawodny, *J. Mol. Struct.* **29**, 105 (1975).
(50) D. M. Dennison, *Rev. Modern Phys.* **24**, 175 (1940).
(51) K. Kuchitsu, T. Oka and Y. Morino, *J. Mol. Spectrosc.* **15**, 51 (1965).
(52) J. L. Duncan and I. M. Mills, *Spectrochim. Acta* **20**, 523 (1964).
(53) A. Burneau, *Spectrochim. Acta* **30A**, 1861 (1974).
(54) J. H. Meal and S. R. Polo, *J. Chem. Phys.* **24**, 1119, 1126 (1956).
(55) D. Kivelson and E. B. Wilson, *J. Chem. Phys.* **21**, 1229 (1953).
(56) L. S. Bartell, *J. Chem. Phys.* **23**, 1219 (1955); K. Kuchitsu and L. S. Bartell, *ibid.* **35**, 1945 (1961).
(57) S. Cyvin (ed.), *Molecular Structures and Vibrations*, Elsevier, Amsterdam, 1972.
(58) D. R. Herschbach and V. W. Laurie, *J. Chem. Phys.* **40**, 3142 (1964).
(59) N. Mohan and A. Müller, *J. Mol. Struct.* **27**, 255 (1975).
(60) W. B. Person and D. Steele, in *Chemical Society Specialist Reports on Molecular Spectroscopy*, Vol. 2, (R. F. Barrow, D. A. Long and D. J. Millen, eds), 1974, p. 357; D. Steele, in *Advances in Infrared and Raman Spectroscopy*, Vol. 1, (R. J. H. Clark and R. E. Hester, eds), 1975, p. 232.
(61) D. A. Long, *Proc. R. Soc.* **A217**, 203 (1953).
(62) R. E. Hester, in *Chemical Society Specialist Reports on Molecular Spectroscopy*, Vol. 2, (R. F. Barrow, D. A. Long and D. J. Millen, eds), 1974, p. 439.
(63) R. J. H. Clark and P. D. Mitchell, *J. Chem. Soc. Faraday II* 515 (1975).
(64) R. J. H. Clark and P. D. Mitchell, *J. Mol. Spectrosc.* **51**, 458 (1974).

(65) V. A. Padma, S. P. Kumar and R. N. Rao, *Indian J. Pure Appl. Phys.* **13**, 31 (1975).
(66) J. W. Nibler and D. M. Barnhart, *J. Mol. Spectrosc.* **44**, 236 (1972).
(67) R. L. Hildebrand, *J. Mol. Spectrosc.* **44**, 599 (1972).
(68) L. S. Mayants and G. B. Shalputer, *J. Mol. Struct.* **24**, 409 (1975).
(69) S. J. Cyvin and J. Brunvoll, *J. Mol. Spectrosc.* **40**, 431 (1971).
(70) L. A. Curtiss, *J. Mol. Spectrosc.* **44**, 605 (1972).
(71) F. Baltagi, A. Bauder, T. Ueda and H. H. Günthard, *J. Mol. Spectrosc.* **42**, 112 (1972).
(72) I. J. McNaught, *J. Mol. Spectrosc.* **39**, 163 (1971).
(73) J. C. Decius, *J. Chem. Phys.* **16**, 1025 (1948).
(74) J. C. Whitmer, *J. Mol. Struct.* **27**, 443 (1975).
(75) T. Henshall, *J. Chem. Educ.* **43**, 600 (1966); J. M. Freeman and T. Henshall, *J. Mol. Struct.* **1**, 172 (1967).
(76) J. M. Freeman, *J. Mol. Spectrosc.* **30**, 51 (1969).
(77) J. H. Carter, J. M. Freeman and T. Henshall, *Spectrochim. Acta* **23A**, 1463 (1967).
(78) P. Gans, *Spectrochim. Acta* **26A**, 281 (1970).
(79) H. O. Dessyn, B. J. Van Der Veken and M. A. Herman, *J. Mol. Struct.* **13**, 219 (1972).
(80) M. Gussoni and G. Zerbi, *Chem. Phys. Lett.* **2**, 145 (1968).
(81) I. M. Mills, *Chem. Phys. Lett.* **3**, 267 (1969).
(82) H. Hunzinger, *J. Mol. Spectrosc.* **17**, 131 (1965).
(83) D. M. Adams and R. G. Churchill, *J. Chem. Soc.* (*A*) 697 (1970).
(84) G. O. Sørensen, *J. Mol. Spectrosc.* **36**, 359 (1970).
(85) J. E. Bertie, R. J. Andersen and P. G. Wright, *Can. J. Spectrosc.* **19**, 153 (1974).
(86) J. H. Schachtschneider and R. G. Snyder, *Spectrochim. Acta* **19**, 117 (1963).
(87) J. M. Reeves, F. F. Cleveland, C. A. Fienzel and E. B. Bradley, *Can. J. Spectrosc.* **19**, 24 (1974).
(88) M. Gussoni, G. Dellepiane and S. Abbate, *J. Mol. Spectrosc.* **57**, 323 (1975).
(89) D. A. Long, R. B. Gravenor and M. Woodger, *Spectrochim. Acta* **19**, 937 (1963).
(90) J. Tyson, H. H. Claassen and K. Kim, *J. Chem. Phys.* **54**, 3142 (1971).
(91) W. D. Gwynn, *J. Chem. Phys.* **55**, 477 (1971).
(92) T. Miyazawa, *J. Chem. Phys.* **29**, 246 (1958).
(93) J. Aldous and I. M. Mills, *Spectrochim. Acta* **18**, 1073 (1962).
(94) R. S. Martin and J. H. Wilkinson, *Numerische Mathematik* **11**, 99 (1968).
(95) D. L. Cummings and J. L. Wood, *J. Mol. Struct.* **26**, 393 (1975).
(96) M. R. Aliev, *J. Mol. Struct.* **23**, 411 (1974).
(97) L. Beckmann, L. Gutjahr and R. Mecke, *Spectrochim. Acta* **19**, 1541 (1963).
(98) W. J. Lehmann, L. Beckmann and L. Gutjahr, *J. Chem. Phys.* **44**, 1654 (1966).
(99) W. T. King and A. J. Zelano, *J. Chem. Phys.* **47**, 3197 (1967).
(100) R. R. Gaughan and W. T. King, *J. Chem. Phys.* **57**, 4530 (1972).
(101) W. T. King, *Spectrochim. Acta* **31A**, 1421 (1975).
(102) W. T. King, *J. Chem. Phys.* **57**, 4535 (1972).
(103) E. Rytter, *J. Chem. Phys.* **60**, 3882 (1974).
(104) P. Adamek, *J. Mol. Spectrosc.* **57**, 164 (1975).
(105) A. J. P. Alix and A. Müller, *J. Mol. Struct.* **24**, 229 (1975).
(106) C. D. Needham and J. Overend, *Spectrochim. Acta* **22**, 1383 (1966).
(107) R. E. Christopher and P. Gans, *J. Chem. Soc. Dalton Trans.* 153 (1975).
(108) P. Gans, *J. Chem. Soc.* (*A*) 2017 (1971).
(109) H. Margenau and G. M. Murphy, *The Mathematics of Physics and Chemistry*, Van Nostrand, New York, 1956.

(110) D. A. Long and R. B. Gravenor, *Spectrochim. Acta* **19**, 951 (1963).
(111) P. Gans, *Coord. Chem. Rev.* **19**, 99 (1976).
(112) D. Papoušek, S. Toman and J. Plíva, *J. Mol. Spectrosc.* **15**, 502 (1965).
(113) K. Levenberg, *Quart. Appl. Math.* **2**, 164 (1944).
(114) J. M. Freeman and T. Henshall, *J. Mol. Spectrosc.* **25**, 101 (1968).
(115) B. Gellai and G. Jancsó, *J. Mol. Struct.* **12**, 478 (1972).
(116) R. Fletcher, *A.E.R.E. Report* R-6799 (1971).
(117) M. J. Bruton and L. A. Woodward, *Spectrochim. Acta* **23A**, 175 (1967).
(118) L. Nemes, *Spectrochim. Acta* **24A**, 300 (1968).
(119) E. C. Curtis, *Spectrochim. Acta* **27A**, 1989 (1971).
(120) J. S. Rollett, in *Crystallographic Computing* (F. R. Ahmed, ed.), Munksgaard, Copenhagen, 1970, pp. 173–174.
(121) T. Shimanouchi and I. Suzuki, *J. Chem. Phys.* **42**, 296 (1965).
(122) H. Susi and J. R. Scherer, *Spectrochim. Acta* **25A**, 1243 (1969).
(123) R. Fletcher and M. J. D. Powell, *Computer J.* **6**, 163 (1963).
(124) P. Gans, *Chem. Comm.* 1504 (1970).
(125) P. Gans, *J. Mol. Struct.* **12**, 411 (1972).
(126) L. J. Pitzner and R. H. Atalla, *Spectrochim. Acta* **31A**, 911 (1975).
(127) J. Overend and J. R. Scherer, *J. Chem. Phys.* **32**, 1289, 1296, 1720 (1960).
(128) J. C. Decius, *J. Chem. Phys.* **38**, 241 (1963).
(129) L. H. Jones and R. R. Ryan, *J. Chem. Phys.* **52**, 2003 (1970).
(130) J. Wright and C. V. S. R. Rao, *J. Mol. Spectrosc.* **51**, 520 (1974).
(131) I. M. Mills, *J. Mol. Spectrosc.* **5**, 334 (1960).
(132) A. A. Chalmers and D. C. McKean, *Spectrochim. Acta* **22**, 251 (1966); D. C. McKean, *ibid*, **22**, 269 (1966).
(133) M. Tsuboi, *J. Mol. Spectrosc.* **19**, 4 (1966).
(134) G. Strey, *J. Mol. Spectrosc.* **17**, 265 (1965); **19**, 229 (1966).
(135) S. O. Sørensen, *J. Mol. Spectrosc.* **39**, 533 (1971).
(136) D. Papoušek and J. Plíva, *Spectrochim. Acta* **21**, 1147 (1965).
(137) C. V. S. R. Rao, *J. Mol. Spectrosc.* **41**, 105 (1972).
(138) D. C. Moule and C. V. S. R. Rao, *J. Mol. Spectrosc.* **48**, 560 (1973).
(139) V. Špirko and J. Morávek, *J. Mol. Spectrosc.* **33**, 368 (1970).
(140) V. Špirko and G. K. Speirs, *J. Mol. Spectrosc.* **55**, 151 (1975).
(141) G. K. Speirs and V. Špirko, *J. Mol. Spectrosc.* **56**, 104 (1975).
(142) G. I. Bezverkhnaya, N. T. Storchai and V. P. Morozov, *Opt. Spektrosk.* **38**, 1044 (1975).
(143) P. N. Ghosh, *J. Mol. Struct.* **26**, 343 (1975).
(144) L. Piseri and G. Zerbi, *J. Mol. Spectrosc.* **26**, 254 (1968).
(145) I. R. Beattie, N. Cheetham, M. Gardner and D. E. Rogers, *J. Chem. Soc. (A)* 2240 (1971).
(146) B. Orel, R. Tubino and G. Zerbi, *Mol. Phys.* **30**, 37 (1975).
(147) G. Taddei, H. Bonadeo and S. Califano, *Chem. Phys. Lett.* **13**, 136 (1972).
(148) A. K. Dublish and D. K. Sharma, *Spectrosc. Lett.* **5**, 387 (1972).
(149) A. N. Pandey, D. K. Sharma, N. Kumar and V. Kumar, *Spectrosc. Lett.* **8**, 413 (1975).
(150) D. C. McKean and J. L. Duncan, *Spectrochim. Acta* **27A**, 1879 (1971).
(151) J. Heicklen, *J. Chem. Phys.* **36**, 721 (1962).
(152) A. J. P. Alix, H. H. Eysel, B. Jordanov, R. Kebabçioglu, N. Mohan and A. Müller, *J. Mol. Struct.* **27**, 1 (1975).
(153) W. J. Taylor, *J. Chem. Phys.* **18**, 1301 (1950).
(154) F. Billes, *Acta Chim. Hungary* **47**, 53 (1966).
(155) M. Gussoni and G. Zerbi, *J. Mol. Spectrosc.* **26**, 485 (1968).
(156) D. E. Freeman, *J. Mol. Spectrosc.* **27**, 27 (1968).

(157) M. P. Drazin, J. W. Dungey and K. W. Gruenberg, *J. London Math. Soc.* **26**, 221 (1951).

(158) D. E. Freeman, *J. Mol. Spectrosc.* **22**, 305 (1967).

(159) A. Alix and L. Bernard, *Compt. Rend.* **268B**, 1307 (1969).

(160) J. Herranz and F. Castaño, *Anales Real Soc. Espan. Fis. Quim.* **A62**, 199 (1966).

(161) J. Herranz and F. Castaño, *Spectrochim. Acta* **22**, 1965 (1966).

(162) P. Pulay, *Z. Angew. Math. Mech.* **46**, 151 (1966); P. Pulay and F. Török, *Acta Chim. Acad. Sci. Hungary* **47**, 273 (1966); **44**, 287 (1965).

(163) M. Larnaudie, *J. Phys. Rad.* **15**, 365 (1954).

(164) C. J. Peacock and A. Müller, *J. Mol. Spectrosc.* **26**, 454 (1968).

(165) H. J. Becher and K. Ballein, *Z. Phys. Chem. Neue Folge*, **54**, 302 (1967).

(166) P. Thirugnanesambandam and G. J. Srinivasan, *J. Chem. Phys.* **50**, 2467 (1969).

(167) N. K. Sanyal, L. Dixit, B. R. Subramanyam and A. N. Panday, *Indian J. Phys.* **47**, 37 (1973).

(168) P. Thirugnanesambandam and S. Mohan, *J. Chem. Phys.* **61**, 470 (1974).

(169) N. K. Sanyal, D. N. Verma and L. Dixit, *Indian J. Pure Appl. Phys.* **13**, 273 (1975).

(170) A. J. P. Alix, A. Müller and N. Mohan, *J. Mol. Struct.* **27**, 440 (1975).

(171) C. J. Peacock, U. Heidborn and A. Müller, *J. Mol. Spectrosc.* **30**, 338 (1969).

(172) D. E. Freeman, *J. Mol. Struct.* **4**, 145 (1969).

(173) L. H. Jones, *J. Mol. Spectrosc.* **33**, 375 (1970).

(174) P. Gans, *J. Mol. Struct.* **33**, 315 (1976).

(175) A. Fadini, *Z. Naturforsch.* **21A**, 2055 (1966).

(176) H. J. Becher and R. Mattes, *Spectrochim. Acta* **23A** 2449 (1967).

(177) H. O. Dessyn, B. J. Van Der Veken, L. Van Haverbeke and M. A. Herman, *J. Mol. Struct.* **13**, 227 (1972).

(178) E. Wendling and L. Mahmoudi, *Bull. Soc. Chim. France* **12**, 4248 (1970).

(179) O. Chacón and R. Matzke, *J. Mol. Struct.* **9**, 243 (1971).

(180) R. L. Hildebrand, *J. Mol. Struct.* **13**, 33 (1972).

(181) B. Van Der Veken, *J. Mol. Struct.* **15**, 300 (1973).

(182) V. P. Zhukov and V. A. Gubanov, *J. Mol. Struct.* **24**, 214 (1975).

(183) A. D. Rae, *J. Mol. Spectrosc.* **56**, 357 (1975).

(184) P. Torkington, *J. Chem. Phys.* **17**, 357 (1949).

(185) G. Strey, *J. Mol. Spectrosc.* **24**, 87 (1967).

(186) D. E. Freeman, *Chem. Phys. Lett.* **2**, 615 (1968).

(187) D. E. Freeman, *Z. Naturforsch.* **24A**, 1964 (1969).

(188) A. Alix, D. E. Freeman and L. Bernard, *Compt. Rend.* **273B**, 247 (1971).

(189) D. E. Freeman, *Chem. Phys. Lett.* **8**, 271 (1971).

(190) P. Gans, *Chem. Phys. Lett.* **12**, 471 (1972).

(191) D. E. Freeman, *Chem. Phys. Lett.* **14**, 335 (1972).

(192) P. Gans, *Chem. Phys. Lett.* **14**, 612 (1972).

(193) D. E. Freeman, *Chem. Phys. Lett.* **18**, 345 (1973).

(194) H. Johansen, *Z. Phys. Chem.* **230**, 240 (1965).

(195) A. Alix and L. Bernard, *Compt. Rend.* **272B**, 528 (1971).

(196) A. Alix and L. Bernard, *J. Chim. Phys.* **68**, 1611 (1971).

(197) A. Alix and L. Bernard, *Compt. Rend.* **270B**, 66 (1970).

(198) A. Alix and L. Bernard, *Z. Naturforsch.* **27A**, 593 (1971).

(199) T. R. Ananthakrishnan and G. Aruldhas, *J. Mol. Struct.* **13**, 163 (1972).

(200) A. Alix and L. Bernard, *Compt. Rend.* **269B**, 812 (1969).

(201) T. R. Ananthakrishnan, C. P. Girijavallabhan and G. Aruldhas, *J. Mol. Struct.* **16**, 149 (1973).

(202) T. R. Ananthakrishnan and G. Aruldhas, *J. Mol. Struct.* **23**, 316 (1974).

(203) T. R. Ananthakrishnan and G. Aruldhas, *J. Mol. Struct.* **26**, 1 (1975).

(204) W. Sawodny, *J. Mol. Spectrosc.* **30**, 56 (1969).

(205) B. S. Averbukh, L. S. Mayants, G. B. Shaltuper, *J. Mol. Spectrosc.* **30**, 310 (1969).
(206) M. Pfeiffer, *J. Mol. Spectrosc.* **31**, 181 (1969).
(207) S. Isotani, *J. Mol. Struct.* **28**, 61 (1975).
(208) K. H. Schmidt and A. Müller, *J. Mol. Struct.* **18**, 135 (1973).
(209) A. Müller and S. N. Rai, *J. Mol. Struct.* **24**, 59 (1975).
(210) R. L. Redington and A. L. K. Aljibury, *J. Mol. Spectrosc.* **37**, 494 (1971).
(211) H. Johansen, *Z. Phys. Chem.* **227**, 305 (1964).
(212) B. Jordanov, *Dokl. Bolg. Akad. Nauk.* **28**, 1073 (1972).
(213) B. Jordanov and B. Nikolova, *J. Mol. Struct.* **13**, 21 (1972).
(214) B. Jordanov and B. Nikolova, *J. Mol. Struct.* **15**, 7 (1973).
(215) N. F. Stepanov, G. S. Koptev and Yu. N. Panchenko, *J. Mol. Struct.* **27**, 423 (1975).
(216) B. Nikolova and B. Jordanov, *J. Mol. Struct.* **15**, 19 (1973).
(217) B. Jordanov, *J. Mol. Struct.* **15**, 165 (1973).
(218) B. Jordanov, *J. Mol. Struct.* **27**, 423 (1975).

Chapter 4

RAMAN POLARIZATION TECHNIQUES IN THE STUDY OF MACROMOLECULES

I. W. Shepherd

Physics Department, Manchester University, Manchester M13 9PL, U.K.

1 INTRODUCTION

The great length of backbone chain gives rise to many of the interesting and important properties of both synthetic and biological polymers. These chains take an enormous variety of conformations, depending on the ambient conditions, and the biological function or physical properties will depend critically on these conformations. Determination of structure as a function of experimental parameters is therefore a matter of importance and this is true both at the level of the complete chain and at the level of the individual monomer units which comprise the chain. Many techniques have been employed in such studies; some examples are X-ray diffraction,[1,2] light scattering (both elastic[3] and inelastic[4]), nuclear magnetic resonance,[5] electron microscopy[6] and neutron scattering.[7] Each of these has particular advantages and disadvantages. For instance, to obtain maximum information from X-ray measurements the samples are normally required to be in solid, often crystalline, form so the technique is of little use in the study of liquids or solutions. However, extremely accurate measurements can be made of structure in the range 1–100 Å which are not possible by other methods. Electron microscopy requires careful sample preparation and the measurements are destructive, yet clear visual representation can be obtained of structure with resolution to 20 Å. Lack of space precludes further remarks along these lines but the interested reader can consult the references for further details. Suffice it to say that no single technique will provide all the desirable information and polymer structure can only be understood by making full use of many techniques. Raman scattering is one technique that has recently been playing an increasingly important role. In this paper the particular contributions made by polarized Raman studies in the understanding of polymer structure will be discussed.

For many years Raman scattering has been used routinely in conjunction with infrared absorption spectroscopy to determine chemical composition by observing bands at frequencies characteristic of particular species. Such chemical characterization will not be dealt with in this review; details of such work can be found in several general discussions of Raman spectroscopy of polymers.[8-13] In the present work, recent sophisticated polarization experiments are emphasized which have been concerned with vibrational mode assignments and chain conformation or secondary structure. There are severe experimental difficulties in this work because, in order to make accurate polarization measurements, the samples must not only be optically clear but also free from fluorescence. There are many interesting polymers in which these criteria have not yet been realized so that the work discussed in this review is limited to a relatively small number of systems. However it will be shown that, in cases where accurate work is possible, extremely detailed information can be obtained and that this information cannot be obtained by other methods.

There are several advantages of the Raman technique which make it particularly important in polymer studies:

(i) It is conservative and measurements can be made on minute quantities of material. This can be important in studies of biological systems where the extraction can be tedious.

(ii) Because the Raman spectrum of water is very weak, it is possible to study molecules in aqueous solution which is the natural environment for biopolymers. In this respect Raman spectroscopy has a clear advantage over infrared absorption spectroscopy.

(iii) Using polarization measurements it has proved possible to gain information about chain conformation in isotropic amorphous materials. This is a great advantage because, although each molecule may have a definite regular structure, the distribution of orientations is frequently random, as for instance in a solution of helical molecules.

To these particular points must be added the general advantages of good sensitivity and high resolution and, in the case of polarization measurements, the wealth of symmetry information that is in principle obtainable. There are, therefore, many advantages and much important information can be obtained if the experimental difficulties can be overcome. We shall see that Raman spectroscopy has made contributions to such diverse topics as the study of denaturation in biological molecules, the underlying molecular basis of rubber elasticity and the details of molecular orientation in both biopolymers and synthetic plastics.

The review is divided into four main sections, not counting the introduction and conclusion. First, the theory section outlines the points that are important in understanding the polarization data and discusses the problems of interpretation. The section on experimental detail makes no attempt to cover in detail the general design features of Raman spectrometers, but rather seeks to emphasize the special features of importance to polarization measurements. There is also a brief sub-section on sample preparation. The discussion of important experiments is divided into two main sections, the first on pure materials and the second on solutions. Each of these has several sub-sections designed to emphasize one particular aspect.

2   THEORY

This section contains a brief outline of that part of the theory of the Raman effect necessary for understanding the polarization data and the concept of the Raman tensor is introduced. The close relationship of the elements of this tensor to the molecular symmetry is emphasized and the problems of interpreting polarization data are discussed.

2.1   Polarization in the Raman Effect

Raman scattered intensities from molecular vibrations can be calculated using third-order perturbation theory.[14−18] Three distinct processes are envisaged in the scattering. (i) The incident photon of energy $\hbar\omega_0$ interacts with the electrons in the scattering medium, promoting one electron from the ground state g to a virtual excited state α' and annihilating the photon. (ii) A vibrational quantum $\hbar\Omega_a$ is either created or annihilated with an accompanying shift of the electron to a second virtual state β'. This is caused by the dependence of the electronic energy on the nuclear positions and is described by the Herzberg-Teller interaction Hamiltonian of the form $(\partial H/\partial Q_a)_0$, where Q_a refers to the ath normal vibrational coordinate. (iii) A photon of energy $\hbar\omega_s$ is created, and the electron falls back to the ground electronic state but in a different vibrational level f. The transition probability for this event is given by:[14]

$$W \propto \left[\sum_{\alpha,\beta} \frac{\langle f'|e^s\cdot\mu|\beta'\rangle\langle\beta'|(\partial H/\partial Q_a)_0|\alpha'\rangle\langle\alpha'|e^0\cdot\mu|g'\rangle}{(E_{\beta g}\pm\hbar\Omega_a-\hbar\omega_0)(E_{\alpha g}-\hbar\omega_0)} \right]^2 \tag{1}$$

$+$ five similar terms

where the summation is over all intermediate electronic states. The five similar terms correspond to the other possible time-orderings of the three processes. $E_{\alpha g}$ and $E_{\beta g}$ refer to the energy differences between the ground electronic state and the excited levels α and β respectively; e^0 and e^s are unit vectors for the incident and scattered polarizations; and μ is the dipole-moment operator. The vibrational mode will be Raman active if the product of matrix elements in the numerator is non-vanishing. This will be the case if, in a given molecular symmetry, the irreducible representation of the normal mode Γ_{Q_a} is contained in the direct product of the irreducible representations of the incident and scattered polarization directions Γ_0 and Γ_s.[19] Thus, for Raman activity we must have

$$\Gamma_{Q_a} = \Gamma_0 \times \Gamma_s \tag{2}$$

and this forms a basis for a nine-component tensor for the ath normal mode which is known as the Raman tensor $\mathbf{R}^a$, and is in effect a derived polarizability tensor. The scattered intensity can then be written in the form:[20]

$$I = A(\sum_{\lambda,\nu=x,y,z} e_\lambda^0 R_{\lambda\nu}^a e_\nu^s)^2 \tag{3}$$

where A is a constant which depends on experimental factors and the properties of the system under study, e_λ^0 and e_ν^s are the polarization components of the incident and scattered photons respectively, and $R_{\lambda\nu}^a$ is the $\lambda\nu$th component of the Raman tensor for the ath vibrational mode. The Raman tensor is strictly symmetrical when the frequencies of electronic transitions and molecular vibrations are far removed from the radiation frequencies.[20] In this case there are six independent components. The form of the tensors will depend on the molecular symmetry, and Loudon[20] lists them for the 32 crystal point groups. Equation (3) shows that it is possible in crystalline structures to measure individual tensor elements by making appropriate choices of incident and scattered polarization directions. In isotropic amorphous material, with which we are mainly concerned in this paper, the molecular axes are randomly oriented with respect to the laboratory axes and the polarization measurements of Raman bands are an average over all orientations. A convenient quantity to consider in this case is the depolarization ratio ρ which is the ratio of the scattered intensities polarized perpendicular and parallel to the direction of polarization of the incident radiation. In the usual 90° scattering geometry and for linearly polarized incident light we have: [21–23]

$$\rho = \frac{3\gamma'^2}{45\bar{\alpha}'^2 + 4\gamma'^2} \tag{4}$$

where $\bar{\alpha}'^2$ is the isotropic part of the tensor and γ'^2 the anisotropic part. These quantities are defined in terms of the components α_{ij}' of the derived polarizability tensor as

$$\bar{\alpha}' = \tfrac{1}{3}(\alpha_{xx}' + \alpha_{yy}' + \alpha_{zz}')$$

and

$$\gamma'^2 = \tfrac{1}{2}[(\alpha_{xx}' - \alpha_{yy}')^2 + (\alpha_{xx}' - \alpha_{zz}')^2 + (\alpha_{yy}' - \alpha_{zz}')^2] + 3(\alpha_{xy}'^2 + \alpha_{yz}'^2 + \alpha_{xz}'^2).$$

The values of α_{ij}' are dependent on the molecular symmetry, and so measurement of ρ can in principle give symmetry information in spite of the random molecular orientation.

The maximum value of $\rho = \tfrac{3}{4}$ predicted by eqn. (4) occurs when $\bar{\alpha}'^2 = 0$. However this expression is only valid when the scattering tensor is symmetric; when the exciting radiation approaches resonance with electronic transitions of the molecule the tensor may become asymmetric. This resonance condition is characterized by zeros in the denominators of eqn. (1) and gives rise to large increases in the scattering cross-section. Because of the possibility of an asymmetric tensor it can also give rise to values $\rho > \tfrac{3}{4}$. This problem has been treated by Placzek.[24] Two anisotropic invariants of the tensor are now required, instead of just the one, γ'^2, of eqn. (4). These are a symmetric part $\gamma_s'^2$ and an asymmetric part $\gamma_{as}'^2$ both of which are defined in terms of the tensor elements as

$$\gamma_s'^2 = \tfrac{1}{2}[(\alpha_{xx}' - \alpha_{yy}')^2 + (\alpha_{xx}' - \alpha_{zz}')^2 + (\alpha_{yy}' - \alpha_{zz}')^2]$$
$$+ \tfrac{3}{4}[(\alpha_{xy}' + \alpha_{yx}')^2 + (\alpha_{xz}' + \alpha_{zx}')^2 + (\alpha_{yz}' + \alpha_{zy}')^2]$$

and

$$\gamma_{as}'^2 = \tfrac{3}{4}[(\alpha_{xy}' - \alpha_{yx}')^2 + (\alpha_{xz}' - \alpha_{zx}')^2 + (\alpha_{yz}' - \alpha_{zy}')^2].$$

The expression for ρ can now be obtained by averaging procedures,[21] keeping track of each tensor element individually and is

$$\rho = \frac{3\gamma_s'^2 + 5\gamma_{as}'^2}{45\bar{\alpha}'^2 + 4\gamma_s'^2} \tag{5}$$

If the tensor is symmetric $\gamma_s'^2 = \gamma'^2$, $\gamma_{as}' = 0$ and we obtain eqn. (4). It is easy to see from eqn. (5) that so-called anomalous values of $\rho > \tfrac{3}{4}$ are possible. In the extreme case where both $\bar{\alpha}'^2$ and $\gamma_s'^2$ are zero and yet where γ_{as}' is finite we have the phenomenon of inverse polarization, where $\rho = \infty$. This can only occur when the tensor is antisymmetric, i.e. $\alpha_{ij}' = -\alpha_{ji}'$. Measurements of anomalous depolarization have proved of value in the study of some biological systems; these will be discussed in Section 5.

2.2 Interpretation of Polarization Data

Equation (3) shows us that Raman polarization measurements on crystalline systems will give relative values of the elements of the Raman tensor appropriate to the mode being studied. Group theoretical analysis based on knowledge of the crystal symmetry then permits unambiguous assignment of the mode to a particular representation. This has proved a valuable technique in the study of single crystals and a selection of recent work can be found in recent conference reports.[25,26] It is sometimes possible to obtain polymer samples in highly regular form. The chains are then usually in helical or chain-extended (all *trans*)form and similar techniques can be employed to assign the various modes. The selection rules and intensities for Raman scattering have been considered for the important case of a helix.[27] The helix is supposed to be infinite, composed of identical units and characterized by a helical space group. Each frequency Ω_i of an isolated unit gives rise in the helically-linked polymer to a band of frequencies $\Omega_i(\theta)$, where θ is the phase difference between motions of adjacent units. Group theoretical arguments show that first-order Raman-active modes have $\theta = 0$ (*a* modes), $\theta = \pm\Psi$ (e_1 modes) and $\theta = \pm2\Psi$ (e_2 modes) where Ψ is the screw-rotation angle of the helix. The Raman selection-rules for linearly polarized light are summarized in Table 1. Here z is the helix-axis direction and x, y are equivalent axes perpendicular to this; a_{0i} etc. are elements of the Raman tensor of the full helix expressed in complex coordinates

$(x \pm iy, z)$ and g_i is a frequency factor. The intensities can be expressed also as a coherent sum of contributions from individual units

$$I_{pq}|\Omega_i(\theta)| \propto \left| \frac{\sum\limits_{n=-\infty}^{\infty} \alpha'_{pq}|n, \Omega_i(\theta)|}{\sum\limits_{n=-\infty}^{\infty} 1} \right|^2 \tag{6}$$

in which p and q denote polarizations of the incident and scattered beams respectively and $\alpha'_{pq}|n, \Omega_i(\theta)|$ is the pqth component of the differential polarizability tensor of the nth unit in mode $\Omega_i(\theta)$. If the coupling between units is weak the intensities can be related to the principal elements of the Raman tensor

TABLE 1
Raman selection rules for scattering of linearly polarized light from a helix.[a]

| Polarization | | Mode | | |
Incident	Scattered	Symmetry	Frequency	Intensity
z	z	a	$\Omega_i(0)$	$g_i(a_{0i})^2$
x	x	a	$\Omega_i(0)$	$g_i(a_{0i})^2$
y	y	e_2	$\Omega_i(2\Psi)$	$g_\nu|a_{2i}|^2$
x	z			
z	x	e_1	$\Omega_i(\Psi)$	$g_i|a_{1i}|^2$
z	y			
y	z			
x	y	e_2	$\Omega_i(2\Psi)$	$g_i|a_{2i}|^2$
y	x			

[a] The helix axis is along z; a_{0i} etc. are elements of the Raman tensor of the full helix and g_i is a frequency factor.

of an isolated unit. In this case the tensor α_i for a unit in mode Ω_i is specified by the diagonal components $\alpha'_{ri}(r = 1, 2, 3)$ and by the orientation angles Φ_{ri} between the principal axes and the helix axis. The general expressions contain many unknown parameters, but great simplification is possible if the Raman tensor is axially symmetric ($a_{2i} = a_{3i} = \alpha_i$, $a_{1i} = \alpha_i'$). In Section 4 we shall consider an example involving vibrations consisting mainly of stretching of single bonds in which this approximation is valid.

However the more usual situation with polymers is to have a mixture of isotropic amorphous and ordered or crystalline regions. The percentage of the sample that is crystalline varies enormously from material to material and with the thermal history of the sample. It rarely approaches 100% and even then there is a distribution of orientations. It is frequently possible partially to orient polymers by an applied stress and the distribution of the chain orientations under such stress is of both theoretical and practical importance. In such situations the simple and elegant approach adopted for single crystals is inappropriate and we now consider the interpretation of Raman polarization data in amorphous isotropic and partially oriented samples.

In oriented systems the measured intensity of the scattered light from the ath mode is given by quantities of the form $A \sum R_{\lambda\nu} R_{\varepsilon\delta}$ (see eqn. (3)) that contain information about the distribution of orientations of the scattering units. This can be seen by expressing the $R_{\lambda\nu}$ as linear combinations of the principal components of the tensor, R_1, R_2, R_3, in which the coefficients depend on the angles defining the principal axes with respect to the symmetry axes of the specimen. It has been shown[28] that in principle it is possible to obtain fairly detailed information about the orientation of scattering units in a solid polymer by expanding the distribution of orientations of the principal axes in a series of generalized spherical harmonics.[29,30] The relationships between the coefficients in the expansion can then be obtained from suitable Raman polarization measurements.

In the case of a truly isotropic amorphous sample only quantities which are averages over all orientation directions are measurable. Such a quantity is the depolarization ratio, ρ, defined in eqn. (4). Depolarization data can be a direct, if approximate, help in assigning the more obvious bands in a polymer spectrum. In this respect, the Raman technique is used in much the same way as in the study of a liquid of low molecular weight. However, the complicated conformations of a polymer system make the problem at once more difficult and more intriguing by providing a variety of environments for the vibrating molecules. The quantities $\bar{\alpha}'$ and γ' depend on the polarizability properties of the molecule under the normal vibration and will be a function of the immediate surroundings. Thus in principle ρ measurements can provide a method of observing changes in polymer conformation at the level of the monomer units, such as changes in rotational isomeric states. The problem is to obtain a theoretical relationship between ρ and the polymer parameters of interest. The complexity of polymer structure with the many associated degrees of freedom makes this an impossible task in general. Under certain simplifying assumptions, however, some progress has been made. If we assume that a monomer can exist in either a *trans* or *gauche* state and that the polarizability properties of a molecular group associated with a given monomer depend on the rotational isomeric state of that monomer alone, we can write the measured ρ of a Raman mode as:[31-33]

$$\rho = \frac{n_g I_{\perp g} + n_t I_{\perp t}}{n_g I_{\parallel g} + n_t I_{\parallel t}}. \tag{7}$$

$I_{\perp g}$ is the intensity scattered from a *gauche* isomer polarized perpendicular to the incident beam and averaged over all orientations; the other intensity terms are defined similarly; n_g and n_t are the *gauche* and *trans* rotamer populations respectively. This general expression provides a formal link between measured ρ and the physical parameters n_g and n_t but, without further simplification, provides no quantitative information because the intensity terms are unknown. In the cases where the bands are highly polarized or where the population of one of the rotamers is known to be very small, further simplification becomes possible. We shall see in later sections that many important polymer parameters can be deduced from ρ data using simplified forms of eqn. (7). However it should be remembered that important assumptions have been made which can only be expected to be valid for simple polymer systems. The general problem of connecting ρ measurements of polymers with physical parameters remains intractable and much of the data is of qualitative rather than quantitative value.

3   EXPERIMENTAL DETAIL

Perhaps the most striking feature of the Raman spectra of polymers is the large number of bands. Such crowded spectra are to be expected because, as polymers are long molecules with a large number of repeat units N and each unit contains a number of atoms m, there may be of the order $3mN$ vibrations, all of which are Raman active. The situation is not generally so bad because many bands will be weak and, if there is some symmetry in the chain conformation, certain vibrations may be inactive. It is, however, generally a problem to find a well-resolved band on which to make detailed polarization measurements. The complexity of the chemical composition and the preparative techniques also means that there will usually be a relatively high impurity content and frequently this causes high levels of fluorescence. A final problem, and this time specific to polarization studies, is the scrambling caused by multiple scattering in a heterogeneous system. These problems must be tackled by a combination of careful chemical purification and sophisticated measurement techniques. Even with best effort, really accurate data have only been obtained on relatively few systems.

In this section we discuss first the special features of equipment used to measure polarized spectra and then touch briefly on sample preparation.

3.1   Equipment

In studies involving accurate polarization measurements, usually only the strongest bands are considered and in general the very low frequency region (<10 cm^{-1}) has not been investigated. Thus spectrometers including only two gratings (e.g. Spex 1401) are normally sufficient, especially if holographic gratings are used. It is convenient to cater for both the more usual 90° scattering and also for back scattering which can be useful for studying thin films. The collection optics must include a high quality rotatable polarizer and it is often convenient to use a half-wave plate in the laser beam to permit rotation of the incident polarization by 90°. An efficient polarization scrambler is essential, placed after the polarizer in the scattered beam, to ensure that the polarization dependence of the spectrometer throughput does not confuse the measurements. Detection is normally accomplished using a high-gain photomultiplier and photon counting. If it is desired to investigate the low frequency region then a triple-grating instrument must be used and it may be necessary to include an iodine filter in the scattered beam.[34]

The basic equipment, then, is fairly standard and details have been published in many places (see, for example, Shepherd,[4] Hendra[12] and Gilson and Hendra[23]). However, if one of the problems outlined above is particularly troublesome then sophisticated modifications become necessary. We start by considering the problem of an overcrowded spectrum. Equation (1) shows that the Raman-scattering cross-section can be significantly increased when the exciting frequency is tuned to that of an absorption band in the material under study. This resonance technique can be used to amplify bands arising from vibrations in the region of a chromophore relative to the other bands in a complex molecule. This has been used in the study of haeme proteins and the work has been reviewed by Spiro.[35] The technique does not have wide application as yet because most polymers do not absorb in the visible region of the spectrum. However, in the case of biological systems, the chromophores (haemes, flavins, metal ions) are frequently at the sites of biological activity, and this technique is promising. The exciting source in such experiments is a tunable dye laser, the mos tfrequently used dye being rhodamine 6G; other dyes permit scanning through the absorptions in, for instance, ferrocytochrome c where the α and β bands are at approximately 18 200 and 19 300 cm^{-1} respectively. Polarization data on this and the related systems will be discussed in Section 5. Continuing development of tunable lasers at higher frequencies into the u.v. may well permit the use of resonance techniques to study a wider range of systems in the future.

We come now to a discussion of experimental modifications designed to suppress unwanted fluorescence. In principle, because the fluorescence is delayed by a characteristic time τ relative to the (prompt) scattering, it is possible to discriminate in favour of the scattering by using pulsed techniques. Equipment designed for this purpose and at present under construction in our laboratory is shown in Fig. 1. The source is a mode-locked argon ion laser. In this configuration the output is a train of pulses, width approximately 0.5 ns and separation twice the round trip time in the laser cavity, approximately 10^{-8} s. Roughly 2% of the beam is extracted as reference and the remainder is focused onto the sample. The scattered beam is collected, analysed and detected in a conventional manner; the only special criterion is that transit time dispersion in the photomultiplier be minimized. The signal and reference pulses are fed to the 'START' and 'STOP' inputs of a time-to-amplitude converter (TAC) respectively and the delayed fluorescence is blocked by the window of the single-channel analyser.

The common values of τ for fluorescence arising from impurities in polymers lie in the range 1–10 ns, and the important biological compound tryptophan fluoresces with $\tau = 3$ ns. With these τ values it should be possible to suppress the fluorescence intensity relative to the Raman by better than an order of magnitude. The signal-to-noise ratio is not improved by such a factor because the upper limit of the power output in the mode-locked configuration is only 35% of the c.w. value. The best improvement is expected to be by a factor 4. The limiting experimental factor appears to be the relative timing of the reference and signal pulses. Previous attempts[36] have not achieved the full predicted improvement because of poor control of this timing caused by an inadequate photomultiplier tube, by the use of a low gain preamplifier and by use of the mode-lock driver to trigger the 'STOP' channel. In our laboratory the

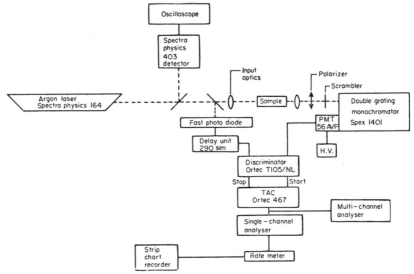

Fig. 1. Equipment designed to discriminate against fluorescence using pulsed-laser excitation and gated detection.

photomultiplier tube has a transit time dispersion <0.5 ns, no preamplifier is used and the 'STOP' channel is triggered by the reference beam. We have obtained a suppression factor of seven in a benzene/rhodamine 6G sample.[37]

It is also possible to avoid the effects of fluorescence by using the technique of coherent anti-Stokes Raman spectroscopy (CARS). First observed in 1963,[38] interest has been revived following the development of tunable lasers.[39] Two pulsed laser beams are focused into the sample, a pump beam of fixed frequency ω_p and a tunable beam ω_t. When the difference between these frequencies is tuned to that of a Raman band, a third beam at the anti-Stokes frequency of $2\omega_p - \omega_t$ is generated providing the momenta are matched. In addition to avoiding fluorescence, this technique has high efficiency and may well prove of value in polymer studies.[40]

The third problem, that of polarization scrambling caused by multiple scattering, cannot be dealt with at the measurement stage. The only actions to be taken are obvious ones of using samples in the form of thin films or, in solutions, of choosing solvents to match the polymer refractive index. Otherwise improvements can only be made in the sample preparation.

3.2 Sample Preparation

The unwanted fluorescence signals that obscure Raman spectra usually arise from impurities in the polymer. Very low impurity concentrations can give rise to substantial fluorescence intensities and the only way to improve the spectra is

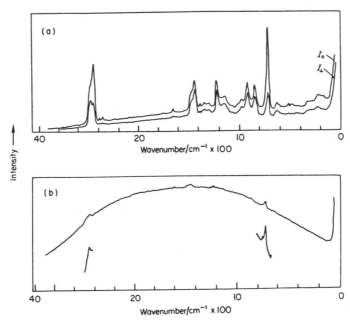

Fig. 2. Raman spectra of polyisobutylene (PIB) (a) pure (b) after cross-linking with zinc diethylamine carbonate. The cross-linking process induces a large fluorescence signal (Maxfield, Ref. 33).

by purification. The technique will vary somewhat from sample to sample but usually involves repeated precipitation. Most synthetic and biological polymers can be purified sufficiently to give reasonable Raman spectra, though not necessarily well enough to permit accurate polarization measurements.

The problem is accentuated where samples are required in the form of networks. The cross-linking process involves the breaking and re-forming of covalent bonds, and the effect of attempting this chemically is illustrated in Fig. 2. Here the spectrum of polyisobutylene (PIB) is shown before and after cross-linking using zinc diethylamine carbonate (Ref. 33, p. 118). The deliberately introduced chemical impurity has introduced an unacceptable level of fluorescence and this is a frequent problem when chemical agents are used. In certain cases, for instance, polypropylene oxide and polystyrene,[41,42] it has neverthe-less proved possible to use chemical means to form clear gels with low fluores-cence. It has been our experience with polydimethylsiloxane (PDMS) that the best way to form networks which show clear Raman spectra is by the use of γ irradiation.[33]

There is little that can be accomplished to reduce scrambling caused by multiple scattering. Careful attention to sample purity and annealing, and to choice of a matching solvent are about the only things to be done. When samples are oriented, this unavoidably introduces a birefringence and therefore a depolarization. Care must be taken to use sufficiently thin samples or to correct for the spurious depolarization. Partially crystalline samples will, of course, scatter strongly yet some progress has been made by studying thin films. These effects will be discussed further in Section 4.1.2.

The problem of overcrowded spectra may be alleviated by attaching chromo-phores at selected positions and then studying the resonance Raman spectra of the molecular groups near the point of attachment. It might be possible to do this without significantly disturbing the spectra, and it remains an interesting possibility for the future.

4 PURE SYSTEMS

Most of the polarized Raman work in polymers has been done on pure systems, that is on systems containing only one component. The reason for this is that the spectra of even relatively simple synthetic systems are complex and crowded compared with, for example, the spectra of solid-state crystals or low molecular-weight liquids. Spectra of more complicated systems, such as block co-polymers which contain two or more distinct components, are generally so crowded that there are few, if any, bands that are resolved well enough to permit accurate polarization measurements. The same is true of most naturally occurring proteins and nucleic acids, which have a wide selection of side groups, and most detailed Raman work on systems of biological interest has been done on model polypeptides or polynucleotides.[43] In these model compounds only very few, say one or two, of the amino acids or bases are involved and the spectra are greatly simplified. A further complication that frequently occurs with multi-component systems is an increase in fluorescence, which can seriously impair experimental accuracy (Section 3). The optical clarity of complex systems can also be poor so that, even in the absence of fluorescence, polarization data may be inaccurate. Thus it is not surprising that most Raman experiments on poly-mers do not involve accurate polarization measurements. It was noted in the introduction that there are several reviews which can be consulted for general details of polymer spectra and Refs 8–13 represent a selection. In this section we make no attempt to rival in quantity these comprehensive works, but rather seek to demonstrate the important information that can be derived from polarization measurements on those polymer systems that conform to certain standards of purity. This information includes definite mode assignments, measurement of conformational changes and associated thermodynamic parameters, and determination of average orientation of structural units within strained samples. The discussion is divided between oriented and isotropic amorphous systems.

4.1   Oriented Systems

In most polymer systems some degree of uniaxial orientation can usually be achieved by the use of appropriate techniques.[44] This can greatly facilitate the assignment of the normal vibrations to the various symmetry representations following Raman polarization measurements (eqn. (3)). The orientation of the polymer structural units themselves can be studied, as can the conformation of the molecule as a whole. The changes in the rotational isomeric states under extension can be observed, which is an observation of conformational change at the monomer level. Examples of work along these lines will be discussed in turn and a final section includes an assessment of future prospects.

4.1.1   Mode assignments

There are many polarization experiments that have permitted definitive mode assignments and it is with difficulty that three have been selected for discussion here. The first example, on polyethylene (PE), shows an experiment of appropriate geometry in a carefully prepared sample unambiguously resolving an assignment problem that had provoked much argument over several years. The second example, isotactic polypropylene (IPP), shows that, even in relatively poorly oriented systems of poor optical quality, polarization data can give firm assignments over the whole spectral range. The last example considers a biological sample, the model polypeptide poly-L-alanine (PLA). In this work the detailed form of the Raman tensor for an α-helix is obtained and measurements are made in several scattering geometries.

The polarization character of the 1418 cm^{-1} and 1370 cm^{-1} modes in PE was studied in highly oriented fibres[45] with the aim of determining which of these was the methylene wagging mode. PE crystallizes in an orthorhombic form (D_{2h}) with two chains per unit cell[46] and with the chain direction coincident with the c-axis. In a completely oriented crystal the vibrations corresponding to the four symmetry representations, $a_g, b_{1g}, b_{2g}, b_{3g}$, can be uniquely determined by suitable polarization experiments. This is made clear by considering the Raman tensors appropriate to the line group species, which are

$$a_g\begin{pmatrix} a & & \\ & b & \\ & & c \end{pmatrix} \quad b_{1g}\begin{pmatrix} & d & \\ d & & \\ & & \end{pmatrix} \quad b_{2g}\begin{pmatrix} & & e \\ & & \\ e & & \end{pmatrix} \quad b_{3g}\begin{pmatrix} & & \\ & & f \\ & f & \end{pmatrix}$$

where all components unlabelled are zero. However, even if the c-axis is uniquely defined, as in cases of very high orientation, the random orientation of the *a*- and *b*-axes makes unique assignment difficult. Measurements were made both with the fibre perpendicular to both incident beam and collection direction and with the fibre parallel to the collection direction and perpendicular to the incident beam. These data are shown in Fig. 3. It was observed that the band at

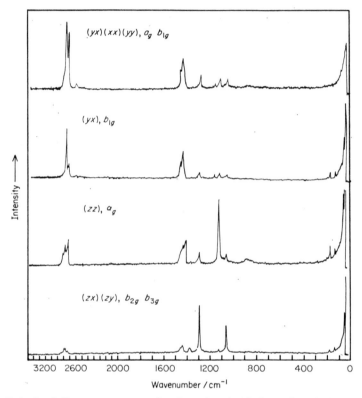

Fig. 3. Polarized Raman spectra of oriented polyethylene; bands below 200 cm^{-1} and at 2903 cm^{-1} are grating ghosts. The incident and scattered polarization directions, and the symmetry species are indicated in each trace (Carter, Ref. 45).

1418 cm^{-1} only contributed to α_{zz} and was therefore assigned to the a_g line-group representation. The 1370 cm^{-1} band appeared strongest in $\alpha_{xz} + \alpha_{yz}$, and was therefore assigned to either b_{2g} or b_{3g}. The methylene wagging mode, about which there had been some conjecture,[47,48] belongs to line group species b_{2g} and can therefore be assigned to the band observed at 1370 cm^{-1}. Thus the Raman experiment was able to determine which of these two bands could be the methylene wagging mode even though, taken by itself, it could not provide a definitive assignment.

Another polymer on which polarized Raman work has been helpful with mode assignments is IPP. This polymer exists in a 3_1 helical form, that is, a helix with three monomers per turn. The normal vibrations can be treated as belonging to a group isomorphous with the point group C_3 and 25 are classified as a modes and 52 as e modes. The Raman tensor for a modes has all off-diagonal elements zero and therefore experiments on uniaxially oriented IPP should permit accurate assignment of modes. Such experiments have been performed[49] under a variety of geometries and some of these data are shown in Fig. 4. The orientation axis is perpendicular to the observation direction in these spectra, with the incident polarization either parallel or perpendicular to the scattered polarization. The direction of collection is perpendicular to the incident direction.

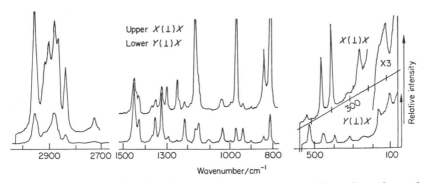

Fig. 4. Raman spectra of oriented isotactic polypropylene. The orientation axis is perpendicular to both the observation axis Y and the laser beam direction Z. In each spectrum the scattered polarization is X; the incident polarization is X (upper) or Y (lower). Bands showing significant polarization are assigned to the a representation (Bailey *et al.*, Ref. 49).

Similar data were obtained with the unique sample axis parallel to the observation direction. Significant degrees of polarization were observed, in spite of the incomplete orientation and the scrambling of polarization caused by imperfect optical clarity. The two species a and e could in most cases be clearly distinguished, and the assignments agree well with previous infrared[50] and Raman[51] results.

As a final example in this section we consider work on a biological sample, poly-L-alanine (PLA). PLA is the simplest model polypeptide that exists in the α-helical conformation and it has been the subject of considerable study. In the α-helix there are 18 peptide residues in five turns and the group is isomorphous with the C_{18} point group. Selection rules for Raman scattering from helical molecules were first considered by Higgs,[27] and the detailed form of the Raman tensor for the Pauling α-helix was obtained by Fanconi *et al.*[52] In this latter paper a theory for the angular dependence of the light scattered from helical molecules is given. The PLA Raman spectrum has been measured,[52,53] as has the infrared absorption,[53,54] and normal-coordinate analyses have been given.[55,56] The clearest polarized Raman data have been obtained from oriented PLA fibres prepared from saturated solutions. A total of eight different scattering geometries were obtained by mounting the fibres with the orientation axis parallel or perpendicular to the spectrometer slit. The data are used to make tentative assignments which are presented in more detail in a later publication.[56] The Raman data have been compared with infrared work[53,54,57,58] and the agreement at low frequencies with calculated assignments[57] is generally good. Above 900 cm^{-1} there are significant disagreements which may be a result of differences in degree of orientation or in the amount of β-structure present.

The work of Fanconi et al.[52] also included Raman experiments on several polyribonucleotides in which differences in both band frequency and polarization between monomer and polymer were studied. The substances studied were poly(guanylic acid) (polyG), poly(uridylic acid) (poly U), poly(cytidilic acid) (poly C) and poly(adenylic acid) (poly A). These samples were not oriented.

From these few examples it can be seen that Raman polarization data on oriented polymer systems, taken by themselves or in conjunction with other data, can provide valuable help in making band assignments. This is true even when orientation is far from complete.

4.1.2   Measurement of molecular orientation

An important field of research in polymer science is the study of how the mechanical and other physical properties of a polymer are influenced by the molecular orientation induced by drawing. It is therefore important to have means of measuring the distribution of orientations of the structural units, which may be crystallites or molecular segments. Several different techniques have been employed in such studies including measurements of fluorescence polarization, nuclear-magnetic-resonance line-shapes, infrared-, visible- and ultraviolet dichroism and birefringence; details may be found in a recently published book[44] and conference report.[59] The various techniques differ both in terms of the type of structural information which they can yield and in the amount of information they can provide about the distribution of orientations. It has been seen in Section 2 that, in principle, polarized Raman data can give detailed information about orientation in both crystalline and non-crystalline regions. These ideas have been developed in experiments on oriented poly(methylmethacrylate) (PMMA)[60,61] and poly(ethylene terephthalate) (PET).[60,62] In the work on PMMA lines at 468, 562, 604 and 1732 cm^{-1} were studied. Values of the averages $\overline{\cos^2 \theta}$ and $\overline{\cos^4 \theta}$ were deduced for the structural units, where θ is the angle between a unique axis in the unit and the draw direction. These results are in good agreement with n.m.r. data.[63] In the sample of highest birefringence, $\Delta n = -14.8 \times 10^{-4}$, where Δn is the difference in refractive indices measured parallel and perpendicular to the strain axis, values of $\overline{\cos^2 \theta} = 0.52$ and $\overline{\cos^4 \theta} = 0.43$ were obtained. In the work on PET several bands were studied, but only in the cases of 1616 cm^{-1} and 632 cm^{-1} bands did the data analysis give values of the averaged orientation parameters, in these cases $\langle P_2(\theta) \rangle$ and $\langle P_4(\theta) \rangle$ where $P_n(\theta)$ is the nth order Legendre polynomial. Both $90°$ and back-scattering geometries were used and intensities proportional to α_{33}^2, α_{11}^2, α_{13}^2, α_{32}^2 and α_{12}^2 could be recorded. The average quantities $\langle P_2(\theta) \rangle$ and $\langle P_4(\theta) \rangle$, deduced from intensities of the 1616 cm^{-1} band, are plotted in Fig. 5 as a function of

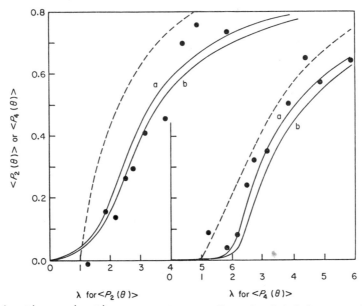

Fig. 5. $\langle P_2(\theta) \rangle$ and $\langle P_4(\theta) \rangle$ for the 1616 cm^{-1} line of poly(ethylene terephthalate) (PET) plotted against draw ratio, λ. Curves (a) and (b) represent predictions of a model based on rubber networks for values of the parameter $N = 5$ and 6 respectively. The dashed curves represent predictions according to an aggregate model (Purvis and Bower, Ref. 62).

draw ratio λ. Also plotted are curves showing the predicted relationships according to two deformation models. Curves (a) and (b) are obtained from a rubber model in which the chains are assumed to form a network, whose junction points are entanglements or other kinds of interactions between chains. The curves are based on calculations previously reported[64] and are fitted to the experimental data by adjusting the parameter N, the number of units between effective cross-links. The dashed curves represent the relationship based on an aggregate model in which the polymer is assumed to consist of rigid units embedded in a continuum in which each unit can rotate, but without change of length. The data are not entirely conclusive, but there are indications that the drawing is equivalent to the stretching of a network.

There has been much recent interest in the properties of highly oriented PE (see, for example, Refs 44 and 59) and polarization measurements have been made[65] with the aim of studying the orientation of both the crystalline and amorphous phases. This work demonstrates that, providing the sample is thin enough, the polarization scrambling caused by the different phases in a semi-crystalline system does not preclude the obtaining of meaningful data. This was shown by measurements of depolarization ratios ρ of bands in the region 1000–1500 cm^{-1} in unoriented samples of various thicknesses. Up to a thickness of 0.25 mm there was no apparent polarization loss due to multiple scattering and ρ values measured were less than those obtained previously.[66] There have also been procedures suggested to correct for depolarization arising from multiple Rayleigh scattering.[67] The orientation was studied by analysing the polarization data from three bands, in a highly oriented film; two 'crystalline' bands at 1170 cm^{-1} and 1296 cm^{-1} and one 'amorphous' band at 1081 cm^{-1}.

TABLE 2
Orientation functions for oriented polyethylene films[a]

| Band | Assignment | From Raman data | | From i.r. data | Theoretical | |
$\tilde{\nu}$/cm^{-1}		$\overline{\cos^2\theta}$	$\overline{\cos^4\theta}$	$\overline{\cos^2\theta}$	$\overline{\cos^2\theta}$	$\overline{\cos^4\theta}$
1081	Amorphous (*gauche* isomer)	0.415	0.334	0.45	0.45[b]	0.31[b]
1170	$a_g + b_{1g}$	0.831	0.763	0.85	0.83[c]	0.74[c]

[a] Ref. 65.
[b] Based on Ref. 64.
[c] Based on Ref. 69.

The band at 1170 cm^{-1} is a CH$_2$ rocking mode with symmetry a_g plus b_{1g}; the 1296 cm^{-1} band is a CH$_2$ twist with symmetry b_{2g} plus b_{3g}; the amorphous band at 1081 cm^{-1} is attributed to *gauche* methylene units.[68] The values of $\overline{\cos^2\theta}$ and $\overline{\cos^4\theta}$ deduced from the Raman polarization data are given in Table 2. Also included are estimates of $\overline{\cos^2\theta}$ from infrared measurements and the agreement between the two sets of data is good. Calculations have been made of these averages using a rubber elasticity model for the amorphous band[64] and the agreement is surprisingly close considering that no account is taken of the fact that the amorphous chain segments are lying between lamellae in this semicrystalline material. The crystalline orientation averages are calculated using a spherulitic model[69] and again agreement is good.

There have been a few other studies of the polarized Raman spectra in oriented synthetic polymers. Hendra and Willis have studied oriented fibres of polypropylene[70] and linear polyethylene[71] but made no attempt to characterize the molecular orientation. Derouault *et al.*[72] have measured the spatial variation of the polarized scattering in inhomogeneous PET, again without quantitative estimates of orientation. In their comprehensive work on PE, Gall *et al.*[66] have noted the correlation between Raman-active line and space-group modes, and confirmed the assignments of Carter.[45]

The Raman spectra of oriented biopolymers have been the subject of relatively few papers. Studies of PLA have already been discussed,[52] and we saw that, while the spectra showed the expected qualitative effects sufficient for making mode assignments, there had been no attempt at further quantitative analysis. Work has been reported[73] on another α-helical biopolymer, poly-γ-benzyl-L-glutamate (PBLG) in which the orientations of certain groups have been calculated relative to the helix axis. Highly-oriented thin films were prepared from solution following the method of Tsuboi,[74] and the observed spectra contained all the bands observed earlier in unoriented, thicker samples.[75] Three bands were analysed in detail (1) the amide I band at 1651 cm^{-1} (2) the ester carbonyl band at 1732 cm^{-1} (3) the N-H stretching band at 3290 cm^{-1}. These were chosen because they arise from stretching vibrations of relatively small amplitude for which the assumption of a uniaxial Raman tensor will be a good approximation. In this approximation the helix tensor-components a_{0i}, a'_{0i}, a_{1i} and a_{2i} (Table 1) can be written in a relatively simple form in terms of the diagonal components of α_{ri} of the vibrating unit and the angle Φ_i between the principal axis and the helix axis. Data for amide I and C=O ester stretching modes in several different geometries are shown in Fig. 6. The angles Φ were deduced to be Φ(amide I) = $39\pm2°$, Φ(C=O ester) = $53\pm3°$ and Φ(N—H) = $28\pm3°$ which were in remarkably good agreement with the orientation angles for the infrared transition moment.[74] For some weak components, the measured intensities differed from the predictions of the model by amounts which were outside the uncertainty in measurement. This could well be because the tensor is

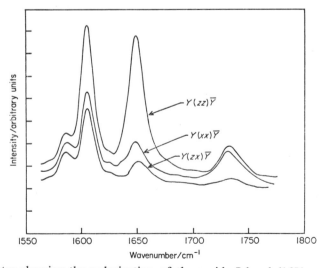

Fig. 6. Spectra showing the polarization of the amide I band (1651 cm^{-1}) and the C=O ester stretching mode (1732 cm^{-1}) in oriented poly-γ-benzyl-L-glutamate (PBLG). The letters in parentheses indicate the incident and scattered polarization directions; the axis of orientation is Z. (Wilser and Fitchen, Ref. 73).

not in fact axially symmetric. A tensor of more general form could undoubtedly improve the fit at the expense of introducing many parameters.

In this section we have seen that polarized Raman data can yield detailed information about the orientation of structural units in synthetic polymers which are partially oriented and also provide accurate estimates of the orientation of molecular groups relative to the chain axis in biological systems.

4.1.3 Determination of molecular conformation

Polarized Raman spectroscopy can be used to differentiate between models of polymer chain conformation by taking into account the different selection rules in each case. This proves to be especially valuable when combined with infrared absorption data. Vibrational modes for structures having no symmetry are all Raman active; in symmetrical structures, as we have seen in Section 2, selection rules are imposed determined by the nature of the symmetry. The absence of certain bands may then be taken as an indication of the molecular symmetry, but as the apparent absence of a spectral feature may be a result of experimental limitations, it is risky to base decisions on such evidence (or lack of evidence) alone. Generally it is better to base decisions on the polarization of well characterized bands. Such a study has been made on standard commercial polyvinylchloride (PVC) of low crystallinity and on highly crystalline syndiotactic PVC.[76] Depolarization measurements were made on the stronger lines and, taken together with infrared data, indicate that in the highly crystalline material the chains are in an extended planar zig-zag conformation rather than in the alternative, folded structure. This extended chain structure typical of the syndiotactic polymer is also present in the standard PVC which has low crystallinity. In the amorphous regions the structure is expected to be irregular and this is confirmed by the presence of bands not observed in crystalline material.

This study of PVC is an example in which the overall conformation of the polymer chain is deduced from the Raman data. It has been shown in Section 2 that the polarization of Raman bands is, in principle, sensitive to the rotational isomeric (rotamer) state of the unit containing the vibrating atoms and so the data are also sensitive to the conformation of the polymer at the monomer level. In general the change from a *trans* to a *gauche* state causes a change in the environment of a vibrating molecule which is reflected in the polarization of the Raman scattered light. In certain cases these changes can be observed and related to the changes in rotamer population (eqn. (7)). It might be expected, then, that the effects of macroscopic orientation on the rotamer states could be observed. This technique has been employed in polydimethylsiloxane (PDMS) networks in order to understand the underlying molecular basis of rubber elasticity.[31,32] A major problem in the formation of the network was the prevention of sample fluorescence and γ-irradiation proved to be better in this regard than chemical techniques. Depolarizations were measured for both the CH_3 stretching vibration at 2907 cm^{-1} and the Si—O backbone mode at 491 cm^{-1} as a function of network extension and some of the data are shown in

Fig. 7. Both of these bands are highly polarized and in this case the relationship between ρ and rotamer population as expressed in eqn. (7) takes the simple form

$$\rho = \rho_g \left(\frac{x}{1+x}\right) \qquad (8)$$

where x is the ratio of rotamer populations n_g/n_t and ρ_g is the depolarization characteristic of a *gauche* isomer. The data in Fig. 7 are interpreted as demonstrating an increase in *gauche* rotamer population n_g with extension, accompanied by a corresponding decrease in n_t. These population changes are the adjustment of the monomer conformation to the macroscopic extension of the network. The theoretical relationship between the macroscopic and microscopic quantities has been obtained in calculations by Abe and Flory[77] in which n_η, the change in population of rotamer η, is connected with the extension ratio α by a proportionality constant, D_2. This constant can be evaluated from the appropriate statistical weight matrices and for the *trans* isomer in PDMS is found to be[32] -1.2. An experimental value of -8 was obtained from the depolarization data,[32] in

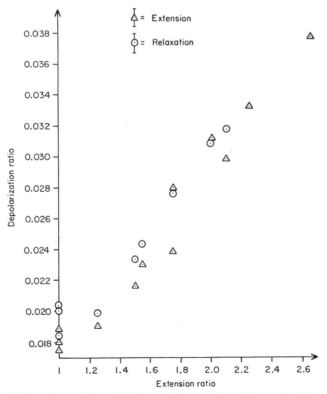

Fig. 7. Depolarization of the 2907 cm^{-1} Raman band in poly(dimethylsiloxane) rubber plotted as a function of sample extension. (Maxfield and Shepherd, Ref. 32).

poor agreement with the theoretical prediction. The discrepancy is believed to be due to non-uniformities in the network and later work on PDMS in solution, to be discussed in Section 5, leads to much closer agreement with theory. A disadvantage of these measurements is that, in the absence of an independent method of characterization, there will always be an uncertainty in the number of chains in the network.[78]. However, the technique is unique in providing a measurement of rotamer populations directly and it is to be regretted that problems of sample preparation have up to now prevented extension of this work to other systems.

4.1.4 Prospects for the future

In this section we report some preliminary measurements on two different systems which show great promise for the future. They also illustrate the diverse nature of problems that can be tackled by Raman polarization experiments. The first concerns the metallic polymer $(SN)_n$, polymeric sulphur nitride. Recent interest has been generated by the novel properties of this material, which even becomes superconducting.[79] It now appears that $(SN)_n$ is a highly aniso-tropic semi-metal.[80,81] There have been two reported Raman studies in this material, the first in unoriented thin films[82] and the second in oriented crystals.[83] The scattering from the crystals is surprisingly strong, considering that the penetration depth in metals is small, and very anisotropic. Principal bands observed are at 454, 621, 658 and 782 cm^{-1} and are all intrachain optical modes. There are two chains per unit cell and the symmetry is C_{2h}^5. Thus there are expected to be a_g and b_g modes Raman active. The polarization data are shown in Fig. 8 and it is clear that all features are present only in YY polarization. These are then a_g modes and no b_g modes are detected. This implies that the dominant electronic transition-dipole-moments which contribute to the

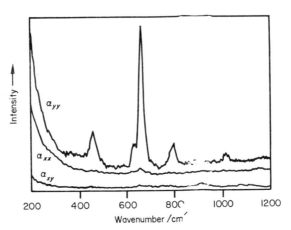

Fig. 8. Polarized spectra of oriented crystalline $(SN)_n$ at room temperature. Excitation wavelength 457.9 nm (Temkin and Fitchen, Ref. 83).

polarizability are directed along the chain axis. Further measurements at different excitation wavelengths may reflect coupling between the longitudinal optic modes and the conduction electrons. Thus it appears from these preliminary data that Raman studies will contribute to understanding of both the structure and interactions of this interesting system.

The second example is a polarization study of longitudinal acoustic (LA) modes in chain-folded PE crystals. There has been much recent interest in studies of these modes following their first observation by Peticolas et al.[84] because of their potential value in understanding the morphology of chain folding. Several groups have centred their investigations on the relationship between the chain length calculated from the observed frequencies of these vibrations in a Raman experiment and the lamellar thickness obtained from low-angle X-ray diffraction.[85-87] Recently a polarization experiment has been reported[88] in which the symmetry of the LA mode is investigated. A sample of PE having relatively good optical quality was prepared by cold-drawing followed by careful annealing at 100°C. Wide-angle X-ray measurements indicated a high degree of orientation of chain c-axes along the draw direction z. The polarization data showed a large signal in a scattering geometry designed to measure α_{zz} and a very small signal for α_{xz}. On the basis of the space group D_{2h} the observations are consistent with a vibrational species a_g (see Section 4.1.1). This is the symmetry of an accordion-like vibration of the extended chain, a model proposed for LA modes in n-alkanes.[89,90] Thus the observed mode has the symmetry characteristics expected for an accordion-like vibration of the extended chains between fold surfaces. Such polarization studies could be extended to other systems where chain folding is known to occur, for instance polyethylene oxide,[91] and is expected to be of value in understanding orientation and deformation behaviour.

4.2   Isotropic Amorphous Systems

In an amorphous system the polymer chains take on no regular array, and there is no possibility of attempting subtle polarization measurements designed to measure scattering from single vibrational species such as we have discussed in previous sections. However, in certain cases measurements of the average quantity ρ, as defined in eqn. (4), can lead to detailed information about the polymers. For example ρ data have been related to the rotamer states in the chain (eqn. (7)) and it has also proved possible to obtain values for thermodynamic parameters and to observe cooperative conformational changes. The experimental problems are formidable. In work accomplished to date the changes in ρ have been small, at most 6×10^{-2}, requiring extreme precision in measurement. This means that the polymers must be essentially free of fluorescence, must be optically clear in order to minimize polarization scrambling, and the spectra must contain bands that are well resolved and highly polarized. Furthermore, to facilitate interpretation of the data, the polymer must have a small number of rotamer states on which the polarizability of the vibrating units depends. Thus the number of systems that can be studied in this way are limited. The effort is worthwhile, however, because the method is unique in measuring monomer conformations in amorphous systems and the information, where obtainable, is detailed and important.

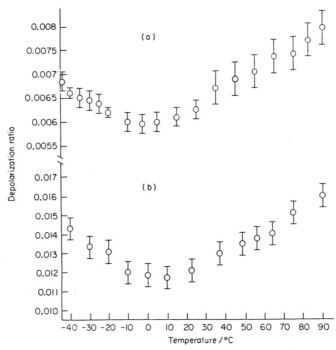

Fig. 9. Depolarization ratios of (a) the 2907 and (b) the 491 cm⁻¹ bands of poly-dimethylsiloxane (PDMS) plotted as a function of temperature. (Hartley and Shepherd, Ref. 92).

The polymer on which most experimental work has been done is PDMS which has already been discussed in the context of strained networks (Section 4.1.3). This system has reasonably well defined *trans* and *gauche* rotamer states which differ substantially in energy. Depolarization measurements have been made on two bands 2907 cm⁻¹ and 491 cm⁻¹ as a function of temperature.[92] These data are shown in Fig. 9 and represent an extension of previous work[31,32] to a wider range of temperature. The data from the two bands show the same feature of a minimum in the region of 0°C. In the region above this minimum the increase is believed to arise from the increase in *gauche* states resulting from the changes in Boltzmann population factor. In the approximation of independent bonds, which appears to be valid to about 10% in this region,[32] and for small x in eqn. (8), the energy difference between rotamer states can be evaluated as $\Delta E = 3.56 \text{ kJ mol}^{-1}$ which is in good agreement with previous estimates from chain dimensions.[93] An interesting comparison is provided by similar measurements on polyisobutylene (PIB) in which the energy difference between *gauche* and *trans* states is small, approximately $0.017 \text{ kJ mol}^{-1}$. In this case the ρ values were constant as a function of temperature, within experimental error.[94]

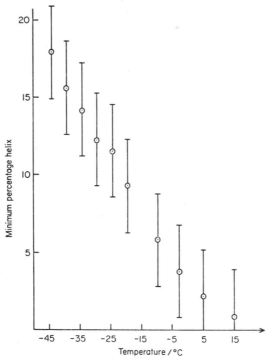

Fig. 10. Helix content in polydimethylsiloxane (PDMS) as calculated from the depolarization data of Fig. 9. The crystallization temperature is $-55°C$. (Hartley and Shepherd, Ref. 92).

The success of these measurements shows that, in this system at least, the polarization properties seem to be influenced by the conformation of individual bonds and that longer range interactions are unimportant. This makes the interpretation easier, but precludes obtaining important information on bond sequences, for example *tt*, *tgt*, etc.

The temperature region below $0°C$ and above the crystallization temperature is more difficult to understand, but at the same time more informative. PDMS crystallizes in a 6_1 helical form[95] at $-55°C$, and at this temperature the measured ρ value increases towards unity because of the multiple random scattering. No information has been obtained below this temperature from ρ data. The monotonic increase in ρ with decreasing temperature from $0°C$ to

$-45°C$ is explained as a precrystallization ordering in which helical sections are forming in each chain. The form of the monomers in the helix is believed to be a distorted *trans*[96] and ρ must now be expressed in terms of this state as well as the *gauche* and *trans* of the non-helical chain sections. The form adopted,[92] following eqn. (7), is

$$\rho = \frac{n_g I_{\perp g} + n_t I_{\perp t} + n_h I_{\perp h}}{n_g I_{\|g} + n_t I_{\|t} + n_h I_{\|h}} \tag{9}$$

where n_h is the number of monomers in a helical form and the other quantities are as in eqn. (7). It proved possible, under certain approximations, to obtain both the enthalpy and entropy of helix formation ($\Delta H = 13.4 \pm 2.5$ kJ mol^{-1} $\Delta S = 70 \pm 12$ J K^{-1} mol^{-1}) and the percentage of helix as a function of temperature (Fig. 10).

Thus it appears possible to obtain detailed information about polymers in the amorphous state from depolarization measurements. It is clear, however, that the experiments are difficult and the limits of experimental accuracy are approached as, for instance, in the extremely low ρ values of 0.006 shown in Fig. 9.

5   STUDIES OF POLYMERS IN SOLUTION

The conformation of polymers in solution, especially biopolymers, is a subject of great current interest both for theoretical and practical reasons. Because water has a relatively weak Raman spectrum, Raman spectroscopy should be a powerful technique for studying polymers in aqueous solution and much has been published in this line.[9,13] An obvious extension of this work is to study the polarization of the Raman scattering. There are, however, at least three intrinsic problems.

(i)   The solutions must frequently be dilute, usually concentrations no greater than 1%, in order to reduce polymer–polymer interactions and aggregation. Thus the Raman signals are weak.

(ii) The spectrum of the solvent, even of water at such low polymer concentrations, can interfere with the measurements.

(iii) The refractive index difference between polymer and solvent gives rise to random scattering which introduces errors into ρ measurements.

When these problems are added to the general problem of sample fluorescence it is not surprising that work to date has been limited. The situation is similar to the studies of pure amorphous polymers in Section 4.2. When a system is suitable for study, the information obtained is detailed, but relatively few systems are suitable. In this section we shall review the work in three parts: (1) studies of random coils, both in dilute and concentrated solution; (2) measurements of cooperative transitions; and (3) ρ measurements in resonance Raman conditions.

5.1   Random Coils in Solution

In this section we confine the discussion to synthetic polymers in a more or less random configuration. Studies of such 'random coils' in solution have been important since the early days of polymer science. The interest arises because of the opportunity to study individual molecules, unperturbed by polymer–polymer interaction, and because under certain conditions known as θ conditions, the chains can take on a configuration unperturbed by long-range intramolecular interactions. This experimental condition becomes of great importance when attempts are made to calculate macroscopic chain dimensions from theoretical models. The conditions, originally proposed by Flory,[97] can be visualized as an exact cancellation between two opposing effects; (1) the long-range interactions or excluded-volume effects which tend to extend the chain relative to its unperturbed dimension and (2) the solvent–polymer interaction χ. The interaction χ is usually strongly dependent on temperature and for a given polymer-solvent system in which such a condition exists, there is a well defined θ-temperature, θ_T.

It was clearly an experiment of some importance to obtain direct measurement of polymer dimensions in solution and this was first accomplished by Zimm[98] using his now celebrated elastic light-scattering technique in which the total scattered intensity is measured as a function of angle. A comprehensive review of the background to such work can be found in the book by Tanford.[99] The elastic light-scattering measures only the dimension of the molecule as a whole and gives no information about the state of the monomer units in the chain. As we have seen in Section 4.2, Raman polarization measurements can yield such information and we now discuss some ρ measurements on polymers in solution as a function of temperature.

Measurements have been reported on two systems. PDMS dissolved in benzene for which $\theta_T = -3°C$,[100] and PS dissolved in cyclohexane for which $\theta_T = 35°C$.[101] Depolarization measurements were made as a function of temperature on the 2907 cm^{-1} band of PDMS[102] and on the 1002 cm^{-1} band of polystyrene (PS)[102,103] and these data are shown in Fig. 11. Speak and Shepherd[103] also report measurements on PS in benzene and methyl ethyl ketone solution. Because of the polarization scrambling induced by the refractive-index increment between polymer and solvent, the measured values of ρ are not the correct ones for the polymer bands. However, for highly polarized bands it is possible to obtain the correct temperature dependence of ρ.[102] Increased solubility is observed as the temperature increases from θ_T and the chains become more extended. In the case of PDMS, because of the alternating bond angles, this means an increase in n_g and hence of ρ; in the case of PS n_t increases and ρ decreases. By measuring the chain extension in PDMS over the same temperature range using conventional elastic light-scattering techniques it is possible, using the form of eqn. (8), to obtain the changes in rotamer state populations with chain extension. A value of the constant

$D_2 = -3.9 \pm 0.9$ was deduced in this way and is to be compared with the value deduced from measurements in strained networks (Section 4.1.3). The difference here is that there is no problem of network characterization; stated more precisely there is no possibility of very short chains which become over-extended and contribute excessive increases in ρ. Thus the value of D_2 deduced

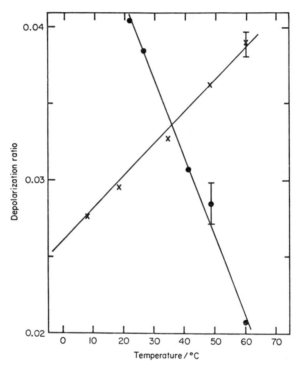

Fig. 11. Depolarization ratios of the 2907 cm^{-1} band of polydimethylsiloxane (PDMS) dissolved in benzene ($\times$) and 1002 cm^{-1} band of polystyrene (PS) dissolved in cyclo-hexane ($\bullet$) plotted as a function of temperature. The molecular weight in each case is 10^4; θ_T for PDMS $= -3°$C, θ_T for PS $= 35°$C. Solution concentration 10% by weight.

in solution is reliable, and the disagreement with theory is probably due to the approximations of rotational isomeric theory when applied in PDMS.

It is more difficult to obtain quantitative data from the PS measurements because of the more complex nature of the rotamers in this polymer (Ref. 96, Chapter 6). No simple relationship is obtainable connecting ρ and the rotamer populations and further progress will have to be by numerical techniques. This matter has not been pursued, but represents a potentially fruitful line of research because there have been recent calculations of PS conformational energy parameters[104] for which there are as yet no experimental data for comparison. However, an interesting deduction can be made from ρ measurements at different molecular weights. Such data taken at fixed concentration are shown in Fig. 12, where the ordinate represents decreases from ρ measured at the lowest temperature in each case. The gradients, $d\rho/dt$, are inversely proportional to the molecular weight, at least for the highest four values, implying that the change

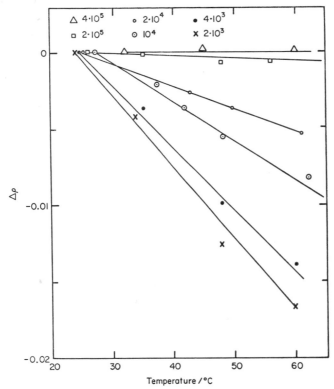

Fig. 12. Depolarization change $\triangle\rho$ of the 1002 cm^{-1} band in polystyrene (PS) plotted as a function of temperature for several molecular weights. The zero is chosen to be the depolarization ratio at the lowest temperature studied for each molecular weight. Solution concentrations 10% by weight (Speak and Shepherd, Ref. 102).

in isomeric population depends only on chain extension and not on molecular weight. This is in agreement with the rotamer theory of Abe and Flory.[77] The inverse proportionality is not maintained to the lowest molecular weights. This is believed to be because in these cases the chains are relatively short, 40 and 20 monomer units respectively, and are becoming 'over-extended' at the higher temperatures. The theoretical treatment[77] is only valid for long chains where the deformation is small, remaining well below the maximum extension. There is the possibility of using these techniques to study such over-extended chains.

Other interesting effects can be observed by extending the range of temperature. Figure 13 shows ρ data obtained[105] from both pure PDMS and PDMS dissolved in benzene in the range 0–200°C. In pure PDMS ρ increases mono-tonically with temperature, representing the continuing increase in the number of *gauche* isomers, n_g. In the solution ρ first increases as the solubility increases and the chains extend; then, as the solvent expands the solubility decreases and the chains become more convoluted leading to a decrease in ρ. The temperatures

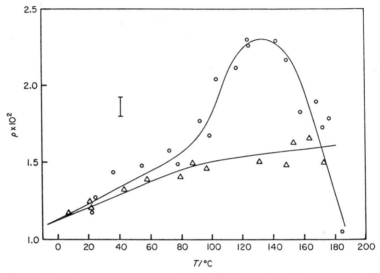

Fig. 13. Depolarization measurements of the 2907 cm⁻¹ band in pure polydimethyl-siloxane (PDMS) ($\triangle$) and in PDMS/benzene solution ($\bigcirc$) (10% by weight) plotted versus temperature. The upper and lower θ points are at -3 and 171°C where the curves intersect. (Thornley and Shepherd, Ref. 105).

are defined approximately by the intersections of the two curves and thus the data provide a measure of the upper $\theta_T = 171 \pm 3$°C. (A good source of back-ground information on polymer solutions is to be found in Ref. 106).

Thus measurements of ρ can provide detailed information about the mono-meric configuration of random-coil polymers in solutions. Up to now, because of the manifest experimental and interpretational problems involved, few systems have been studied. One most interesting possibility for the future is to use the technique in the study of concentrated solutions,[107] which are at present but poorly understood and to which few experimental techniques can be applied.

5.2   Cooperative Transitions of Polymers in Solution

Cooperative transitions in model biopolymers have been studied by various techniques including circular dichroism (c.d.), optical rotatory dispersion (o.r.d.), and calorimetry. Examples of these transitions are the changes from random-coil form to α-helix or extended β-structure and in some cases estimates of the values of the thermodynamic parameters governing the transitions have been made.[108-110] The importance of such parameters lies in the close connection between these model systems and proteins or nucleic acids where the analogous quantities are determining factors in biological function. There has also been considerable theoretical interest.[111-115] The techniques mentioned above are

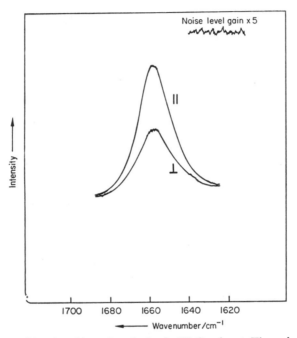

Fig. 14. Raman amide I band in poly-L-lysine in ^2H_2O solvent. The gain of the spectrometer in perpendicular relative to parallel polarization is $\times 2$. The noise level is shown with gain $\times 5$. The molecular weight was 6.5×10^4, the temperature 18°C and concentration 3%.

sensitive to the long-range structure and only detect the helix formation, for instance, when several turns have formed. They are not sensitive to the conformation of the individual units. Raman scattering clearly has an important role to play in such studies, particularly as the solvent is invariably water, and several studies have been published on polypeptides[116-118] in general and poly-L-lysine (PLL) in particular.[119,120] The only detailed polarization study to date has been on PLL[121] in which the amide I band at about 1660 cm^{-1} was studied; sample traces are shown in Fig. 14. ^2H_2O was used as solvent because the Raman bands of H_2O obscure the amide I spectral region. Measurements of ρ were made as a function of methanol content in aqueous-methanol solvent and are plotted in Fig. 15. There are two features of interest: first a relatively slow increase with concentration up to approximately 87% methanol and then a sharp increase to a constant value. The sharp increase is quite comparable with o.r.d. measurements on the same system[122] (also shown in Fig. 5) where the sharp increase was interpreted as occurring at the coil-α-helix transition. These data illustrate rather well the strength of the Raman polarization technique. The sharp change in ρ is a manifestation of the cooperative transition, measured at the level of the individual monomer unit. This is then

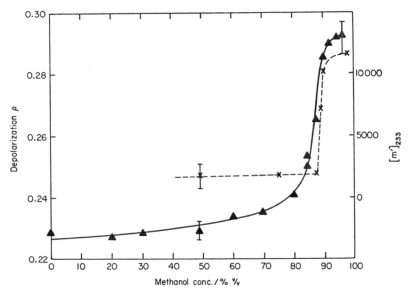

Fig. 15. Depolarization of the amide I band of poly-L-lysine —(▲)— and mean residue optical rotation at 233 nm - -(×)- - plotted as a function of methanol concentration in an aqueous-methanol solvent. (O.r.d. data from Epand and Scherage, Ref. 122).

complementary to the o.r.d. data. However, ρ measurements can also detect changes in the coil state, as evidenced by the slow increase at lower methanol concentrations. In this region the o.r.d. data are featureless, as would be expected for measurements sensitive to the longer-range order, and the Raman technique provides new information in this case.

Measurements of ρ were made as a function of temperature at constant solvent composition,[121] and the data used to estimate energy parameters of the system. This could only be accomplished by making the radical assumption that the polymer conformation in the coil state could be characterized by two monomer conformations, one *trans*-like, corresponding to values of dihedral angles (Ref. 96, Chapter 7) $\Phi = \Psi \approx 0°$, and the other *gauche*-like with $\Phi = \Psi = 120°$. The latter values are consistent with helix formation. The enthalpy difference between these states, ΔH, was evaluated for several methanol concentrations and was observed to decrease with increasing concentration and to have a value of 8.8 ± 0.7 kJ mol^{-1} at 85%. This difference is connected with the parameters ν[115] and $\sigma^{\ddagger}$[113] which represent the difficulty in starting a section of helix relative to extending it. When combined with values of the enthalpy change observed in helix-coil transitions by calorimetric techniques,[123] the helix stabilization-energy is determined to be 9.3 kJ mol^{-1}.

There is also evidence that polarization measurements are sensitive to transitions from coil to other ordered structures, for instance β-structures, and the technique should prove of value in studying these other transitions both in PLL and in other systems.

5.3 Studies of Anomalous Depolarization Ratios in Haem-related Compounds

Placzek[24] was the first to demonstrate theoretically that depolarization ratios greater than $\frac{3}{4}$ were possible for randomly oriented systems near resonance. In the extreme case of inverse depolarization, where $\rho = \infty$, the scattering tensor must be antisymmetric. The first observations of such effects were in dilute solutions of haemoglobin and cytochrome c.[124] The chromophore in this case is an iron-porphyrin complex. Since then there have been many further experiments[125−131] on compounds of the same type, but only few reports of similar effects in unrelated systems[132,133] viz. $[IrCl_6]^{2-}$, $[IrBr_6]^{2-}$ and $[FeBr_4]^{-}$. Spiro and Loehr[35,134] have published reviews of the measurements on biological samples.

An immediate benefit of these observations is in the assignment of the modes of the haem group. The Raman spectra are dominated by the porphyrin vibrational modes and the strongest bands are in the region 1000–1700 cm^{-1}, characteristic of the in-plane stretching modes of the ring. If D_{4h} tetragonal symmetry can be assumed for this group, the depolarization ratios for the vibrational modes can be predicted: $\rho_{a_{1g}} = \frac{1}{8}$, $\rho_{a_{2g}} = \infty$, $\rho_{b_{1g}} = \rho_{b_{2g}} = \frac{3}{4}$. In spite of the fact that the experimental ρ measurements are not limited to these discrete values and that there is a dependence on the exciting frequency, the ρ-values have been used to make band assignments.

Spiro and Strekas[127] have studied several compounds including both ferro- and ferri-cytochrome c and cyanomethaemoglobin. In the case of cytochrome c, assuming D_{4h} symmetry for the planar chromophore and ignoring the peripheral substituents, there are 81 normal modes classified as $7a_{1g} + 6a_{2g} + 7b_{1g} + 7b_{2g} + 14e_u$ all in-plane and $2a_{1u} + 5a_{2u} + 4b_{1u} + 3b_{2u} + 6e_g$ all out-of-plane. This apparently complicated situation is greatly simplified because the Raman scattering is dominated by in-plane modes in as much as the electronic transitions are polarized in-plane. Also the e_u modes are, of course, inactive in Raman scattering unless the symmetry is lowered. In the region studied, 1000–1650 cm^{-1}, there are expected to be four a_{2g} modes and four anomalously polarized bands are observed at 1129, 1312, 1399 and 1584 cm^{-1}. Three of four expected polarized bands are observed at 1362, 1483, 1594 cm^{-1} and these must therefore have a_{1g} symmetry. Only four of nine expected b_{1g} or b_{2g} depolarized bands are observed, at 1174, 1230, 1548 and 1620 cm^{-1}. It is not clear why the other bands are not observed, but it is argued that accidental degeneracy may be the reason. The spectrum of cyanomethaemoglobin corresponds closely to the cytochrome spectrum, except that the former has some additional features: two polarized bands at 1625 and 1005 cm^{-1}, two depolarized bands at 1552 and 1432 cm^{-1} and an anomalously polarized band at 1345 cm^{-1}. Similar extra features are observed in all the other haemoglobin spectra studied and it is believed that these are caused by the two vinyl substituents at the periphery of the protohaeme groups. The effect can be direct arising from the new double bonds which are saturated in cytochrome c, or indirect caused by lowering the effective symmetry.

Kitagawa et al.[130] have studied metalloporphyrins with the aim of assigning the stretching vibrations of the methine bridge. There are expected to be eight such modes of which four are Raman active in D_{4h} symmetry, one each in the species a_{1g}, a_{2g}, b_{1g} and b_{2g}. Thus one polarized, two depolarized and one anomalously polarized bands should be observed. The assignments in two compounds, Pd^{2+} and Fe^{3+} octaethylporphyrin, could be made as follows, the value for the Fe^{3+} compound being given first: a_{1g} 1493, 1504 cm^{-1}; b_{1g} or b_{2g} 1629, 1635 cm^{-1}; a_{2g} 1568, 1585 cm^{-1}. In fact, in the region of these bands, extra ones were observed. Substitution of deuterium for the methine hydrogens, however, clearly showed that these modes were not associated with the methine bridge but most likely with pyrrolic ring vibrations.

A final example in this section relates to the work on Ni, Co and Cu chelates of mesoporphyrin IX dimethyl ester.[128] Several vibrational frequencies were observed to vary with the metal in a systematic manner Ni > Co > Cu. These bands were in the higher frequency range, the values for Cu being 1640, 1581, 1573, 1505 and 1467 cm^{-1}. The 1313 cm^{-1} band, however, showed a reverse trend. In this work it is emphasized that, because of the peripheral substituents, the rigorous symmetry is C_s. It is nevertheless suggested that the higher frequency bands are associated with ring-stretching modes, which is consistent with the frequency shifts observed with change in metal atom.

It appears to be clear that some vibrational assignments are possible in biological systems containing chromophores. These assignments are incomplete in that only the region of the chromophores can be studied by the resonance technique; they rely on approximations in the symmetry and in some cases they are ambiguous. However, the fact that any detailed work at all can be done on these extremely complex systems is remarkable and it may be that further work in which samples are selectively doped with chromophores will allow extension of the technique.

In the resonance measurements the depolarization shows a dependence on the excitation frequency which is still not completely understood. Collins et al.[125] have studied several bands of ferrocytochrome c using argon and krypton laser lines near resonance with the β-absorption band. The ρ-values for anomalously polarized bands rise to maxima when the frequency is mid-way between the α- and β-absorption bands. A previously suggested explanation assumed that the observed peaks were superpositions of independent modes of different symmetries having different resonance behaviour. This explanation is rejected because it is unlikely that there should be similar degeneracies for each of the several bands exhibiting this dispersion in ρ and furthermore there is no evidence of band splitting. Instead, it seems that the mixing of the D_{4h} representations required to explain the observations is an indication that the electronic or

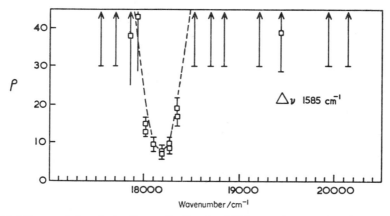

Fig. 16. Measured depolarization ratio for the 1585 cm⁻¹ Raman band of ferrocyto-chrome c as a function of laser excitation wavenumber. The peak of the absorption band occurs at 18 180 cm⁻¹. The arrows indicate ρ-values greater than 30. The line shows the theoretical prediction based on a model incorporating interference between electronic states (Collins, Champion and Fitchen, Ref. 131).

vibrational states are perturbed.[125] Model compound studies,[128] using non-symmetrical peripheral substituents on the haem group, also display the increase of ρ as the laser frequency is increased through the α band. Later work on ferrocytochrome c,[131] showed a minimum in ρ for the anomalously polarized a_{2g} bands at 1310 and 1585 cm⁻¹ when the laser frequency matched the α-absorption band at 18 180 cm⁻¹. Data for the 1585 cm⁻¹ band are shown in Fig. 16. These observations could not be explained by a simple reduction in symmetry. However, such minima are expected if there is near-degeneracy among excited electronic states,[131] and the agreement with theoretical predic-tion based on these ideas is good. The technique may prove useful in measuring splitting and line widths of the absorption arising from transitions from the ground state to the degenerate excited electronic states. These data show that the value of ρ measured at resonance can be misleading. For example, as can be seen from Fig. 16, the 1585 cm⁻¹ mode, which has a_{2g} symmetry, might be construed as being a symmetry-mixed mode if ρ were measured at resonance where the value is ≈ 7. If the laser frequency is changed by as little as 250 cm⁻¹

to $17\,930\ cm^{-1}$ the value is > 30. It is therefore important to measure ρ at several exciting frequencies.

These novel ρ-data can therefore be of use in mode assignments and perhaps also in studying electronic states. At the moment the origin of the anomalous ρ-values is not in doubt, but more experimental and theoretical work is required before the details of the dependence on laser frequency is fully understood. Recent preliminary data on haem proteins[135] at low temperatures, down to 68 K, show that there are no observable changes in vibrational frequencies from room temperature and thus that the haem group is apparently not significantly distorted. This shows that considerable experimental advances can be expected because the dispersion effects become more pronounced as the absorption bands sharpen at low temperature. Another line of work which has not been developed fully is the study of porphyrin modes using circularly polarized light.[136,137]

6 SUMMARY

Polarized Raman studies are subject to severe experimental problems of impurity fluorescence and optical clarity. Thus it has been possible, up to now, to make accurate measurements and gain quantitative information on only relatively few samples. However, as we have seen, where samples are suitable for study, the information obtained can be detailed and accurate and in many cases unobtainable by other methods. The technique is unique in studies of amorphous systems and solutions and has provided a direct measurement of monomer rotational states. Because a water environment is frequently the natural condition for biological molecules, Raman scattering is of particular value in investigating transitions and in estimating the thermodynamic parameters of such systems. We have also seen that, if some degree of orientation is introduced to the material under study, then more detailed information can be obtained. This has been used to make or confirm band assignments, to study molecular conformation both of the monomer and of the polymer as a whole, and to make estimates of the average orientation of structural units. All these questions are of great theoretical and practical interest. Of course, when studying such complex materials many techniques are employed, each with its own particular merits, and in each case we have tried to show how the Raman data complement data from other sources.

It is obviously desirable in the future to expand measurements to a wider range of samples. This will rely on improvements in sample preparation and purification methods. A particularly attractive possibility is to introduce chromophores selectively into the polymer thereby enhancing the scattering from different parts of the molecule. Experiments so far confined to haem compounds could then be extended to other systems. Development of u.v. tunable lasers should also allow the more general application of resonance techniques. Further experimental effort may also permit the application of the circular intensity differential in the scattering as a structural probe. This technique is involved with the measurement of the difference between the scattering of left- and right-circularly polarized light from optically active molecules. The difference is small, amounting to only about 10^{-3} of the Raman intensity and experimental artefacts make the measurements difficult, but the technique provides a novel method for studying dissymmetric molecules. It is clear that this field of study continues to be active on both the instrument-developmental and the sample-preparation sides. Further important work can therefore be expected.

ACKNOWLEDGMENTS

I would like to thank all those people who allowed me to quote their work and who made their most recent unpublished results available. Several members of the Polymer Physics Group at Manchester made helpful suggestions which are gratefully acknowledged, and Mr. John Rowcroft and Miss Janet Ridings are to be thanked for respectively drawing the figures and typing the manuscript. Finally I thank my wife Pat for help with proof reading.

REFERENCES

(1) L. E. Alexander, *X-ray Diffraction Methods in Polymer Science*, Wiley, New York, 1969.
(2) D. W. L. Hukins, in *Structure of Fibrous Biopolymers* (E. D. T. Atkins and A. Keller, eds) Butterworth, London, 1975, p. 293.
(3) M. B. Huglin, ed. *Light Scattering From Polymer Solutions*, Academic Press, London, 1972.
(4) I. W. Shepherd, *Rep. Prog. Phys.* **38**, 565 (1975).
(5) I. D. Robb and G. J. T. Tiddy, in *Nuclear Magnetic Resonance*, Vol. 4 (R. K. Harris ed.) (Specialist periodical reports) The Chemical Society London, 1975, p. 202.
(6) P. H. Geil, in *Encyclopedia of Polymer Science and Technology*, Vol. 5, Wiley, 1966, p. 662.
(7) G. Allen and J. S. Higgins, *Rep. Prog. Phys.* **36**, 1075 (1973).
(8) J. L. Koenig, *Appl. Spectrosc. Rev.* **4**, 233 (1971).
(9) J. L. Koenig, *J. Polym. Sci.* **D6**, 59 (1972).
(10) W. L. Peticolas, *Proc. Nucleic Acid Res.* **2**, 94 (1971).
(11) W. L. Peticolas, *Adv. Polym. Sci.* **9**, 285 (1972).
(12) P. J. Hendra, in *Polymer Spectroscopy* (D. O. Hummel, ed.) Weinheim: Verlag Chemie, 1974 Chapter 2.3.
(13) B. G. Frushour and J. L. Koenig, in *Advances in Infrared and Raman Spectroscopy*, Vol. 1, (R. J. H. Clark and R. E. Hester, eds) Heyden, London, 1975, pp. 35 *et seq.*
(14) W. L. Peticolas, L. Nafie, P. Stein and B. Fanconi, *J. Chem. Phys.* **52**, 1576 (1970).
(15) A. C. Albrecht, *J. Chem. Phys.* **34**, 1476 (1961).
(16) F. A. Savin, *Opt. Spectrosc.* **19**, 308 (1965).
(17) F. A. Savin, *Opt. Spectrosc.* **19**, 412 (1965).
(18) J. Tang and A. C. Albrecht, in *Raman Spectroscopy*, Vol. 2 (H. A. Szymanski, ed.) Plenum, New York, 1970, p. 33.

(19) M. Tinkham, *Group Theory and Quantum Mechanics*, McGraw Hill, New York, 1964.

(20) R. Loudon, *Adv. Phys.* **13**, 423 (1964).

(21) E. B. Wilson, J. C. Decius and P. C. Cross, *Molecular Vibrations*, McGraw-Hill, New York, 1955.

(22) S. P. S. Porto, *J. Opt. Soc. Am.* **56**, 1585 (1965).

(23) T. R. Gilson and P. J. Hendra, *Laser Raman Spectroscopy*, Interscience, New York, 1970.

(24) G. Placzek, *Handbuch der Radiologie VI.2* Akademische Verlagsgesellschaft, Leipzig, 1934, p. 205.

(25) M. Balkanski, ed., *Proc. 2nd Int. Conf. on Light Scattering in Solids*, Flammarion, Paris, 1971.

(26) J. P. Mathieu, ed., *Advances in Raman Spectroscopy*, Vol. 1, Heyden, London, 1973.

(27) P. Higgs, *Proc. R. Soc. (London)* **A220**, 472 (1953).

(28) D. I. Bower, *J. Polym. Sci.* **A-2 10**, 2135 (1972).

(29) R.-J. Roe, *J. Appl. Phys.* **36**, 2024 (1965).

(30) R.-J. Roe, *J. Appl. Sci.* **A-2 8**, 1187 (1970).

(31) J. Maxfield and I. W. Shepherd, *Chem. Phys. Lett.* **19**, 541 (1973).

(32) J. Maxfield and I. W. Shepherd, *Chem. Phys.* **2**, 433 (1973).

(33) J. Maxfield, *Ph.D. Thesis*, Manchester University (1974).

(34) G. E. Devlin, J. L. Davis, L. L. Chase and S. Geschwind, *Appl. Phys. Lett.* **19**, 138 (1971).

(35) T. G. Spiro, *Biochim. Biophys. Acta* **416**, 169 (1975).

(36) R. P. Van Duyne, D. L. Jeanmaire and D. F. Shriver, *Anal. Chem.* **46**, 213 (1974).

(37) S. Burgess and I. W. Shepherd, *J. Phys. E.* (to be published).

(38) R. W. Terhune, *Bull. Am. Phys. Soc.* **8**, 359 (1963).

(39) M. D. Levenson and N. Bloembergen, *J. Chem. Phys.* **60**, 1323 (1974).

(40) R. F. Begley, A. B. Harvey, R. L. Byer and B. S. Hudson, *J. Chem. Phys.* **61**, 2466 (1974).

(41) G. Allen, P. A. Holmes and D. J. Walsh, *Faraday Discuss. Chem. Soc.* **57**, 19 (1974).

(42) R. J. Walsh, G. Allen and G. M. Ballard, *Polymer* **15**, 366 (1974).

(43) W. L. Peticolas, E. W. Small and B. Fanconi, in *Polymer Characterization: Interdisciplinary Approaches* (C. D. Craven, ed.) Plenum, New York, 1971, p. 47.

(44) I. M. Ward, ed. *Structure and Properties of oriented Polymers*, Applied Science, London, 1975.

(45) V. B. Carter, *J. Mol. Spectrosc.* **34**, 356 (1970).

(46) C. W. Bunn, *Trans. Faraday Soc.* **35**, 482 (1939).

(47) P. J. Hendra, *J. Mol. Spectrosc.* **28**, 118 (1968).

(48) R. G. Snyder, *J. Mol. Spectrosc.* **31**, 464 (1969).

(49) R. T. Bailey, A. J. Hyde and J. J. Kim, *Spectrochim. Acta* **30A**, 91 (1973).

(50) H. Tadakoro, M. Kobayashi, M. Ukita, K. Yasufuku and S. Murahashi, *J. Chem. Phys.* **42**, 1432 (1965).

(51) P. D. Vasko and J. L. Koenig, *Macromolecules* **3**, 597 (1970).

(52) B. Fanconi, B. Tomlinson, L. A. Nafie, W. Small and W. L. Peticolas, *J. Chem. Phys.* **51**, 3993 (1969).

(53) J. L. Koenig and P. L. Sutton, *Biopolymers* **8**, 167 (1969).

(54) K. Itoh, T. Nakahara and T. Shimanouchi, *Biopolymers* **6**, 1759 (1968).

(55) K. Itoh and T. Shimanouchi, *Biopolymers* **9**, 383 (1970).

(56) B. Fanconi, E. W. Small and W. L. Peticolas, *Biopolymers* **10**, 1277 (1971).

(57) T. Miyazawa, K. Fukushima and S. Sugano, in *Conformation of Biopolymers* (G. N. Ramachandran, ed.) Vol. 2, Academic Press, New York, 1967, p. 557.

(58) C. H. Bamford, A. Elliot and W. E. Hanby, *Synthetic Polypeptides* Academic Press, New York, 1956, Chapter 5.

(59) Proceedings of 5th Europhysics conference '*Orientation effects in solid Polymers*' Budapest, April 1976. To be published *J. Polym. Sci.* C (1976).

(60) D. I. Bower, Ref. 44 Chapter 5.

(61) J. Purvis and D. I. Bower, *Polymer* 15, 645 (1974).

(62) J. Purvis and D. I. Bower, *J. Polym. Sci.* (*Poly. Phys.*) 14, 1461 (1976).

(63) M. Kashiwagi, M. J. Folkes and I. M. Ward, *Polymer* 12, 697 (1971).

(64) R.-J. Roe and W. R. Krigbaum, *J. Appl. Phys.* 35, 2215 (1964).

(65) J. Maxfield and R. S. Stein, *J. Poly. Sci.* to be published.

(66) M. J. Gall, P. J. Hendra, C. J. Peacock, M. E. A. Cudby and H. A. Willis, *Spectrochim. Acta* 28A, 1485 (1972).

(67) R. E. Prud'homme, L. Bourland, R. Natarajan and R. S. Stein, *J. Polym. Sci., Poly. Phys. Ed.* 12, 1955 (1974).

(68) M. J. Gall, P. J. Hendra, C. J. Peacock, M. E. A. Cudby and H. A. Willis, *Polymer* 13, 104 (1972).

(69) D. Y. Yoon, C. Chang and R. S. Stein, *J. Polym. Sci.* A2 12, 2091 (1974).

(70) P. J. Hendra and H. A. Willis, *Chem. Ind.*, 2146 (1967).

(71) P. J. Hendra and H. A. Willis, *Chem. Commun.* 225 (1968).

(72) J. L. Derouault, P. J. Hendra, M. E. A. Cudby and H. A. Willis, *Chem. Commun.* 1187 (1972).

(73) W. T. Wilser and D. B. Fitchen, *J. Chem. Phys.* 62, 720 (1975).

(74) M. Tsuboi, *J. Polym. Sci.* 59, 139 (1962).

(75) W. T. Wilser and D. B. Fitchen, *Biopolymers* 13, 1435 (1974).

(76) J. L. Koenig and D. Drusedow, *J. Polym. Sci.* 7A2, 1075 (1969).

(77) Y. Abe and P. J. Flory, *J. Chem. Phys.* 52, 2814 (1970).

(78) J. Maxfield and I. W. Shepherd, *Polymer* 16, 227 (1975).

(79) R. L. Greene, G. B. Street and L. J. Suter, *Phys. Rev. Lett.* 34, 577 (1975).

(80) C. H. Chen, J. Silcox, A. F. Garito, A. J. Heeger and A. G. Macdiarmid, *Phys. Rev. Lett.* 36, 525 (1976).

(81) W. E. Rudge and P. M. Grant, *Phys. Rev. Lett.* 35, 1799 (1975).

(82) H. J. Stolz, A. Otto and L. Pintschovius, in *Light Scattering in Solids* (M. Balkanski, R. C. C. Leite and S. P. S. Porto, eds.) Flammarion, Paris, 1976 p. 737.

(83) H. Temkin and D. B. Fitchen, *Solid State Commun.* 19, 1181 (1976).

(84) W. L. Peticolas, G. W. Hibler, J. L. Lippert, Λ. Peterlin and H. G. Olf, *Appl. Phys. Lett.* 18, 87 (1971).

(85) H. G. Olf, A. Peterlin and W. L. Peticolas, *J. Polym. Sci.* 12, 359 (1974).

(86) J. L. Koenig and D. L. Tabb, *J. Macromol. Sci., Phys.* B9, 141 (1974).

(87) M. J. Folkes, A. Keller, J. Stejny, P. L. Goggin, G. V. Fraser and P. J. Hendra, *Colloid Polym. Sci.* 253, 354 (1975).

(88) G. V. Fraser, A. Keller and D. P. Pope, *J. Polym. Sci., Poly Lett. Ed.* 13, 341 (1975).

(89) R. F. Schaufele and T. Shimanouchi, *J. Chem. Phys.* 47, 3605 (1967).

(90) T. Shimanouchi and M. Tasumi, *Ind. Pure Appl. Phys.* 9, 958 (1971).

(91) A. J. Hartley, Y. K. Leung, C. Booth and I. W. Shepherd, *Polymer* 17, 354 (1976).

(92) A. J. Hartley and I. W. Shepherd, *J. Polym. Sci., Polym. Phys. Ed.* 14, 643 (1976).

(93) P. J. Flory, V. Crescenzi and J. E. Mark, *J. Am. Chem. Soc.* 86, 146 (1964).

(94) I. W. Shepherd, unpublished data.

(95) G. Damaschun, *Kolloid-Z.* 180, 65 (1962).

(96) P. J. Flory, *Statistical Mechanics of Chain Molecules*, Wiley, New York, 1969, p. 178.

(97) P. J. Flory, *Principles of Polymer Chemistry*, Cornell U.P., Ithaca, 1953, p. 425.

(98) B. H. Zimm, *J. Chem. Phys.* **16**, 1099 (1948).

(99) C. Tanford, *Physical Chemistry of Macromolecules*, Wiley, New York, 1961.

(100) N. Kuwahara, Y. Miyake, M. Kanebo and J. Furuchi, *Rep. Prog. Polym. Phys. (Japan)* **5**, 1 (1962).

(101) P. Outer, C. I. Carr and B. H. Zimm, *J. Chem. Phys.* **18**, 830 (1950).

(102) R. Speak and I. W. Shepherd, *J. Polym. Sci., Polym. Phys. Ed.* **13**, 997 (1975).

(103) R. Speak and I. W. Shepherd, *J. Polym. Sci., Symposium 44*, 209 (1974).

(104) D. Y. Yoon, P. R. Sundararajan and P. J. Flory, *Macromolecules* **8**, 776 (1975).

(105) P. W. Thornley and I. W. Shepherd, *J. Polym. Sci.* (to be published).

(106) Polymer Solutions, *Discuss Faraday Soc.* **49** (1970).

(107) P. W. Thornley and I. W. Shepherd, *J. Polym. Sci.* (to be published).

(108) R. T. Ingwall, H. A. Scheraga, N. Lotan, A. Berger and E. Katchalski, *Biopolymers* **6**, 331 (1968).

(109) P. Y. Chou and H. A. Scheraga, *Biopolymers* **10**, 657 (1971).

(110) F. T. Hesselink, T. Ooi and H. A. Scheraga, *Macromolecules* **6**, 541 (1973).

(111) J. M. Gibbs and E. A. di Marzio, *J. Chem. Phys.* **30**, 271 (1959).

(112) K. Nagai, *J. Phys. Soc. Japan* **15**, 407 (1970).

(113) B. H. Zimm and J. K. Bragg, *J. Chem. Phys.* **31**, 526 (1959).

(114) B. H. Zimm and S. A. Rice, *Mol. Phys.* **3**, 391 (1960).

(115) S. Lifson and A. Roig, *J. Chem. Phys.* **34**, 1963 (1961).

(116) D. F. H. Wallach and J. M. Graham, *FEBS Lett.* **7**, 330 (1970).

(117) M. C. Chen and R. C. Lord, *J. Am. Chem. Soc.* **96**, 4750 (1974).

(118) P. C. Painter and J. L. Koenig, *Biopolymers* **15**, 241 (1976).

(119) T. J. Yu, J. L. Lippert and W. L. Peticolas, *Biopolymers* **12**, 2161 (1973).

(120) P. C. Painter and J. L. Koenig, *Biopolymers* **15**, 229 (1976).

(121) I. W. Shepherd, *Biochem. J.* **155**, 543 (1976).

(122) R. F. Epand and H. A. Scheraga, *Biopolymers* **6**, 1383 (1968).

(123) D. Pederson, D. Gabriel and J. Hermans, *Biopolymers* **10**, 2133 (1971).

(124) T. G. Spiro and T. C. Strekas, *Proc. Nat. Acad. Sci. U.S.A.* **69**, 2622 (1972).

(125) D. W. Collins, D. B. Fitchen and A. Lewis, *J. Chem. Phys.* **59**, 5714 (1973).

(126) L. A. Nafie, M. Pezolet and W. C. Peticolas, *Chem. Phys. Lett.* **20**, 563 (1973).

(127) T. G. Spiro and T. C. Strekas, *J. Am. Chem. Soc.* **96**, 338 (1974).

(128) A. L. Verma, R. M. Mendelsohn and H. J. Bernstein, *J. Chem. Phys.* **61**, 383 (1974).

(129) R. H. Felton, N. T. Yu, D. C. O'Shea and J. A. Shelnutt, *J. Am. Chem. Soc.* **96**, 3765 (1974).

(130) T. Kitagawa, H. Ogashi, E. Watanabe and Z. Yoshida, *Chem. Phys. Lett.* **30**, 451 (1975).

(131) D. W. Collins, P. M. Champion and D. B. Fitchen, *Chem. Phys. Lett.* **40**, 416 (1976).

(132) H. Hamaguchi, I. Harada and T. Shimanouchi, *Chem. Phys. Lett.* **32**, 103 (1975).

(133) R. J. H. Clark and P. C. Turtle, *J. Chem. Soc. Faraday. Trans. II* **72**, 1885 (1976).

(134) T. G. Spiro and T. M. Loehr, in *Advances in Infrared and Raman Spectroscopy*, Vol. 1, (R. J. H. Clark and R. E. Hester, eds) Heyden, 1975, Chapter 3.

(135) P. M. Champion, D. W. Collins and D. B. Fitchen, *J. Am. Chem. Soc.* (to be published).

(136) M. Pezolet, L. A. Nafie and W. L. Peticolas, *J. Raman Spectrosc.* **1**, 455 (1973).

(137) J. Nestor and T. G. Spiro, *J. Raman Spectrosc.* **1**, 387 (1973).

Chapter 5

VIBRATIONAL SPECTRA OF NON-AQUEOUS SOLUTIONS

Derek J. Gardiner

Newcastle upon Tyne Polytechnic, Department of Chemistry, Ellison Building, Ellison Place, Newcastle upon Tyne NE1 8ST, England

1 INTRODUCTION

The vast majority of chemical reactions are carried out in solution, yet despite extensive research, our understanding of this phase is very limited. For many years this field of research has been in the domain of the electrochemist. Ionization phenomena and alarmingly disparate values for solvation numbers have shed some light upon the complex dynamic equilibria present in many solution systems. Nuclear magnetic resonance, ultraviolet spectroscopy, thermodynamic measurements and other techniques besides, have each contributed valuable results to improve our understanding. Of particular interest are the structures of the species present in solution, the species being generated in a variety of ways. The solute may decompose or ionize and the resulting moieties may then interact with the solvent. The solute may remain intact and yet enter into association either with solvent molecules or with other solute molecules. The solvent may interact with itself, for example by the formation of hydrogen-bonded aggregates. It is highly probable that in any solution all of these basic interactions will be present to a greater or lesser extent. The various interactions will often be present in systems at equilibrium and thus will be affected by concentration. Temperature will also affect the nature of the chemical processes occurring in the solution. With such a complex situation, which of course becomes more complex as the number of solutes is increased or if a mixed solvent is used, it is to be expected that even with the most sophisticated techniques, any one method of study will reveal only a small part of the total picture. There exist many good texts describing the background chemistry of non-aqueous solvents. Those edited by Waddington[1] and Lagowski[2] are particularly helpful.

Vibrational spectroscopy has an important contribution to make here because the technique allows many of the species in solution to be identified and estimated quantitatively. The time scale of a vibrational observation is such that molecular motion in the solution to be studied is 'frozen' and the vibrational transitions of all species present contribute to the spectrum. This latter feature is sometimes a hindrance to straightforward interpretation of the spectroscopic results. Motives for carrying out solution phase studies are many. Often the spectroscopist simply wishes to study the 'free' solute, without the complications of the solid state. It is wise in these cases to use more than one type of solvent, to allow for solute-solvent interactions. The spectroscopist interested in the nature of the solution itself will be concerned primarily with all of the possible inter-actions which make up this complex phase.

In this article an attempt has been made to draw together some of the vast amount of vibrational spectroscopic data relating to all types of solution systems. The review concentrates on solutions which are either totally or partially in-organic and only a few examples of totally organic systems are discussed. The literature reviewed covers the period from 1967 to the time of writing, with a few earlier references to provide background where necessary. The material is organized by solvent type. Inorganic solvents are collected together according to their periodic groups and organic solvents are considered under three headings. These cover solvent-ion interactions and solutions in strongly interacting and weakly interacting solvents.

2   SOLUTION THEORIES

Two theoretical models for the behaviour of solution species should be con-sidered. The first is the *solvent systems concept* which has been developed from the acid-base theories of Brönsted and Lowry to include both protonic and non-protonic solvents. An excellent example of its application is provided by the work of Gutmann.[3] This approach places emphasis upon the auto-ionization of the solvent by comparison with the water system, e.g.

$$2H_2O \rightleftharpoons [H_3O]^+ + [OH]^-$$

$$2NH_3 \rightleftharpoons [NH_4]^+ + [NH_2]^-$$

$$2BrF_3 \rightleftharpoons [BrF_2]^+ + [BrF_4]^-$$

In aqueous systems, an acid is regarded as any molecule acting as a proton donor to increase the concentration of $[H_3O]^+$ cations. A base, on the other hand, is regarded as a proton acceptor which increases the $[OH]^-$ anion concentration. In general, the *solvent systems concept* defines an acid as a cation donor or an anion acceptor and a base as an anion donor or a cation acceptor. Thus in liquid ammonia, NH_4Cl acts as an acid, producing $[NH_4]^+$ cations, whereas $NaNH_2$ acts as a base, generating $[NH_2]^-$ anions. Table 1 lists autoionization cations and anions for several solvents. This concept has found wide application, particularly in electrochemical studies. In some instances, for example the BrF_3 systems, the

TABLE 1

Autoionization species for several inorganic and organic solvents

Solvent	Cation	Anion	Solvent	Cation	Anion
H_2O	H_3O^+	OH^-	HF	H_2F^+	HF_2^-
NH_3	NH_4^+	NH_2^-	HCl	H_2Cl^+	HCl_2^-
N_2H_4	$N_2H_5^+$	$N_2H_3^-$	BrF_3	BrF_2^+	BrF_4^-
N_2O_4	NO^+	NO_3^-	MeOH	$MeOH_2^+$	MeO^-
$POCl_3$	$POCl_2^+$	Cl^-	EtOH	$EtOH_2^+$	EtO^-
SO_2	SO^{2+}	SO_3^{2-}	Et_2O	Et^+	EtO^-
H_2SO_4	$H_3SO_4^+$	HSO_4^-			

concept will explain successfully vibrational spectroscopic results (*vide infra*). However, in many inorganic systems this approach fails to explain the experimental results.

The second theoretical approach is the *coordination model* developed by Drago.[4] This is not an acid-base theory but a general theory applicable to aqueous and non-aqueous solutions. The principal consideration of the concept is that the donor- or acceptor-strength of a solvent, along with its ability to solvate the dissolved species, plays the major role in determining the nature of species in solution. It is assumed that when a solute, MX_n, is dissolved in a solvent, S, the initial step is formation of a Lewis acid-base adduct.

$$MX_n + pS \rightleftharpoons MS_pX_n$$

The addition compound MS_pX_n is then examined to determine what further reactions may occur. Often the groups X are anionic and can be replaced by solvent molecules.

$$MS_pX_n + S \rightleftharpoons [MS_{p+1}X_{n-1}]^+ + X^-$$
$$[MS_{p+1}X_{n-1}]^+ + S \rightleftharpoons [MS_{p+2}X_{n-2}]^{2+} + X^-, \quad \text{etc.}$$

A thermochemical cycle can be written to show which enthalpy terms are involved in the following typical solution equilibrium:

$$S_{(solv)} + MS_pX_{n(solv)} \rightleftharpoons [MS_{p+1}X_{n-1}]^+_{(solv)} + X^-_{(solv)}$$

It must be assumed that all the species are soluble and that the coordination number of M does not change.

$$
\begin{array}{ccccc}
MS_pX_{n(g)} & + & S_{(g)} & \overset{c}{\rightarrow} & [MS_{p+1}X_{n-1}]^+_{(g)} & + & X^-_{(g)} \\
a\uparrow & & b\uparrow & & d\downarrow & & e\downarrow \\
MS_pX_{n(solv)} & + & S_{(solv)} & \rightleftharpoons & [MS_{p+1}X_{n-1}]^+_{(solv)} & + & X^-_{(solv)}
\end{array}
$$

The various terms involved are the enthalpy of solvation of S (*b*), the difference in the solvation enthalpies of $MS_pX_{n(g)}$ and $[MS_{p+1}X_{n-1}]^+_{(g)}$ (*d−a*), the solvation enthalpy of $X^-_{(g)}$ (e) and the difference in donor strengths of $X^-_{(g)}$ and $S_{(g)}$ (c). The donor-acceptor strengths are measured as enthalpies of the donor-acceptor interaction in the absence of solvation.

Unfortunately, few of the enthalpy terms involved can be obtained for most systems, although indirect methods can be employed. The general approach of the *coordination model* is suited to vibrational spectroscopic studies. In many instances much useful information concerning the nature of species of the type MS_pX_n can be obtained by observing M–S vibrations and measuring changes in the spectrum of the solvent.

3   TECHNIQUES

There are two principal difficulties encountered when making infrared measurements on solvent systems. Both of the difficulties relate to the fact that the liquid solutions under study must be contained in a vessel which is transparent to infrared radiation in the region of interest. First, the vapour pressure of the liquid must be retained by the cell. This generally involves the construction of cryostat cells when working with low-boiling solvents, or the construction of cells able to withstand high pressure. Second, and perhaps more limiting, is the chemical reactivity of the solvent in contact with the infrared cell windows. When liquids such as the interhalogens or oleum are to be studied, the use of conventional salt cell windows is precluded. In many instances, polar solvents will dissolve salts like CsI and KBr quite readily. However, the ingenuity of the spectroscopist seems to be unlimited when it comes to designing sample cells for uncooperative liquids.

Several cells have been described for studying liquefied gases.[5,6] Overend *et al.*[7] have used a cell consisting of a 2 cm diameter by 40 cm length copper cylinder with CsI windows. The cell was thermally connected to a liquid-nitrogen dewar. Liquid argon at 900 Torr (1.20×10^5 Pa) was used as the solvent and the infrared bands of CF_4 as solute were examined. Jander *et al.*[8] give details of a cell which can be used for condensed gases, liquids and solids. The cell windows are interchangeable and temperatures as low as 103 K can be attained. To overcome the problem of chemical reaction with, or dissolution of, the cell windows by the solvent, one relies upon being able to select window materials which cover the correct spectral range and are sufficiently unreactive. A technique which has proved successful in some instances involves coating the infrared windows with a thin film of polystyrene. This is achieved by dipping the windows into a solution of polystyrene in toluene and allowing the toluene to evaporate. In this way a very thin film of polystyrene remains on the windows and contributes very little to the spectrum.

Raman spectroscopy encounters the same two problems. However, as Raman cells are required to be transparent to visible radiation, the choice of suitable materials is considerably widened. In most cases Pyrex glass cells can be used.

With highly corrosive liquids like hydrogen fluoride, cells must be constructed from Teflon-type plastics or synthetic sapphire (Al_2O_3). Cornut and Huong[9] have described a useful Raman cell for corrosive fluids, having four windows and a working pressure $\leqslant 60$ atm (6.08 MPa). In general, however, the design of a Raman cell will be dictated to a large extent by the optical geometry and sample-compartment size of the spectrometer to be used.

4   SOLVENT SPECTRA

As a prerequisite of any vibrational spectroscopic investigation into a solvent-solute system, it is desirable that a thorough assignment of the pure solvent spectrum is available. This situation often does not obtain. In many instances spectroscopists have found it necessary to re-examine pure solvent spectra before the solution systems could be studied. In some systems addition of a specific solute will help to clarify the solvent assignment. Many solvent spectra are complicated by solvent-solvent interactions which can be reduced by choice of a suitable structure-breaking solute. With some of these problems in mind, Table 2 has been devised to provide a background of available spectroscopic data on solvent systems. A comprehensive table for the organic solvents has been compiled by Irish[10] and, except for a few instances, Table 2 concentrates on inorganic solvents. The references given are not always the most recent and gaps in the list do not necessarily imply that no spectroscopic studies have been reported in that area. The list simply provides a source of readily available results from which a more thorough literature search may begin. Table 2 does include several liquids which have not yet been studied as solvents by vibrational spectroscopy; they are included for completeness. Melting points, boiling points, dielectric constants and references to normal coordinate analyses are listed. The data for water are included for comparison.

5   LIQUID AMMONIA

Liquid ammonia is probably one of the most frequently studied inorganic, non-aqueous solvents. Vibrational studies have been made over a range of temperatures and pressures. In order to discuss the spectra arising from species in solution it is essential that the spectra of the pure solvent be fully understood. The free gaseous ammonia molecule has C_{3v} symmetry and as such will have a vibrational representation $\Gamma_{vib} = 2a_1 + 2e$, all the vibrational modes being both infrared and Raman active. In the liquid phase, ammonia is well known as an extensively hydrogen-bonded system and thus some departure from C_{3v} symmetry is to be expected. However, to a first approximation, assuming C_{3v} symmetry in the liquid phase, four vibrational bands should be observed: $\nu_1(a_1)$ the N—H symmetric stretch; $\nu_2(a_1)$ the NH_3 symmetric deformation; $\nu_3(e)$ the N—H asymmetric stretch and $\nu_4(e)$ the NH_3 asymmetric deformation. In the

TABLE 2
Liquid ranges, dielectric constants[a] (ϵ) and references to infrared spectra (i.r.), Raman spectra (R) and force constant analyses (F) for a selection of solvents in the liquid phase

Solvent	Formula	m.p./°C	b.p./°C	ϵ^b	i.r.	R	F
ammonia	NH_3	−78	−33.4	22.4 (−33)	11	12	13
antimony(V) fluoride	SbF_5	7	150	—	—	14	—
antimony(III) bromide	$SbBr_3$	97	280	20.9 (100)	—	15	—
antimony(III) chloride	$SbCl_3$	73	221	33 (75)	—	16	—
arsenic(III) bromide	$AsBr_3$	35	220	8.8 (3.5)	17	17	18
arsenic(III) chloride	$AsCl_3$	−13	130	12.6 (17)	19	—	18
bromine(V) fluoride	BrF_5	−61	40.5	8 (25)	—	20	21
bromine(III) fluoride	BrF_3	9	126	—	—	22	21
chlorine(III) fluoride	ClF_3	−83	12	4.6 (12)	—	20	21
dinitrogen tetroxide	N_2O_4	−12.3	21.3	2.5 (15)	23	23	24
formamide	$HCONH_2$	2.6	211	109 (20)	25	26	25
formic acid	$HCOOH$	8.4	101	58 (16)	27	27	—
hydrazine	N_2H_4	1.4	114	52 (20)	28	29	30
hydrogen bromide	HBr	−87	−67	7.3 (−87)	31	31	—
hydrogen cyanide	HCN	−14	26	123 (16)	—	32	32
hydrogen fluoride	HF	−83	19.5	84 (0)	33	34	—
iodine(V) fluoride	IF_5	9.4	101	36.2 (35)	—	35	36
nitric acid	HNO_3	−42	83	50 (14)	37	38	39
oleum	H_2SO_4/SO_3	—	—	—	—	40	—
oxygen difluoride	OF_2	−224	−145	—	—	41	—
phosphorus trichloride oxide	$POCl_3$	1.0	108	13.9 (22)	42	—	43
sulphur dioxide	SO_2	−75	−10	15.4 (0)	44	44	45
sulphuric acid	H_2SO_4	10	290	100 (25)	—	46	47
sulphur dichloride dioxide	SO_2Cl_2	−54	69	10 (22)	48	48	—
sulphur dichloride oxide	$SOCl_2$	−105	79	9.3 (20)	48	48	49
water	H_2O	0	100	78.5 (25)	50	51	13

[a] Relative permittivity.
[b] Measurement temperature (°C).

infrared and Raman spectra at ambient temperatures, two bands are observed at *ca.* 1046 cm^{-1} and *ca.* 1640 cm^{-1} which can be attributed to v_2 and v_4 respectively. In the N—H stretching region, however, the situation is not so straightforward. The complex band envelope clearly shows three maxima: a component at *ca.* 3385 cm^{-1} can be assigned to v_3, leaving two others at *ca.* 3300 cm^{-1} and *ca.* 3215 cm^{-1} to be assigned. In the Raman spectrum these two bands appear with comparable intensities and they have been assigned as v_1 and $2v_4$, intensity enhanced through Fermi resonance with v_1. However, which band is v_1 and which is $2v_4$ has been the subject of several pieces of research. The situation is further complicated in the N—H stretching region where band resolution reveals

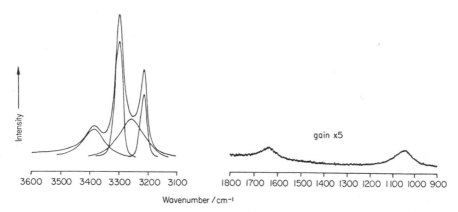

Fig. 1. Raman spectrum of liquid ammonia at 293 K (Gardiner *et al.*, Ref. 12).

the presence of a broad, medium intensity, band centred at *ca.* 3260 cm^{-1} in the Raman spectrum.[12,52,53]

The argument for assigning the higher frequency band as $2\nu_4$ and the lower frequency band as ν_1 is based upon the intensity behaviour as a function of temperature.[54,55] Supporting evidence from a coupled-damped-oscillator calculation and further temperature/intensity studies has been provided by Schwartz and Wang.[56] In opposition, and following more directly from the gas-phase spectrum,[57] are the results of several other investigators. Gardiner *et al.*,[12] recognizing the additional complication of the extra broad band at *ca.* 3260 cm^{-1}, which appears to arise from hydrogen-bonding interactions in the liquid, examined the Raman spectra of dilute solutions of ammonia in carbon tetrachloride and acetonitrile. In this situation the spectrum was simplified by removal of the band due to associated ammonia and the true intensities of ν_1 and $2\nu_4$ could be observed. In the dilute solutions the band at *ca.* 3300 was clearly more intense than the band at *ca.* 3215 cm^{-1}, suggesting that the former is more properly assigned to ν_1 and the latter to $2\nu_4$. Further evidence has been provided by Roberts and Lagowski[58] who measured the infrared frequencies in the overtone region of the N—H stretching fundamentals. They observed a band at 6541 cm^{-1} which was assigned to $2\nu_1$ of ammonia, implying a minimum value of 3270 cm^{-1} for the ν_1 fundamental frequency. These results support the assignment of Gardiner *et al.*[12] The results of earlier infrared work on ammonia dissolved in a variety of solvents[11, 59–64] also conform most satisfactorily to this assignment. A typical, curve-resolved Raman spectrum of liquid ammonia at ambient temperature is shown in Fig. 1.

5.1 Metal-Ammonia Solutions

The blue solutions which result upon dissolving alkali metals in liquid ammonia have been the subject of theoretical and experimental studies for several years. The general consensus considers the solutions to contain solvated electrons. Ammonia is peculiar in this respect, being particularly capable of stabilizing the electron. The theoretical model utilized by vibrational spectroscopists is that of the electron existing in a cavity created by orientated ammonia molecules. This model predicts two main vibrational spectroscopic features: a shift of the ammonia fundamental frequencies from those of the pure solvent, due to the polarized ammonia molecules forming the cavities, and a vibration of the cavity itself. This latter vibration can be described as the symmetric breathing mode of the cavity molecules. The frequency of this mode, which should be Raman active, has been calculated by Copeland *et al.*[65] to be between 25 and 60 cm^{-1}. Rusch and Lagowski[66] have performed a single-configuration normal-coordinate calculation on the cavity model and arrive at frequencies of between 143 and 266 cm^{-1}, depending upon the concentration of the solution.

TABLE 3
Infrared band frequencies from metal-ammonia solutions at 203 K

Concentration of metal	Frequency/cm^{-1}		
	ν_1	ν_3	$2\nu_4$
pure NH$_3$	3281	3449	3155
5×10^{-4} mol dm^{-3}	3267	3428	3157
5×10^{-2} mol dm^{-3}	3251	3411	3153

Infrared spectra of lithium- and potassium-ammonia solutions at 203 K in the N—H stretching region, using a cell with sapphire windows, have been reported by Rusch and Lagowski.[67,68] Both ν_1 and ν_3 are seen to shift from their pure NH$_3$ values of 3281 and 3449 cm^{-1}, respectively, while the frequency of $2\nu_4$ remains little affected. The shifts to lower frequency with increasing concentration were independent of the metal in solution. In Table 3 the observed frequencies for the two different metals are listed. These results indicate a weakening of the N—H bonds in the molecules of the cavity. The use of sapphire windows in the infrared cell precludes the observation of any lower frequency vibrations.

In marked contrast to the infrared results, two Raman studies, one of sodium-ammonia solutions[69,70] and the other of potassium-ammonia solutions,[71] reveal only minor spectral changes from that of the pure solvent. A weak, broad band at 300 cm^{-1}, which appears in the Raman spectrum of pure liquid ammonia, decreases to zero intensity as the metal concentration increases. This band is believed to be due to unresolved rotational structure which is lost as the ammonia solutions become more ordered. The spectra also show an overall decrease in intensity upon concentration, which is probably a result of the increasing electronic absorbance of the solutions. There were no frequency shifts and no band was detected which could be attributed to the cavity breathing mode. No explanation is offered for this surprising lack of infrared- and Raman- frequency coincidence in identical systems. The failure to observe a cavity breathing mode leaves a question mark over the theoretical models used. Furthermore, there appears to be some discrepancy between infrared and Raman frequencies of the pure solvent at similar temperatures. More detailed infrared studies would clearly be of great value here.

5.2   Electrolyte-ammonia Solutions

Owing to the similarities between liquid ammonia and water, infrared and Raman studies of electrolytes in both solvents are a rewarding field of enquiry. Many electrolytes are soluble in liquid ammonia and in Table 4 the solubilities

TABLE 4
Solubilities of salts in liquid ammonia at 298 K (g/100 g solvent)

Salt	Solubility	Salt[a]	Solubility
AgCl	0.83	NaBr	137.95
AgBr	5.92	NaI	161.9
AgI	206.84	NaSCN	205.5
$AgNO_3$	86.04	$NaNO_3$	97.6
$Ba(NO_3)_2$	97.22	NH_4Cl	102.5
KBr	13.5	NH_4Br	237.9
KI	182.0	NH_4I	368.4
KNO_3	10.4	NH_4SCN	312.0
$LiNO_3$	55.2	NH_4ClO_4	137.9
NaF	0.35	NH_4NO_3	390.0
NaCl	3.02	NH_4OAc	253.2

[a] Ac = acyl.

of a representative selection of these are listed. In general, salts of monovalent cations and polarizable, monovalent anions have the greatest solubilities. The effects of alkali and alkaline-earth cations on the Raman spectrum of liquid ammonia have been investigated in some detail by Plowman and Lagowski.[72] Except for the ν_2 fundamental, which is shifted to higher frequency, they report little cation-dependent effect upon the Raman spectrum of liquid ammonia. In the low-frequency region, bands assigned to the symmetric stretching mode of solvated cations were detected for Li^+, Na^+, Mg^{2+}, Ca^{2+}, Sr^{2+} and Ba^{2+} at 241, 194, 328, 266, 243 and 215 cm^{-1}, respectively. These frequencies were also estimated using an electrostatic cation-solvent interaction model by calculating a force constant from the interaction energy as a function of cation geometry. These calculations led Plowman and Lagowski to the conclusion that the primary solvation sphere of the alkali-metal cations contains four ammonia molecules, whilst that of the alkaline-earth cations contains six. Raman-active metal-nitrogen stretching modes have been recorded in the 200–450 cm^{-1} range for several salts in liquid ammonia by Gans and Gill.[73] The spectra were obtained at 243–213 K for salt concentrations between 0.5 and 4.0 mol dm^{-3}. The results suggest that Zn^{2+} ions, at concentrations of *ca.* 1 mol dm^{-3}, are present in both 4- and 6-coordinate forms, whereas Ag^+ and Hg^{2+} are apparently only 4-coordinate. Infrared spectra at room temperature of solutions of $[NH_4]^+$ salts in liquid ammonia indicate the simultaneous existence of the hydrogen-bonded systems; $[NH_4]^+ \ldots NH_3$, $[NH_4]^+ \ldots X^-$ and $NH_3 \ldots X^-$, by analogy with the solid ammoniate $NH_4Cl.3NH_3$.[11,74]

The effect of the anions present in these solutions is often marked, producing frequency shifts and intensity changes in the ammonia spectra. In many cases, where the anions possess internal vibrational modes, these may be studied as a function of concentration to yield valuable information concerning anion-cation and anion-solvent interactions. Frequency shifts of fundamental modes are enhanced in the overtone and combination region. This fact has been used by Roberts and Lagowski[58] to determine the influence of anions on the solvent structure. It was found that the chlorate(VII) ion produced the greatest frequency shift in $2\nu_1$ and that nitrate and thiocyanate produced no measurable shifts in the solutions studied. These observations indicate that chlorate(VII) has a structure-breaking function in liquid ammonia, comparable to that in aqueous solutions. These infrared results have been supported by measurements in the fundamental region by Raman spectroscopy.[52,53]

Lithium nitrate is particularly soluble in liquid ammonia. This, coupled with the high polarizing power of the Li^+ cation, is expected to produce strong interactions in such solutions. In contrast, ammonium nitrate, though remarkably soluble, has a cation which is only weakly polarizing. These two solution systems have been investigated by Gardiner et al.[75] using infrared and Raman spectroscopy. In Fig. 2 the N—H stretching region of ammonia is shown for a range of $LiNO_3$ concentrations. The most striking feature of these spectra is the changes in intensity of ν_3 and $2\nu_4$ as a function of concentration. Subsequent studies have revealed that this behaviour is typical for any simple salt solution in liquid ammonia and is attributable to a decrease in NH_3—NH_3 H-bonded interactions. The NH_3 (a_1) deformation at 1046 cm^{-1} in pure liquid NH_3 shifts to *ca.* 1150 cm^{-1} in $LiNO_3$ solutions. This, and the observation of bands attributable to Li^+—NH_3 modes between 250 and 550 cm^{-1}, point to strong Li^+—NH_3 interactions. In very concentrated solutions, changes in the $[NO_3]^-$ vibrations suggest that ion pairs are present.

Lemley and Lagowski[76] have examined the Raman spectra of $NaNO_3$, $NaSCN$, NH_4NO_3, NH_4SCN, $LiNO_3$ and $LiSCN$ in liquid NH_3. Results indicate that Na^+ and $[NH_4]^+$ cations interact only weakly with the solvent but that Li^+ cations compete with $[NO_3]^-$ and $[SCN]^-$ anions for interaction with the solvent. The $[SCN]^-$ anion appears to enter into strong NH_3 interactions through the sulphur atom. Lundeen and Tobias[77] have found Raman evidence for ion pairing and solvation in liquid ammonia solutions of $[NH_4]^+$, Ag^+, K^+, Na^+ and Ca^{2+} nitrates. Measurements of nitrate ν_3 and ν_4 mode splittings revealed that the latter are not necessarily a good indication of contact ion-pair formation with weakly polarizing cations in these solutions.

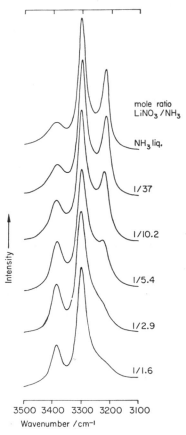

Fig. 2. Raman spectra of $LiNO_3/NH_3$ solutions and liquid ammonia in the N—H stretching region. (Gardiner *et al.*, Ref. 75).

A recent Raman study of thallium(I) nitrate solutions[78] suggests that Tl^+ ions produce species in liquid ammonia solution which are quite different from those in the alkali-metal salt and alkaline-earth salt solutions. In Fig. 3, part of the Raman spectrum of a $TlNO_3/3NH_3$ solution is shown. The polarized band at 830 cm^{-1} is assigned to the $\nu_2(a_2'')$ mode of $[NO_3]^-$. Under the D_{3h} point group this mode is Raman inactive and its presence here indicates that the $[NO_3]^-$ ion is in an environment of lower symmetry; a C_{3v} or C_3 environment would imply a π-interaction model for Tl^+—$[NO_3]^-$ ion pairs, with Tl^+ ions positioned on the principal axis of the $[NO_3]^-$ anions. The spectrum of Fig. 3 also reveals an intense band at *ca.* 1100 cm^{-1}. Further studies using ND_3 solutions, and the absence of this high-intensity band in the Raman spectra of $LiNO_3$ solutions, suggest that it is $\nu_2(a_1)$ of NH_3 coordinated to Tl^+ ions. The anomalous intensity requires further study.

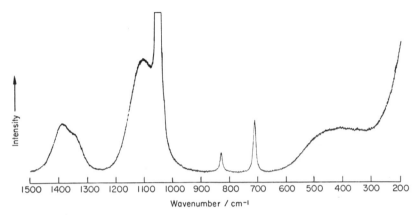

Fig. 3. Raman spectrum of a TlNO₃/NH₃ solution in (mole ratio 1:3) the 200–1500 cm⁻¹ region. (Gardiner *et al.*, Ref. 78).

Birchall and Drummond have studied liquid ammonia and dimethoxymethane solutions of $KGeH_3$ and $KGeD_3$ by infrared[79] and Raman spectroscopy.[55] The anions $[GeH_3]^-$ and $[GeD_3]^-$ were identified and ν_1, ν_2 and ν_4 were measured. Using a simple valence force-field calculation, an inter-bond angle of 93° was determined for the ions.

6   GROUP VI SOLVENTS

This group contains the excellent solvent, water, beside which the other solvents of this group appear less important. However, several interesting solvent systems have been investigated, from the fairly inert liquid sulphur dioxide to oleum and the super-acids.

6.1   Liquid Sulphur Dioxide and Sulphur Hexafluoride

Sulphur dioxide is liquid under readily attainable conditions and forms a convenient and often inert solvent for several systems. Despite its frequent use as a solvent, the recent literature reveals but a few spectroscopic studies of its solutions. The existence of induced dipole moments in HCl have been inferred from integrated intensity measurements of the $1 \leftarrow 0$ and $2 \leftarrow 0$ vibrational bands of HCl in CCl_4 and liquid SO_2 solutions. The signs of the induced moments for the fundamental and its overtone appear to be different. The effect of induced moments on intensity has to be allowed for when deconvolution of the band profiles is undertaken.[80] Spectroscopic studies of HCN complexes[81,82] and the Hg_3^{2+} cation[83] (*vide infra*) in liquid SO_2 have been reported. The reaction between antimony(V) and arsenic(V) fluoride in liquid SO_2 produces $[Sb_n^{+}]$ $[AsF_6^{-}]_n$ which has been examined spectroscopically.[84]

Liquid sulphur(VI) fluoride is frequently used as an inert solvent. The liquid is used as a diluent when studying other liquid systems in order to observe polymerization and rotation effects. Le Duff and Holzer[85] have used the Raman spectra from solutions of HF in liquid SF_6 to assess the state of polymerization of the HF molecules. The intensity of the HF polymer band, consisting of two overlapping components centred at 3230 and 3430 cm^{-1}, was found to be 40 times greater than that of the monomer band at 3939 cm^{-1}. This ratio exceeds that of the gas by a factor of almost 7. The polymer band of HF in liquid SF_6 is otherwise essentially unchanged from the gas-phase spectrum of HF. These observations are in accord with previous interpretations in terms of the polymeric species $(HF)_6$ and $(HF)_4$. Evidence for the rotation of HCl in SF_6 solution has been presented. Comparisons of the infrared absorption profiles show that rotational structure of the overtone is more perturbed by the solvent than that of the fundamental.[86] Le Duff[87] has discussed the collision-induced anisotropy of the vibrational Raman band of nitrogen dissolved in liquid SF_6 and with Holzer has recorded spectra from SF_6 solutions of H_2, D_2 and HF.[88]

6.2 Fluorosulphuric(VI) Acid and Oleum

Research using these powerful acids as solvents has lead to the identification and vibrational characterization of several novel cationic species. Gillespie and Morton[89] have recorded the Raman spectrum of brominemonofluorosulphate(VI) in the super-acid HSO_3F—SbF_5—$3SO_3$. The presence of a new species was demonstrated by an intense fundamental at 360 cm^{-1}. This band was attributed to the Br_2^{+} cation. The I_2^{+} cation may be prepared by oxidizing iodine in fluorosulphuric(VI) acid with a solution of $S_2O_6F_2$ in fluorosulphuric-(VI) acid or by oxidation of iodine by oleum. The cation absorbs strongly at 640 nm, giving it an intense blue colour. Gillespie and Morton[90] have used this fact to make a resonance Raman study of I_2^{+} in both fluorosulphuric(VI) acid and oleum solutions. Figure 4 shows the resonance Raman spectrum of I_2^{+} in a 10^{-2} mol dm^{-3} solution in fluorosulphuric(VI) acid. Both Stokes and anti-Stokes overtone progressions can be seen. The fundamental frequency of I_2^{+} occurs at 238 cm^{-1}. Commeyras and Olah[14] have combined the techniques of ^{1}H and ^{19}F n.m.r. with Raman spectroscopy to study some complex solution equilibria in the systems, SbF_5/HSO_3F, $SbF_5/HSO_3F/SO_2$, $SbF_5/HSO_3F/SO_2/H_2O$ and $SbF_5/HSO_3F/SO_2/HCl$. The results suggest that the following equilibria exist in the SbF_5/HSO_3F solutions:

$$HSO_3F + SbF_5 \rightleftharpoons H[SbF_5SO_3F]$$

$$H[SbF_5SO_3F] + HSO_3F \rightleftharpoons [H_2SO_3F]^+ + [SbF_5SO_3F]^-$$

$$2H[SbF_5SO_3F] \rightleftharpoons [H_2SO_3F]^+ + [Sb_2F_{10}SO_3F]^-$$

$$HSO_3F \rightleftharpoons SO_3 + HF$$

$$2HF + 3SbF_5 \rightleftharpoons HSbF_6 + HSb_2F_{11}$$

$$3SO_3 + 2HSO_3F \rightleftharpoons HS_2O_6F + HS_3O_9F$$

Selenium dissolves in sulphuric(VI) and fluorosulphuric(VI) acids in the presence of oxidizing agents to give green or yellow solutions. The yellow solutions have been shown to contain the Se_4^{2+} cation. Gillespie and Pez[91] have

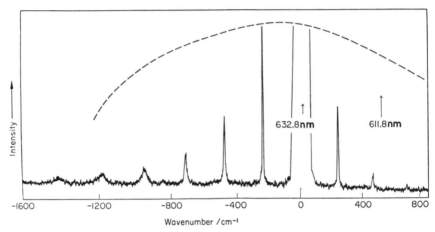

Fig. 4. Resonance Raman spectrum of a 10^{-2} mol dm^{-3} solution of I_2^+ in fluorosulphuric acid. The visible absorption-band contour is shown by the broken line. (Gillespie and Morton, Ref. 90).

recorded infrared and Raman spectra of $Se_4(SO_3F)_2$, $Se_4(HS_2O_7)_2$, $Se_4(S_4O_{13})$ and $Se_4(Sb_6F_{11})_2$ as solids and Raman spectra of their solutions in HSO_3F and oleum. Bands observed at 188 and 327 cm^{-1} in the Raman spectra and at *ca.* 306 cm^{-1} in the infrared spectra are assigned to the b_{2g}, a_{1g} and e_u fundamentals of a D_{4h}, square-planar, Se_4^{2+} cation. A normal coordinate analysis predicts that the b_{1g} mode should appear between 300 and 330 cm^{-1}. Reaction of AsF_5 and SbF_5 with mercury in liquid SO_2 and of mercury with fluorosulphuric(VI) acid, produces the cation Hg_3^{2+}. Gillespie *et al.*[83,92] have recorded Raman spectra from Hg_3^{2+} in solution and report a band at 113 cm^{-1}. This strong, polarized band is attributed to the symmetric stretching mode of the linear Hg_3^{2+} cation.

The cations $[CH_3CO]^+$ and $[PhCO]^+$ are produced when the respective acid chlorides are dissolved in heptaoxodisulphuric(VI) acid, $H_2S_2O_7$. Using infrared measurements, Paul *et al.*[93] located the C=O stretch for the acyl cation at

2300 cm^{-1} and that of the phenyl cation at 2200 cm^{-1}. In the latter, the frequency was lowered due to conjugation with the aromatic ring. Raman spectra of nitryl fluoride, NO_2F, dissolved in $H_2S_2O_7$ demonstrate the presence of the nitryl cation, $[NO]_2^+$. The infrared spectrum of nitrosyl chloride, NOCl, in $H_2S_2O_7$ solution indicates the production of the nitrosyl cation, NO^+, having a band at 2160 cm^{-1}. Related infrared work[94] on solutions of $SeCl_4$ and $TeCl_4$ in HSO_3F confirms the presence of $[SeCl_3]^+[SO_3F]^-$ and $[TeCl_3]^+[SO_3F]^-$ in these systems, according to the reaction:

$$MCl_4 + HSO_3F \rightarrow [MCl_3]^+ + [SO_3F]^- + HCl$$

7 GROUP VII SOLVENTS

Halogen compounds provide us with many different liquids suitable for use as solvents. Compounds of fluorine are the most frequently encountered in this respect. Hydrogen fluoride and some of the halogen fluorides have been subjects of vibrational spectroscopic studies and useful results relating to solvent behaviour and solution interactions have been reported.

7.1 Anhydrous Hydrogen Fluoride

The use of anhydrous hydrogen fluoride as a solvent has grown rapidly since the availability of corrosion-resistant plastics, such as polytetrafluoroethylene, has become widespread. Hydrogen fluoride is liquid over a wide range of temperatures, which makes it a convenient medium for study. The structure of the liquid involves both hydrogen-bonded intermolecular association and self-ionization. The latter generates ions which are expected to be variously solvated in the liquid, viz.

$$2HF \rightleftharpoons [H_2F]^+ + F^-$$

In order to make vibrational measurements on liquid HF systems, corrosion-resistant cells are required. Hyman et al.[95] have given details of a short-path-length diamond-windowed cell for use in the infrared. Sheft and Perkins[34] have described a cell constructed entirely from sapphire for making Raman measurements. Much earlier, using a nickel cell with silver chloride windows, Maybury et al.[33] recorded the infrared spectrum of liquid HF and of HF/SO_2 solutions. In the infrared spectrum, three principal features are apparent: a weak band at 400 cm^{-1}, a very strong band at 3450 cm^{-1} and a medium intensity, broad band between 1000 cm^{-1} and 400 cm^{-1}. The broad band is attributed to absorptions arising from intermolecular interactions. Smith[96] has assigned an infrared band in the 3500 cm^{-1} region to a tetramer and a band in the 3300 cm^{-1} region to a hexamer species in the liquid. The Raman spectrum[34] consists of complex bands at 150, 400–700, 1000–1300 and 3000–3600 cm^{-1}. Measurement of these band frequencies as a function of temperature suggests that a range of different polymer species is present in liquid HF.

7.2 Hydrogen Fluoride Solutions

Many compounds are soluble in liquid HF and many have been studied by vibrational spectroscopy. Simple molecular systems like HCN[97] to complex protein molecules[33] in HF solution have received attention. Of some particular interest are the fluorides of the elements of groups VB, VIB and VIIB. The BrF_3—HF system has been investigated by Hyman et al.[98] The Raman spectra of this system are complex, requiring the use of curve-resolving techniques to determine the positions and intensities of component bands. Bands at 625 and 528 cm^{-1} have been assigned to ν_1 of $[BrF_2]^+$ and $[BrF_4]^-$, respectively. Using intensity data, the equilibrium constant for the process:

$$BrF_3 + HF \rightleftharpoons [HF_2]^- + [BrF_2]^+$$

was calculated to be in the range $(6.14–2.09) \times 10^{-3}$. Christe and Sawodny[99] have recorded the Raman spectra of $IF_5.SbF_5$, $BrF_5.2SbF_5$, $ClF_5.1.08SbF_5$ and $[ClF_2]^+[SbF_5]^-$ adducts in HF solution. Raman spectra and polarization measurements have been reported for $[IF_6]^+[AsF_6]^-$ in HF solution.[100] The results resolve a former controversy over the assignment of ν_1 for $[IF_6]^+$ by establishing that it occurs at 711 cm^{-1}. Line broadening in the spectra reveals that the $[AsF_6]^-$ ion may be involved in H-bonded interactions with the solvent. Similar broadening behaviour has been observed by Gillespie and Schrobilgen[101] in the Raman spectrum of $[BrF_6]^+[AsF_6]^-$, where the $\nu_1(a_{1g})$ and $\nu_2(e_g)$ bands of $[AsF_6]^-$ were most affected.

TABLE 5
Frequencies/cm^{-1} and assignments for the Raman bands of $[ClF_2O]^+[BF_4]^-$ and $[ClF_2O]^+[HF_2]^-$ in anhydrous HF

$[ClF_2O]^+[BF_4]^-$/HF[104]	$[ClF_2O]^+[HF_2]^-$/HF[105]		Assignment
1333	1339	$\nu_1(a')$	$\nu(Cl{=}O)$
741	746	$\nu_2(a')$	$\nu(Cl{-}F)$
512	516	$\nu_3(a')$	$\delta_{sym}(OClF)$
383	409	$\nu_4(a')$	$\delta_{sym}(FClF)$
710	729	$\nu_5(a'')$	$\nu_{asym}(Cl{-}F)$
402	391	$\nu_6(a'')$	$\delta_{asym}(OClF)$

Solutions of $[SF_3]^+$ salts in liquid HF have been examined and characterized by Raman spectroscopy.[102,103] The frequencies for this C_{3v} cation as the $[BF_4]^-$ salt are: $\nu_1(a_1)$ 943, $\nu_3(e)$ 920, $\nu_2(a_1)$ 539 and $\nu_4(e)$ 411 cm^{-1}. The difluoro-oxochloronium(V) cation, $[ClF_2O]^+$, exists in salts with $[BF_4]^-$, $[AsF_6]^-$ and $[SbF_6]^-$. These salts are soluble in anhydrous HF and have been studied by Raman spectroscopy. Chlorine trifluoride oxide, $ClOF_3$ dissolves in anhydrous HF to form $[ClF_2O]^+$ and $[HF_2]^-$ ions.[105] The $[ClF_2O]^+$ ion appears to have C_s symmetry and band assignments on this basis are listed in Table 5 for the two systems, $[ClF_2O]^+[HF_2]^-$ and $[ClF_2O]^+[BF_4]^-$ in HF solution. Potential energy distributions calculated by Christe et al. suggest that the earlier assignments for ν_4 and ν_6 of the $[ClF_2O]^+[HF_2]^-$ system should be reversed. Small differences between the frequencies for the two systems may be attributed to differing cation–anion interactions. Christe et al.,[106] also, have recorded the Raman spectrum of the $ClO_2F_2^+$ cation as the BF_4^- salt in anhydrous HF solution. Polarization measurements were used in assigning the vibrational spectrum which was analysed in terms of a pseudotetrahedral C_{2v} structure.

Addition of water to HF mixtures with the strong Lewis acids SbF_5 and AsF_5 results in the formation of stable $1:1:1$ adducts in quantitative yields, viz.

$$HF + H_2O + MF_5 \xrightarrow{HF} [H_3O]^+[MF_6]^-$$

The adduct is formed by the stronger base, H_2O, displacing $[H_2F]^+$ by the formation of the H_3O^+ cation.

$$SbF_5 + 2HF \rightleftharpoons [H_2F]^+[SbF_6]^-$$
$$[H_2F]^+ + [SbF_6]^- + H_2O \rightarrow [H_3O]^+ + [SbF_6]^- + HF$$

Christe et al.[107] have used vibrational spectroscopy to demonstrate that these adducts are indeed ionic both in the solid state and in HF solution. In the case of $[H_3O]^+[SbF_6]^-$ in HF solution, two Raman bands due to the C_{3v} $[H_3O]^+$ cation were detected: $\nu_1(a_1)$ 3300 cm^{-1} and $\nu_4(e)$ 1630 cm^{-1}. Infrared and Raman measurements on the solid adducts place the remaining modes, ν_2 and ν_3, at 900 and 3150 cm^{-1}, respectively.

It has been demonstrated in many instances that the group VB pentafluorides readily become octahedral in HF solution by the addition of a fluoride ion. It can be argued that this fluoride-ion transfer is expected in these cases due to the geometrical stabilization of the octahedral configuration.[108] On these grounds, hexafluorides are expected to be unaffected by fluoride transfer in anhydrous HF solutions. Frlec and Hyman[109] have recorded the Raman spectra of MoF_6, WF_6, UF_6, ReF_6 and OsF_6 in liquid HF and report only minor frequency shifts from those of the gas or liquid phases. Less predictable is the behaviour of heptafluorides in HF. However, once again, the frequencies are little affected as demonstrated by Selig and Gasner[110] who recorded the Raman spectrum of ReF_7 in HF solution and compared it to the spectra from the liquid and gas phases. The Raman spectrum of IF_7 also remains unchanged in HF solution.[111]

In the solid phase, $ReOF_4$ appears to be associated through cis-fluorine bridges.[112] As the compound is soluble in liquid HF, Paine et al.[113] have recorded the Raman spectrum of the solution and compared it with infrared spectra of matrix-isolated $ReOF_4$, in an attempt to determine the structure of the monomer. The results, though not conclusive, indicate a C_{4v} structure for the monomeric molecule.

A detailed study of HCN ligation of Ag(I) and Cu(I) in anhydrous HF solution has been reported by Dove and Hallett.[81] They also reported infrared

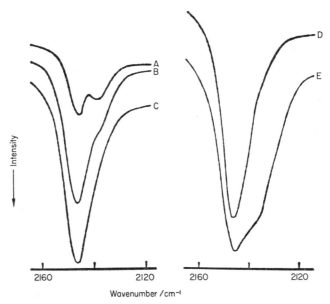

Fig. 5. Infrared spectra of HCN/Ag$^+$ mixtures in HF. Mole ratio CN:Ag, 1:1.43(A); 1:1(B); 1.5:1(C); 2:1(D) and 3.5:1(E). (Dove and Hallett, Ref. 81).

spectra of HCN in SO_2/HF mixtures and in pure SO_2 liquid. The $\nu(C \equiv N)$ frequency of HCN in SO_2 was found at 2097 cm^{-1}, which is the same as the gas phase frequency. In liquid HF, however, this vibration occurs at 2138 cm^{-1}. The increase in frequency is attributed to hydrogen bonding with the solvent. Solutions of AgCN in liquid HF possess two $\nu(C \equiv N)$ bands at 2147 and 2138 cm^{-1} in the infrared spectrum. The chemical stability of these solutions precludes the assignment of the 2138 cm^{-1} band to free HCN. In Fig. 5 spectra in the $\nu(C \equiv N)$ region are shown for a range of these solutions varying in Ag:CN composition ratio. These spectra, linked with some ^{1}H n.m.r. studies led Dove and Hallett to assign the 2147 cm^{-1} band to [(HCN)$_2$Ag]$^+$ and the 2138 cm^{-1} band to [HCNAg]$^+$. In the case of the CuCN solutions, [HCNCu]$^+$ appears to be the only complex formed.

Raman spectra of ethanol, ethoxyethane, tetrahydrofuran and dioxan at various concentrations[114] and of xenon oxide tetrafluoride[115] in anhydrous liquid HF have been reported. The complex cation $[Fe(phen)_2(CNH)_2]^{2+}$ has been shown[82] to have a *cis*-octahedral structure in liquid HF and liquid SO_2 solutions.

7.3   Anhydrous Hydrogen Chloride

As a solvent, anhydrous HCl does not appear to have the same appeal as HF. However, several interesting spectroscopic investigations have been made on liquid HCl solution systems. Petrov *et al.*[116] have identified $[SbCl_4]^-$ (T_d) and $[SbCl_6]^{3-}$ (O_h) in hydrogen chloride solutions of $SbCl_3$. A butoxybutane extract of As(III) in liquid HCl has been shown by infrared and Raman studies[117] to contain the $[AsCl_4]^-$ anion. Long and Davies[19] have recorded the Raman spectrum of $[AsCl_4]^-$ in $AsCl_3/HCl$ solutions and Raman spectra from HCl solutions of $TiCl_4$ have been reported.[118]

Several boron compounds readily dissolve in liquid HCl with the formation of the $[B_2Cl_6]^{2-}$ ion. The tetramethylammonium salt gave rise to infrared absorptions at 694, 665 and 600 cm^{-1} due to the $[B_2Cl_6]^{2-}$ ion.[119] Reactions of some sulphur compounds with BCl_3 in anhydrous HCl have been studied. The chlorocompounds $RSCl_3$ and R_2SCl_2 (R = Me or Et) form the solid products $[RSCl_2]^+[BCl_4]^-$ and $[R_2SCl]^+[BCl_4]^-$ having $\nu(S-Cl)$ in the 496–536 cm^{-1} range. With RSCl, R_2S_2 and R_2S, 1:1 adducts are formed which have B—S bonds.[120] The reaction between Al_2Cl_6 and CH_3COCl in liquid HCl, after removal of excess of solvent, leaves a solid product. The infrared spectrum of this solid suggests that it is a mixture of the covalent species $MeClCO.Al_2Cl_6$ and the ionic compound $[MeCO]^+[Al_2Cl_7]^-$. The carbonyl stretching frequency was observed at 1573 cm^{-1} for the former and at 2310 cm^{-1} for the latter.[121]

7.4   Liquid Halogen Fluorides

Several of the halogen fluorides have been utilized as solvents, though BrF_3 and ClF_3 have received most of the spectroscopic attention. Self-ionization of BrF_3 is thought to occur thus

$$2BrF_3 \rightleftharpoons [BrF_2]^+ + [BrF_4]^-$$

The concentrations of the two ions would be enhanced by acid-base reactions of the type:

$$KF + BrF_3 \rightarrow K^+ + [BrF_4]^-$$
$$SbF_5 + BrF_3 \rightarrow [BrF_2]^+ + [SbF_6]^-$$

By utilizing these reactions, Hyman *et al.*[122] have demonstrated the presence of these ions in liquid BrF_3. Infrared and Raman spectra of BrF_3, KF/BrF_3 and of the solid $KBrF_4$, establish a square planar, D_{4h}, geometry for the $[BrF_4]^-$ anion. The vibrational spectra for the cation-containing systems are not so conclusive because only one band, at *ca.* 700 cm^{-1} in solid $[BrF_2][SbF_6]$ and *ca.* 625 cm^{-1} in liquid BrF_3, was observed. A band at 308 cm^{-1} in the Raman spectra has been tentatively assigned to the bending mode of $[BrF_2]^+$. The observed frequencies for the species BrF_3 and $[BrF_4]^-$ as they occur in liquid BrF_3 are listed in Table 6. The assignment for BrF_3 is based on a T-shaped C_{2v} molecule.

Hyman *et al.*[123] extended their experiments to the reaction

$$ClF_3 + AsF_5 \rightleftharpoons [ClF_2]^+ + [AsF_6]^-.$$

The Raman spectrum of this system reveals a band at 782 cm^{-1} which most likely arises from the ν_1 stretch of $[ClF_2]^+$. In liquid $ClF_3 + BrF_3$ mixtures no band at

TABLE 6
Frequencies/cm^{-1}[122] of bands of BrF_3 and $[BrF_4]^-$ observed in the infrared and Raman spectra of liquid BrF_3

BrF$_3$ liq.			[BrF$_4$]$^-$ in liq. BrF$_3$			
Infrared	Raman		Infrared		Raman	
674	673	ν_1	—		528	ν_1
528	531	ν_2	302		—	ν_2
n.o.	235	ν_3	—		249	ν_3
614	n.o.	ν_4		inactive	—	ν_4
344	341	ν_5	—		455	ν_5
269	265	ν_6	570		—	ν_6
	581	polymer	n.o.		—	ν_7
	490	polymer				
	428	dimer?				

782 cm^{-1} was observed although the bands due to $[BrF_4]^-$ decreased in intensity, consistent with the following equilibrium lying well over to the left

$$BrF_3 + ClF_3 \rightleftharpoons [BrF_4]^- + [ClF_2]^+.$$

Raman intensity studies indicated a value for the equilibrium constant,

$$K = \frac{[ClF_2^+][BrF_4^-]}{[ClF_3][BrF_3]}$$

of $(1 \pm 0.4) \times 10^{-4}$. The Raman spectrum of bromine fluoride dioxide, BrO_2F, in liquid BrF_5 has been recorded by Gillespie and Spekkens.[124] In frozen solutions of BrF_5, evidence for the existence of $[Kr_2F_3]^+$ has been claimed.[125]

8   ORGANIC SOLVENTS

Many organic compounds are used as solvents, from simple molecules like CCl_4

and MeCN to larger and more complex molecules such as propene carbonate and substituted pyridines. Hydrocarbons, alcohols, aldehydes, ketones, ethers, amines, amides, acids, aromatic compounds and several of their derivatives, have all been employed as solvents. Many of these have been investigated by vibrational spectroscopy. An obvious problem of classification exists if the relevant aspects of these studies are to be reviewed. A frequently used grouping is that of donor solvent and non-donor solvent. However, in practice the division between these two types is not clear cut. Most solvents, given a sufficiently powerful acceptor as a solute, will behave as donors. Whether a hydrogen-bonding interaction between solvent and solute may be regarded as evidence for donor behaviour depends upon definitions. One aspect of this subject, which can be treated separately, concerns cation solvation and the measurement of cation-solvent vibrational frequencies.

In order to simplify treatment of the general organic, non-aqueous solvent research, two broad groupings of solvents have been adopted: low-donicity solvents and high-donicity solvents. The concept of donicity or donor number has been developed by Gutmann[126,127] in an attempt to express, in a semi-empirical way, the donor ability of a solvent. The scale is founded on the enthalpy of formation of a 1:1 complex between a given solvent and antimony(V) chloride in dilute 1,2-dichloroethane solution. That is, $-\Delta H^\circ$ for the reaction

$$\text{Solvent} + \text{SbCl}_5 \underset{\text{ClCH}_2 . \text{CH}_2\text{Cl}}{\rightleftharpoons} \text{Solvent-SbCl}_5$$

Donicity values range from zero for 1,2-dichloroethane up to 38.8 for hexamethylphosphoramide. There are indications from n.m.r. experiments[128] that higher values are expected for molecules like ethylamine (55.5) and ammonia (59). For the purposes of this review low-donicity systems will be regarded as those having solvent donicity values less than 10; they are not generally thought to form donor-acceptor complexes. Benzene, having a donicity of 0.1, and nitromethane, with a value of 2.7, are reasonable examples of low-donicity solvents. High-donicity solvents will include those with donicity values greater than 10 and solutions where donor-acceptor complex formation predominates.

8.1 Cation-Solvent Interactions

A considerable amount of effort has been put into measurements of cation-solvent frequencies.[128] In many solvent systems, low frequency modes are detected which are generally not affected by the nature of the anion, are not present in the spectrum of the pure solvent and are sensitive to cation type. The general opinion is that such vibrational bands are due to cation vibrations in a solvent cage. Infrared spectra of lithium salts LiX (X = $[\text{ClO}_4]^-$, Br^-, I^- or $[\text{AlCl}_4]^-$) in THF solution show absorption bands at *ca.* 420 cm^{-1}. These have been attributed by Ashby *et al.*[129] to a vibration of the Li$^+$ ion in a solvent cage formed from four THF molecules. The solvation of Na$^+$ ions by THF in the

THF—Na[AlBu$_4$]-cyclohexane system has been studied using the 900–1150 cm^{-1} region of the infrared spectrum.[130] Cation-solvent cage vibrations have been reported for Li$^+$, Na$^+$, K$^+$ and [NH$_4$]$^+$ in THF and also in some other solvents and they appear to be sensitive to the solvent, anion type and pressure.[131–133] The following frequency regions for the bands were found: Li$^+$, 373–453; Na$^+$, 170–203; K$^+$, 142–150; [NH$_4$]$^+$, 188–203 cm^{-1}.

In dimethylsulphoxide both Li$^+$ and [NH$_4$]$^+$ have characteristic cation-solvent vibrations. Maxey and Popov[134] have measured these at 429 cm^{-1} for LiX (X = Cl$^-$, Br$^-$, I$^-$, [NO$_3$]$^-$ or [ClO$_4$]$^-$) and at ca. 200 cm^{-1} for NH$_4$X (X = Cl$^-$, Br$^-$, I$^-$, [NO$_3$]$^-$, [SCN]$^-$ or [BPh$_4$]$^-$). Maxey and Popov[135] have extended their measurements to alkali metal salts in dipropylsulphoxide and dibutylsulphoxide where the cation-solvent bands are dependent to a small extent on the solvent used, but vary greatly as a function of cation type. Changes in the spectra of the solvents are to be expected in these systems and, indeed, the ν(S=O) band is observed to shift to lower frequencies in the solutions.

Acetone solvation of alkali metal cations has been detected. Popov et al.[136] have reported infrared bands at 425, 195 and 148 cm^{-1} for Li$^+$, Na$^+$ and K$^+$ ions in acetone solutions. That the bands were due to cation-solvent vibrations was demonstrated by observation of an isotopic frequency shift when ^{2}H^6-acetone and ^{6}Li$^+$ salts were used. Solutions of Li$^+$, Na$^+$, Ba^{2+}, Sr^{2+}, Mg^{2+}, Ag^{2+}, Zn^{2+}, Co^{2+} or Cu^{2+}, as chlorate(VII)s, nitrates or halides in acetone, give rise to splittings of the ν(C=O) and δ(C—C—C) infrared bands. In an attempt to analyse the nature of the interactions present in these solutions, Borucka et al.[137] have used c.n.d.o. calculations to predict the electronic structures of Me$_2$O-cation and Me$_2$O-anion complexes. Their results allow correlations to be drawn between cation charge densities and variations in frequency and intensity of the band components. This work has been extended to acetonitrile solutions.[138] Solvation of cations by nitromethane has also been examined by infrared spectroscopy.[139] Far-infrared measurements by Handy and Popov[140] on Li$^+$, Na$^+$ and [NH$_4$]$^+$ salts in 4-methylpyridine again show evidence of ion-solvent interactions. Characteristic bands were observed at 390–350, 175 and 200 cm^{-1} respectively. The Li$^+$-solvent band appeared to be strongly affected by 2-substitution of the methylpyridine. Similar results have been obtained from far-infrared studies of alkali metal salts in 2-pyrolidones[141] and propene carbonate[142] solutions.

Tsatsas et al.[143] have studied the effect of crown ethers as complexing agents upon the far-infrared spectra of alkali metal salts in dimethylsulphoxide and pyridine. In these two solvents the cation-solvent bands are observed at 200 and 180 cm^{-1}, respectively, for Na$^+$ and at 150 and 136 cm^{-1}, respectively, for K$^+$ ions. Addition of dibenzo-18-crown-6 causes these bands to shift to higher frequency, 214 cm^{-1} (Na$^+$) and 168 cm^{-1} (K$^+$), and to become independent of the solvent. These observations imply that the crown ether preferentially complexes the cations and the authors were able to calculate ion-crown force constants using a D_{6h}-symmetry interaction model. Analogous experiments have been performed by Cahen and Popov[144] using cryptands[145] as complexing agents, i.e.

C222, $a = b = c = 1$, C221, $a = 0, b = c = 1$, C211, $a = b = 0, c = 1$.

With alkali metal ions these macrobicyclics form stable inclusion compounds, referred to as cryptates. Addition of a cryptand to solutions of sodium or lithium salts causes the solvent-cation bands to be replaced by new bands which are both anion- and solvent-independent. In pyridine, acetonitrile, nitromethane and dimethylsulphoxide solutions, the vibrational frequencies of Li^+ and Na^+ ions in the cryptand cavity are 234 ± 2, 218 ± 1, 243 ± 3 and 348 ± 1 cm^{-1} for Na^+—C222, Na^+—C221, Li^+—C221 and Li^+—C211 cryptates, respectively.

Infrared spectroscopy has been employed to estimate solvent coordination numbers for Li^+, Na^+ and Mg^{2+} cations present in MeCN solution as chlorate(VII)s. Values of $Li^+(4)$, $Na^+(4)$ and $Mg^{2+}(6)$ were obtained.[146] Regis and Corset[147] have analysed the infrared spectra from ternary mixtures of $LiClO_4$ and two different solvents in terms of preferential solvation of the cation. The solvating power of the several bases studied was shown to decrease in the order: $NH_3 > MeNH_2 > Me_2NH > Me_3N > MeCN > MeNO_3$. In the

TABLE 7
Typical cation-solvent frequencies^a/cm^{-1}

Solvent/Cation	Li^+	$[NH_4]^+$	Na^+	K^+	Rb^+	Cs^+
dimethylsulphoxide	429	214	200	153	125	110
propanone	425(409)	—	195	148	—	—
tetrahydrofuran	413(373)	—	192	146	—	—
1-methyl-2-pyrolidine	398(377)	207	204	140	106	—
propene carbonate	397(385)	184	186	144	115	112
4-methylpyridine	390	290	178(172)	—	—	—
acetic acid	390	—	—	—	—	—
pyridine	385	196	182(170)	—	—	—
2-chloropyridine	355(340)	—	—	—	—	—
nitromethane	340–370	—	—	—	—	—

^{a} Figures in parentheses indicate reported limits of anion-dependent frequencies.

case of solutions containing $Na[BPh_4]$ in pyridine, 1,4-dioxan, piperidine and tetrahydrofuran, the presence of bare ions, rather than solvated ions, is indicated. French and Wood[148] have measured an isotopic shift for the vibrations $\nu([NH_4]^+ - [BPh_4]^-)$ at 198 cm^{-1}, and $\nu([ND_4]^+ - [BPh_4]^-)$ at 183 cm^{-1} which they believe supports the bare-ion model. The interionic vibration for $K^+ - [BPh_4]^-$ was observed at 133 cm^{-1}. Infrared evidence has been presented[149] to demonstrate that tetraalkylammonium salts also are unsolvated in acetonitrile and dimethylformamide solutions.

In Table 7 many of the observed cation-solvent frequencies are collected together. The frequencies, in some systems, are dependent upon the anion to a small extent. This is often the case amongst the halides. However, the variations are relatively small,[128] $\leqslant 20$ cm^{-1}. Where available, the range of anion-dependent frequencies is included in Table 8. It is evident that the cation-solvent frequency is largely dependent upon both the mass of the cation and, to a lesser extent, the nature of the solvent. The lighter cations, Li^+ in particular, have frequencies which are most sensitive to the solvent.

8.2   Low-donicity Systems

Many low-donicity solvents are used to provide a non-interacting medium for solute studies. In order to obtain structural information about a molecule, it is desirable to record the infrared and Raman spectra in a situation where it can be regarded as a 'free' molecule. Clearly this ideal situation can never be attained in solution but, by suitable choice of solvent, a close approximation may result. Nevertheless, weak solute-solvent and solute-solute interactions are frequently present. Collections of data for these systems and, in particular, reporting of weak solvent effects, is invaluable in assisting the analysis of new spectroscopic results.

Hester and Mayer[150] have studied the $Na^+[BH_3 . PH_2 . BH_3]^-$ salt in various solvents and have shown that the anion possesses a C_{2v} structure. Infrared and Raman data on P_2I_4 have been used to demonstrate that the molecule has C_{2h} symmetry in CS_2 solution.[151] Observation of a split ν_3 band of $[CuCl_4]^{2-}$ as the tetraethylammonium salt in nitromethane, has been used as an indication of a distorted tetrahedral structure for the ion.[152] Further examples are studies of PCl_5, $SbCl_5$ and $[Ph_4As]^+[TeCN]^-$ in acetonitrile[153,154] and $CdBr_2$ in tri-n-butylphosphate solution.[155] Shore et al.[156] have examined the self-ionization of PCl_5 in acetonitrile, nitromethane and nitrobenzene solutions by Raman spectroscopy. Figure 6 shows the Raman spectra of PCl_5 in the three solvents. It is clear that $[PCl_4]^+$ (456 cm^{-1}), $[PCl_6]^-$ (354 cm^{-1}) and PCl_5 (393 cm^{-1}) are present in all solutions. In nitrobenzene solution the PCl_5 band at (393 cm^{-1}) is masked by an intense solvent band. However, the presence of PCl_5 in this system can be inferred from the presence of other PCl_5 bands at 262, 273 and 280 cm^{-1}. Acetonitrile appears to react with PCl_5 over a period of about two hours, eliminating the 393 cm^{-1} band from the spectrum and probably generat-

'ing $[PCl_6]^-$ and a complex cation. Above concentrations of about 0.03 mol dm^{-3} equilibrium (1) seems to predominate and at lower concentrations equilibrium (2) appears to be more important:

$$2PCl_5 \rightleftharpoons [PCl_4]^+ + [PCl_6]^- \qquad (1)$$
$$PCl_5 \rightleftharpoons [PCl_4]^+ + Cl^- \qquad (2)$$

Huong and Desbat[157] have shown from Raman spectra that only PCl$_5$ is present in CS$_2$ solutions of PCl$_5$ but that in nitromethane solution equilibrium (1) exists. Addition of [Me$_4$N]Cl to nitromethane solutions leaves only $[PCl_6]^-$ as is also the case for PCl$_5$ dissolved in anhydrous HCl.

Studies by Daly and Brown[158] on Raman spectra of rhombic sulphur dissolved in primary amines have provided evidence for the presence of the S_3^- ion with ν_{sym} at 535 cm^{-1}. Under the same conditions a band observed in the infrared spectrum at 585 cm^{-1} was assigned to ν_{asym}. Raman bands at 400, 440, 462

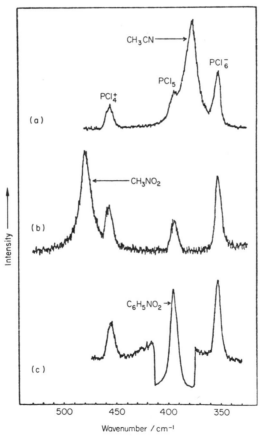

Fig. 6. Raman spectra of phosphorus(V)chloride in acetonitrile, nitromethane and nitrobenzene solutions. (Shore *et al.*, Ref. 156).

and *ca.* 510 cm^{-1} are thought to arise from polysulphides. Raman spectra of WF$_6$ in benzene, acetonitrile and cyclopentane solutions, show that there is very little solute-solvent charge-transfer interaction present.[159] In a Raman study of SO$_2$ in a range of solvents, Le Duff and Ouillon[160] show that both ν_1 and ν_3 are lowered on dissolution. In dioxan solution the I$_2$ molecule vibration is lowered from the gas phase value of 214.5 cm^{-1} to 204.8 cm^{-1}. In CCl$_4$ solution, however, the vibration occurs at 212.6 cm^{-1}, suggesting that relatively free I$_2$ molecules are present. These measurements on iodine were carried out for several solvents by way of the resonance Raman effect.[161] This technique offers the chance to observe spectra from species at extreme dilutions, thus reducing the possibilities of solute-solute interactions.

Several reports of work on ionic systems in organic solvents have been reported. Evidence of ion-pair formation by lithium salts in acetone solution has been presented[162] and infrared spectra of many inorganic nitrates in acetone suggest the presence of C_{2v} nitrate anions.[163] Indications of strong ionic associations between incompletely substituted alkylammonium cations in non-dissociating solvents, like *cis*-1,2-dichloroethene, have been obtained from far-infrared measurements.[164] In the case of [Pr$_4^n$N]$^+$[GaCl$_4$]$^-$, one ν(Ga—Cl) infrared band is observed at 374 cm^{-1}. With [Et$_3$NH]$^+$[GaCl$_4$]$^-$, however, three ν(Ga—Cl) bands are observed, indicating a lowering of symmetry to C_{3v} by Et$_3$N$^+$—H...Cl—GaCl$_3^-$ hydrogen bonding. The ion-pair structure of Ga$_2$Cl$_4$ and Ga$_2$Br$_4$ has been revealed in the 200–500 cm^{-1} infrared spectrum of these compounds in benzene solution.[165]

Trichloromethane, frequently regarded as a non-interacting solvent, has been shown to solvate nitrate anions by detection of $\nu_3(e')$ mode splittings.[166] Silver nitrate solutions in acetonitrile have been the subject of a Raman study by Chang and Irish[167] and infrared spectroscopy has been used to examine acetonitrile solutions of sodium and lithium iodides.[168] Contact ion-pair formation has been observed in acetonitrile solutions of TeF$_5$OAg. Mayer and Sladky[169] have observed two new bands which they assign to Te—O and axial Te—F stretching modes in the complex. Far-infrared spectra of tetrabutylammonium chloride in benzene have been interpreted in terms of vibrations of solvated and solvent-separated aggregates and collisions of strongly polarized benzene molecules.[170] The effect of temperature on these systems has been demonstrated by Irish *et al.*[171] who obtained evidence of ion-pair formation by Zn(NO$_3$)$_2$ in anhydrous MeOH above 243 K but only solvent-separated ion pairs at lower temperatures. Infrared spectroscopy has been used to demonstrate the presence of the species [SCN]$^-$, LiSCN and (LiSCN)$_n$ in solutions of LiSCN in polar solvents.[172]

The influence of solvent type on the degree of aggregation or polymerization of a solute has been investigated for several systems. Phosphorus(III) cyanide appears to be tetrameric in nitromethane solution and dimeric in acetonitrile, dioxan and benzene solutions.[173] Comparisons with the solid state spectra have allowed Green *et al.*[174] to demonstrate that halogenobis(pentafluorophenyl)thallium(III) compounds, $(R_F)_2TlX$ (X = Cl or Br), are dimeric by halogen bridging in benzene but monomeric in acetone. Tantalum(V) fluoride is dimeric in non-polar solvents and yet WCl_5 has been shown to be monomeric.[175] It also has been reported[176] that the complexes $VX_3 . 2L$ (X = Cl or Br, L = Me_2S, Et_2S, C_4H_8S or $C_7H_{13}N$ (quinuclidine)) are monomeric in low-donicity solvents. Duboc[177,178] has used infrared spectroscopy to examine the auto-association of aliphatic alcohols in CCl_4 solutions by measurements in the $\nu(O—H)$ region.

It is possible for solvents to interact with a solute in such a way as to effect isomerization in the solute molecules. Burmeister *et al.*[179] have studied the effects of various solvents on the linkage isomers $[Pd(AsPh_3)_2(SCN)_2]$ and $[Pd(AsPh_3)_2(NCS)_2]$ by infrared spectroscopy. In acetone, pyridine, acetonitrile, benzonitrile and adiponitrile solutions only the S-bonded isomer was detected. In DMF and DMSO, however, the presence of free thiocyanate ions was also detected. In benzene, carbon tetrachloride, trichloromethane, dichloromethane, cyclopentanone and nitrobenzene, three bands were observed, due to bridging thiocyanate ($\nu(CN)$ 2170–2153 cm^{-1}), S-bonded thiocyanate ($\nu(CN)$ 2125–2118 cm^{-1}) and N-bonded thiocyanate ($\nu(CN)$ 2095–2083 cm^{-1}), for each isomer. Interconversion of the two isomers is thought to proceed via a bridge-linked dimer formed by loss of $AsPh_3$, viz.

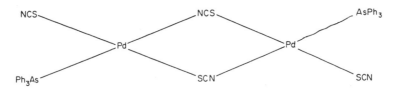

S-bonded, *trans*-$Pd(DMSO)_2Cl_2$ is converted to the *cis*-isomer in acetonitrile solution.[180] Far-infrared and Raman spectroscopy have been used to determine the effect of solvent type on the Br—Br stretching mode of the pyridine–Br_2 complex and on the torsional modes of propenal, trichloroethanal, MeCHO, PhCHO, PrCl and S_2Cl_2. Solvent shifts were measured and were thought to be caused by polarization of the solute molecule in its equilibrium configuration. The solvent shift of trichloroethanal indicates that the staggered O—Cl isomer corresponds to the minimum energy configuration.[181] Frequency shifts have also been noted for binary solvent mixtures containing KI, Me_2SO and PhN:NPh.[182]

Specific solvent effects of cyclohexane towards IBr and ICl compared with hexane have been revealed by infrared intensity measurements.[183] Also, several pieces of evidence for trichloromethane solvent interactions have been reported.[184-186] The barrier to rotation of HCl molecules in both CCl_4 and C_2Cl_4 solutions is reported[187] to be 270 cm^{-1}. Comparison of $\nu(C—D)$ frequencies in $CDCl_3$ solutions of Me_3MNMe_2 and $M(NMe_2)_4$ (M = C, Si, Ge or Sn) with the gas phase value has allowed Mack and Yoder[188] to determine the relative basicities of these amines. The absolute intensities of the bands, ν_3 of MeI and ν_2 and ν_8 of MeCN, in various solvents over a range of concentrations can be rationalized in terms of dipole–dipole interactions in the solutions.[189] Methanol, phenol and p-FC$_6$H$_4$OH appear to be involved in hydrogen-bonded complex formation with Me$_3$NBH$_2$X (X = Cl, Br or I) in CCl$_4$ solutions.[190] This is apparent from the infrared spectra of these solutions which contain a ν(O—H) absorption not observed in the spectrum of the 'free' alcohol. In systems of this type the solvent, in this case CCl$_4$, simply provides a medium in which to observe the species of interest and is not expected to contribute to any of the solute spectral features. This assumption is generally true of low-donicity solvents but caution needs to be exercised, as shown by some of the earlier examples, when interpreting spectra from solutions containing strong acceptor solutes. Solute-solvent interaction can also be reduced by using a reasonably 'inert' solvent. Orville-Thomas and Szczepianak[191] have made extensive measurements on the ν(O—H) vibration of phenols in fluorinated and mixed 'inert' solvents. In all cases, frequency shifts indicated that intermolecular interaction with fluorinated solvents is, in general, reduced from that with the hydrogenated analogues.

Trichloromethane is frequently used as a solvent in spectroscopic work since it is regarded as a weakly interacting solvent. The complexes LPtCl$_2$(CO), where L is an N-containing organic ligand, show the expected single infrared band due to the ν(C=O) mode. In propanone and acetonitrile solutions, however, two bands appear, the second being due to S.PtCl$_2$(CO) species,[192] where S is a solvent molecule which has displaced the ligand L. In some situations, however, CHCl$_3$ does display a strong solvating ability. The ν(Pb—O) vibration of Me$_2$Pb(acac)$_2$ has been found to shift from 388 cm^{-1} in CHCl$_3$ solution to 378 cm^{-1} in HMPA. The effect is attributed to polarization of the Pb—O bond by solvent–Pb coordination.[193] H-bonding plays an important part in CHCl$_3$-solute interactions. In CHCl$_3$ and CHBr$_3$ solutions of Ph$_3$PCl$_2$, Arzoumanidis[194] has detected hydrogen-bonded solvates which can be crystallized from solution. The solvates are thought to have the structure:

Interactions between trichloromethane and phenylamines have been studied by Kolbe and Pracejus.[195] In these systems it appears that the chlorine atoms act as acceptors and that hydrogen bonding, where the nitrogen atoms of the phenylamines act as acceptors for the $CHCl_3$ proton, is relatively unimportant. The enthalpy of hydrogen bonding, determined from the temperature-dependencies of the NH_2 and NH vibrational frequencies, is 5–10 kJ mol^{-1}. Deviations from additivity of u.v. and infrared spectroscopic data have been used[196] to support the suggestion that both $Me_2CO.CHCl_3$ and $Me_2CO.2CHCl_3$ adducts are present in $CHCl_3$ solutions of Me_2CO. The concept of statistical intermolecular complexes has been discussed by Mierzecki[197] in the context of binary solutions of π- and n-donors in $CHCl_3$ solution. Infrared and Raman band intensities were used to determine the compositions and structures of the complexes present.

8.3 High-donicity Systems

This class of solvent systems is loosely defined, as it must be recognized that the acceptor strength of the solute needs to be considered when discussing the formation of donor-acceptor complexes in solution. Nonetheless, it is apparent that in many solvents this type of complex formation is of prime importance. Strong acceptor compounds like $AlCl_3$ and $AlBr_3$ have been shown by infrared studies to form 1:1 and 1:2 complexes with Me_2O and Et_2O at ambient temperatures. At 93 K the solutions contain only $L \rightarrow AlCl_3$ monomers.[198] Infrared and Raman spectra of $MgBr_2$ and MgI_2 solutions in Et_2O have been interpreted by Wieser and Krueger[199] in terms of Et_2O complexes with magnesium, $MgBr_2$ and MgI_2. Addition complexes of the type MeX, AlX_3 and EtX, AlX_3 have been proposed[200] to explain the 600–200 cm^{-1} infrared region of spectra from MeX and EtX solutions of Al_2X_6 (X = Br or I). The symmetric and asymmetric stretches of complexed AlX_3 were observed at 263 and 466 cm^{-1}, respectively, for X = Br and at 225 and 395 cm^{-1}, respectively, for X = I. When a poor acceptor is dissolved in a donor solvent, solute–solute interactions may predominate. Shirk and Shriver[201] have studied the infrared and Raman spectra of the tetrahydroaluminate ion, as the Li$^+$, Na$^+$ or [Et$_4$N]$^+$ salt, and of the tetrahydrogallate ion as the Li$^+$, Na$^+$ or K$^+$ salt, in the solid state and dissolved in various ethers. The formation of three distinct species was reported, viz. tightly and loosely bound aggregates and ion pairs. An unexpected frequency-order for the a_1 ν(M—H) mode for these species was found, such that $[BH_4]^- > [GaH_4]^- > [AlH_4]^-$.

Many boron compounds are recognized as good acceptor species and BF_3 is a frequently quoted example. Vibrational spectra of 30 ketone-BF_3 complexes have been reported by Gates and Mooney,[202] who made correlations with the ketone donor strengths. The effect of solvents on the ν(B—H) of some cyclo-tetrazenoboranes is that the frequency is found to increase as a function of solvent polarity. However, it appears that the solvent interacts with the solute molecules in parts remote from the B—H bond.[203] In compounds of the type R_3GeH, R_2GeH_2 and $RGeH_3$ the effect of solvent on the ν(Ge—H) frequencies has been found to be small ($\leqslant 10$ cm^{-1}). Changes in ν(Ge—H) from the value found in the free compound vary in an approximately linear fashion with $(n^2 - 1)/(2n^2 + 1)$, where n is the solvent refractive index, for each group of compounds.[204] Loehr and Plane[205] have interpreted the Raman spectra from solutions of $AsCl_3$ in alcohols in terms of $ROH.AsCl_3$ species. Greenwood et al.[206] have examined solutions of TeX_4 (X = Cl or Br) in a variety of organic solvents. The ionic species $[L_2TeX_3]^+X^-$, where L is a solvent molecule, was concluded to be present in Me_2SO, EtOH, Me_2CO, MeCN and C_4H_8O solutions. In benzene and toluene solutions, however, $TeCl_4$ and $TeBr_4$ appear to be present as trimeric aggregates. A somewhat different conclusion was arrived at by Katsaros and George,[207] who found $SeCl_4$, $TeCl_4$, $TeBr_4$ and $TeCl_2Br_2$ to be largely monomeric in non-aqueous solutions. However, in DMF, $TeCl_4$ and $TeBr_4$ show signs of being 6-coordinate, as indicated by the observation of low ν(Te—X) frequencies at 245 and 193 cm^{-1}, respectively. Furthermore, $SeBr_4$ shows signs of being fully dissociated to Se_2Br_2, $SeBr_2$ and Br_2 in non-aqueous solutions and a strong infrared band at 290 cm^{-1} is thought to be due to ν(Se—Br).

A correlation between ν(O—H) of some silanols and their acidity has been demonstrated in THF and MeCN solutions.[208] Infrared measurements of ν(O—H) frequency shifts in trimethylsilanol dissolved in a number of different solvents have been used to determine the extent of hydrogen bonding in such solutions.[209] Also, some anionic and neutral complexes of Tl(III) chloride and iodide in polar solvents have been studied in the far-infrared region.[210] Still in the field of non-aqueous solutions is a report of the Raman spectrum of water in DMSO solution.[211] Gentric et al.[212] have analysed the bending vibration of water dissolved in MeCN, Me_2SO, $P(NMe_2)_3$ and dioxan over a wide concentration range by infrared spectroscopy. At low concentrations in some basic solvents, the band was asymmetric or split. Studies of ternary mixtures and of the effect of temperature on binary solutions allowed the two components to be assigned to the bending vibrations of a 1:1 and a 1:2 water:solvent complex in equilibrium. The molecular size of the solvent appeared to determine the proportion of each complex present.

Several examples of solvent coordination to incompletely coordinated transition metal complexes are known. The square pyramidal oxovanadium(IV) complexes provide a good example of a system which has been extensively studied over the past 15 years. For instance, Bozis and McCormick[213] have reported an infrared study of VOL_2 (L = a monothio-β-diketone of general formula, RC(SH)=CHCOR'). In nujol mulls, ν(V=O) appears at ca. 990 cm^{-1}, but in the donor solvents pyridine or DMSO the frequency drops to near 960 cm^{-1}. The solvents interact trans to the V=O bond, increasing the electron density on the vanadium atom and weakening the V=O bond. In contrast, Larsson[214] has shown that ν(V=O) is essentially unaffected in THF and EtOH solutions. When sodium and $Cr(CO)_6$ are dissolved in THF, $[Cr(CO)_5]^{2-}$ ions are produced. In the ν(C=O) region, infrared bands at 1820 (a_2'') and 1772, 1738 (e') were reported by Lindner et al.[215] The ion is believed to have D_{3h}

symmetry, but it is clear from the e' mode splitting that there is some significant interaction with the solvent.

It is frequently expected that the donor part of an acid, ester or amide is the oxygen atom of the C=O bond. However, vibrational studies do not always present clear-cut evidence for this. Raman spectra of concentrated solutions of LiCl in formic acid, containing mainly ion pairs and singly solvated ions, show striking changes in the $\nu(C=O)$, $\nu(C-O)$ and $\nu(C-H)$ bands. Rode[216] has shown that these observations are in good agreement with calculated frequency shifts obtained by semi-empirical molecular-orbital methods applied to simple solvation models. When $TiCl_4$, $SnCl_4$, $SbCl_5$ or $AlCl_3$ is dissolved in $CHCl_2CO_2H$, $\nu(C=O)$ shifts from 1710 to 1680 cm^{-1}, indicating in this case a strong interaction with the C=O bond.[217] Several reports[218-220] of the effects of the presence of Lewis acids in the $\nu(C=O)$ stretching frequency of amides or esters agree that, in all cases studied, the $\nu(C=O)$ infrared band is shifted to lower frequencies. This, it is generally concluded, indicates that C=O is the donor group. Gardiner et al.[221] have used Raman difference spectroscopy to investigate the solvation properties of formamide towards electrolytes. Using a rotating, split-compartment cell, the spectra clearly reveal that the anions $[NO_3]^-$ and Cl^- interact with the $-NH_2$ protons. The interaction site for the cations Li^+ and Na^+ was not so obvious. It seems that there is no great change in $\nu(C=O)$ when the cation is changed from Li^+, which is highly polarizing, to Na^+. However, changes in the $\nu(N-C)$ vibration are apparent and it seems that this vibration is mixed to quite a large extent with the $\nu(C=O)$ vibration. This mixing probably reduces the expected frequency shift in $\nu(C=O)$. Changes in the $\nu(C-H)$ vibration were also detected. Emsley[222] has obtained evidence for hydrogen bonding between F^- and acetic acid from the infrared spectrum of KF in acetic acid solution.

Raman spectra of I_2, Br_2 and ICl have been reported in 33 different solvents by Klaboe.[223] In the pyridine-I_2 solution a band at 163 cm^{-1} is attributed to $\nu(N-I)$. Evidence for the ionization

$$2pyIX \rightleftharpoons [py_2I]^+ + [IX_2]^-$$

where X is Cl, Br, I or CN, has been cited for pyridine-halogen complexes in solutions of polar solvents.[224] The γ-picoline-halogen complexes behave in a similar fashion.[225] N—I vibrations have been observed at 560, 490, 380 and 130 cm^{-1} for NI_3-3-quinoline and NI_3-pyridine adducts.[226] In the gas phase, HF has a vibrational frequency of 3961 cm^{-1}. Solutions of HF in pyridine show an HF vibration at 2713 cm^{-1}. This large drop in frequency is attributed to hydrogen-bonding interactions.[227]

9   CONCLUDING REMARKS

The study of solvents and solutions continues at an increasing pace. This is due, in part, to the introduction of new solvent systems. All compounds in the liquid phase will have some solvent properties, though only a few will find use as reaction media. The contribution which vibrational spectroscopy is making to this research is gaining deserved recognition. The technique allows observations to be made on both weak and strong interactions in solution. The spectroscopic measurements range from small frequency shifts, degenerate-mode splittings and changes in bandwidths, to larger frequency shifts and the detection of normal modes from solute-solvent species. These more common measurements are quite well understood for several solution systems. Solutions of ionic solutes have received particularly close attention and significant advances have been made in this area. Studies of single solvents with a well-defined range of specific solute types, should prove rewarding. This, linked with theoretical calculations of interaction geometries and energies, will provide much needed information towards a more complete understanding of the solution phase.

REFERENCES

(1) T. C. Waddington (ed.), *Non-Aqueous Solvent Systems*, Academic Press, London, 1965.

(2) J. J. Lagowski (ed.), *The Chemistry of Non-Aqueous Solvents*, Academic Press, New York, 1967.

(3) V. Gutmann, *J. Phys. Chem.* **63**, 378 (1959).

(4) R. S. Drago and K. F. Purcell, in *Progr. Inorg. Chem.*, Vol. 6, (F. A. Cotton, ed.), 1964.

(5) V. V. Bertsev, M. O. Bulanin, L. A. Zhigula and T. D. Kolomiitsova, *Mol. Spektrosk.* **2**, 81 (1973).

(6) R. Akhmedzanov, V. V. Bertsev, M. O. Bulanin and L. A. Zhigula, *Opt. Spektrosk.* **36**, 1219 (1974).

(7) A. C. Leannotte, D. Legler and J. Overend, *Spectrochim. Acta A* **29**, 1915 (1973).

(8) L. Bayersdorfer, R. Minkwitz and J. Jander, *Z. Anorg. Allg. Chem.* **392**, 137 (1972).

(9) J. C. Cornut and P. V. Huong, *Appl. Spectrosc.* **27**, 55 (1973).

(10) D. E. Irish, in *Advances in Infrared and Raman Spectroscopy*, Vol. 2, (R. J. H. Clark and R. E. Hester, eds), Heyden, London, 1976.

(11) J. Corset, P. V. Huong and J. Lascombe, *Spectrochim. Acta A* **24**, 1385 (1968).

(12) D. J. Gardiner, R. E. Hester and W. E. L. Grossman, *J. Raman. Spectrosc.* **1**, 87 (1973).

(13) G. Herzberg, *Infrared and Raman Spectra of Polyatomic Molecules*, Van Nostrand, Princeton, N.J., 1945.

(14) A. Commeyras and G. A. Olah, *J. Am. Chem. Soc.* **91**, 2929 (1969).

(15) J. C. Evans, *J. Mol. Spectrosc.* **4**, 435 (1960).

(16) P. D. Simova and R. Angelova, *Izv. Fiz. Inst. Aneb.* **7**, 333 (1959); *Chem. Abs.* **54**, 17048e.

(17) D. J. Stufkens, *Recl. Trav. Chim. Pays-Bas* **89**, 755 (1970); *Chem. Abs.* **73**, 93315g.

(18) M. G. K. Pillai and P. P. Pillai, *Indian J. Pure Appl. Phys.* **6**, 404 (1968).

(19) J. E. D. Davies and D. A. Long, *J. Chem. Soc. A* 1761 (1968).

(20) R. Rousson and M. Drifford, *J. Chem. Phys.* **62**, 1806 (1975).
(21) R. A. Frey, R. L. Redington and A. L. K. Alijbury, *J. Chem. Phys.* **54**, 344 (1971).
(22) H. H. Claassen, B. Weinstock and J. G. Malon, *J. Chem. Phys.* **28**, 285 (1958).
(23) G. M. Begun and W. H. Fletcher, *J. Mol. Spectrosc.* **4**, 388 (1960).
(24) S. J. Cyvin, *Z. Anorg. Allg. Chem.* **378**, 117 (1970).
(25) I. Suzuki, *Bull. Chem. Soc. Japan* **33**, 1359 (1960).
(26) P. G. Puranik and K. V. Ramiah, *J. Mol. Spectrosc.* **3**, 486 (1959).
(27) G. E. Tomlinson, B. Curnette and C. E. Hathaway, *J. Mol. Spectrosc.* **36**, 26 (1970).
(28) P. A. Giguère and I. D. Liu, *J. Chem. Phys.* **20**, 136 (1952).
(29) J. S. Ziomek and M. D. Zeidler, *J. Mol. Spectrosc.* **11**, 163 (1963).
(30) S. J. Cyvin, *Z. Anorg. Allg. Chem.* **378**, 117 (1970).
(31) E. L. Pace, *Spectrochim, Acta A* **27**, 491 (1971).
(32) M. Pezolet and R. Savoie, *Canad. J. Chem.* **47**, 3041 (1969).
(33) R. H. Maybury, S. Gordon and J. J. Katz, *J. Chem. Phys.* **23**, 1277 (1955).
(34) I. Sheft and A. J. Perkins, *J. Inorg. Nucl. Chem.* **38**, 665 (1976).
(35) L. E. Alexander and I. R. Beattie, *J. Chem. Soc. A* 3091 (1971).
(36) E. C. Curtis, *Spectrochim. Acta A* **27**, 1989 (1971).
(37) H. Cohn, C. K. Ingold and H. G. Poole, *J. Chem. Soc.* 4272 (1952).
(38) G. E. McGraw, D. L. Bernitt and I. C. Hisatsune, *J. Chem. Phys.* **42**, 237 (1965).
(39) A. Palm, A. Castelli and C. Alexander, *Spectrochim. Acta A* **24**, 1658 (1968).
(40) R. J. Gillespie and E. A. Robinson, *Canad. J. Chem.* **40**, 658 (1962).
(41) D. J. Gardiner and J. J. Turner, *J. Mol. Spectrosc.* **38**, 428 (1971).
(42) I. R. Beattie and M. Webster, *J. Chem. Soc.* 38 (1963).
(43) S. T. King and R. A. Nyquist, *Spectrochim. Acta A* **26**, 1481 (1970).
(44) H. Gerding and J. W. Ypenburg, *Rec. Trav. Chim. Pays-Bas* **86**, 458 (1967); *Chem. Abs.* **67**, 16293s.
(45) H. J. Becher and K. Ballein, *Z. Phys. Chem.* **54**, 302 (1967).
(46) C. K. Ingold, D. J. Millen and H. G. Poole, *J. Chem. Soc.* 2576 (1950).
(47) S. J. Cyvin, *Acta Chem. Scand.* **24**, 1499 (1970).
(48) R. J. Gillespie and A. E. Robinson, *Canad. J. Chem.* **39**, 2171 (1961).
(49) D. A. Long and T. A. Bailey, *Trans. Faraday Soc.* **59**, 792 (1963).
(50) A. Le Narvor, E. Gentric and P. Saumagne, *Canad. J. Chem.* **49**, 1933 (1971).
(51) G. E. Walrafen, *J. Chem. Phys.* **47**, 114 (1967).
(52) J. H. Roberts, A. T. Lemley and J. J. Lagowski, *Spectrosc. Lett.* **5**, 271 (1972).
(53) A. T. Lemley, J. H. Roberts, K. R. Plowman and J. J. Lagowski, *J. Phys. Chem.* **77**, 2185 (1973).
(54) B. DeBettignies and F. Wallart, *Compt. Rend. Acad. Sci. Paris B* **271**, 640 (1970).
(55) T. Birchall and I. Drummond, *J. Chem. Soc. A* 1859 (1970).
(56) M. Schwartz and C. H. Wang, *J. Chem. Phys.* **59**, 5258 (1973).
(57) W. S. Benedict and E. K. Plyler, *Canad. J. Phys.* **35**, 1235 (1957).
(58) J. H. Roberts and J. J. Lagowski, in *Electrons in Fluids*, (J. Jortner and N. R. Kestner, eds), Springer-Verlag, Berlin, 1973.
(59) C. G. Cannon, *Spectrochim. Acta A* **10**, 425, 429 (1958).
(60) I. V. Demidenkova and L. D. Schcherba, *Izv. Akad. Nauk. S.S.S.R. (Eng. Trans.)*, **22**, 1110 (1959).
(61) J. Corset and J. Lascombe, *J. Chim. Phys.* **64**, 655 (1967).
(62) J. Corset, P. V. Huong and J. Lascombe, *Compt. Rend.* **262**, 959 (1966).
(63) J. Corset, J. Guillermet and J. Lascombe, *Bull. Soc. Chim. France* **42**, 1231 (1966).
(64) J. Corset, P. V. Huong and J. Lascombe, *J. Chim. Phys.* **64**, 1707 (1967).
(65) D. A. Copeland, N. R. Kestner and J. J. Jortner, *J. Chem. Phys.* **53**, 1189 (1970).
(66) P. F. Rusch and J. J. Lagowski, *J. Phys. Chem.* **77**, 1311 (1973).

(67) P. F. Rusch and J. J. Lagowski, in *Electrons in Fluids*, (J. Jortner and N. R. Kestner, eds), Springer-Verlag, Berlin, 1973.

(68) P. F. Rusch and J. J. Lagowski, *J. Phys. Chem.* **77**, 210 (1973).

(69) B. L. Smith and W. H. Koehler, *J. Phys. Chem.* **76**, 2481 (1972).

(70) B. L. Smith and W. H. Koehler, *J. Phys. Chem.* **77**, 1753 (1973).

(71) M. G. DeBacker, P. F. Rusch, B. DeBettignies and G. Lepoutre, in *Electrons in Fluids*, (J. Jortner and N. R. Kestner, eds), Springer-Verlag, Berlin, 1973.

(72) K. R. Plowman and J. J. Lagowski, *J. Phys. Chem.* **78**, 143 (1974).

(73) P. Gans and J. B. Gill, *J. Chem. Soc. Chem. Commun.* 914 (1973).

(74) J. Corset, P. V. Huong and J. Lascombe, *Spectrochim. Acta A* **24**, 2045 (1968).

(75) D. J. Gardiner, R. E. Hester and W. E. L. Grossman, *J. Chem. Phys.* **59**, 175 (1973).

(76) A. T. Lemley and J. J. Lagowski, *J. Phys. Chem.* **78**, 708 (1974).

(77) J. W. Lundeen and R. S. Tobias, *J. Chem. Phys.* **63**, 924 (1975).

(78) D. J. Gardiner, A. H. Haji and B. P. Straughan, *J. Chem. Soc. Faraday Trans. I.* **72**, 93 (1976).

(79) T. Birchall and I. Drummond, *J. Chem. Soc. A* 3162 (1971).

(80) M. Perrot and J. Lascombe, *J. Chim. Phys. Physicochim. Biol.* **70**, 1486 (1973).

(81) M. F. A. Dove and J. G. Hallett, *J. Chem. Soc. A* 2781 (1969).

(82) M. F. A. Dove and J. G. Hallett, *J. Chem. Soc. A* 1204 (1969).

(83) C. G. Davies, P. A. W. Dean, R. J. Gillespie and P. K. Ummat, *J. Chem. Soc. Chem. Commun.* 782 (1971).

(84) P. A. W. Dean and R. J. Gillespie, *J. Chem. Soc. Chem. Commun.* 853 (1970).

(85) Y. LeDuff and W. Holzer, *J. Chem. Phys.* **60**, 2175 (1974).

(86) N. I. Orlova and L. A. Pozdnyakova, *Opt. Spektrosk.* **35**, 1074 (1973).

(87) Y. LeDuff, *J. Chem. Phys.* **59**, 1984 (1973).

(88) Y. LeDuff and W. Holzer, *Chem. Phys. Lett.* **24**, 212 (1974).

(89) R. J. Gillespie and M. J. Morton, *J. Chem. Soc. Chem. Commun.* 1565 (1968).

(90) R. J. Gillespie and M. J. Morton, *J. Mol. Spectrosc.* **30**, 178 (1969).

(91) R. J. Gillespie and G. P. Pez, *Inorg. Chem.* **8**, 1229 (1969).

(92) B. D. Cutforth, C. G. Davies, P. A. W. Dean, R. J. Gillespie, P. R. Ireland and P. K. Ummat, *Inorg. Chem.* **12**, 1343 (1973).

(93) R. C. Paul, V. P. Kapila and K. C. Malhotra, *J. Chem. Soc. A* 2267 (1970).

(94) R. C. Paul, K. K. Paul and K. C. Malhotra, *J. Inorg. Nucl. Chem.* **34**, 2523 (1972).

(95) H. H. Hyman, T. Surles, L. A. Quarterman and A. I. Popov, *Appl. Spectrosc.* **24**, 464 (1970).

(96) D. F. Smith, *J. Chem. Phys.* **28**, 1040 (1958).

(97) R. K. Thomas, *Proc. Roy. Soc. London* **A325**, 133 (1971).

(98) T. Surles, H. H. Hyman, L. A. Quarterman and A. I. Popov, *Inorg. Chem.* **10**, 611 (1971).

(99) K. O. Christe and W. Sawodny, *Inorg. Chem.* 2879 (1973).

(100) K. O. Christe, *Inorg. Chem.* **9**, 2801 (1970).

(101) R. J. Gillespie and G. J. Schrobilgen, *Inorg. Chem.* **13**, 1230 (1974).

(102) D. D. Gibler, C. J. Adams, M. Fischer, A. Zalkin and N. Bartlett, *Inorg. Chem.* **11**, 2325 (1972).

(103) M. Bownstein and J. Shamir, *Appl. Spectrosc.* **26**, 77 (1972).

(104) K. O. Christe, E. C. Curtis and C. J. Schack, *Inorg. Chem.* **11**, 2212 (1972).

(105) R. Bougon, J. Isabey and P. Plurien, *Compt. Rend.* **273C**, 415 (1971).

(106) K. O. Christe, R. D. Wilson and E. C. Curtis, *Inorg. Chem.* **12**, 1358 (1973).

(107) K. O. Christe, C. J. Schack and R. D. Wilson, *Inorg. Chem.* **14**, 2224 (1975).

(108) E. L. Mutterties and W. D. Phillips, *J. Am. Chem. Soc.* **81**, 1084 (1959).

(109) B. Frlec and H. H. Hyman, *Inorg. Chem.* **6**, 1596 (1967).

(110) H. Selig and E. L. Gasner, *J. Inorg. Nucl. Chem.* **30**, 658 (1968).

(111) M. Brownstein and H. Selig, *Inorg. Chem.* **11**, 656 (1972).
(112) A. J. Edwards and G. R. Jones, *J. Chem. Soc.* 2511 (1968).
(113) R. T. Paine, K. L. Trevil and F. E. Strafford, *Spectrochim. Acta A* **29**, 1891 (1973).
(114) J. Shamir and H. H. Hyman, *J. Phys. Chem.* **70**, 3132 (1966).
(115) H. Selig, L. Quarterman and H. H. Hyman, *J. Inorg. Nucl. Chem.* **28**, 2063 (1966).
(116) K. I. Petrov, V. E. Plyushchev, V. V. Formichev and G. V. Zimina, *Russ. J. Inorg. Chem.* **16**, 696 (1971).
(117) J. E. D. Davies and D. A. Long, *J. Chem. Soc. A* 2166 (1968).
(118) M. Craiu and G. Gruder, *Rev. Roumaine Chim.* **13**, 1581 (1968); *Chem. Abs.* **71**, 8239w.
(119) M. E. Peach and T. C. Waddington, *J. Chem. Soc. A* 180 (1968).
(120) M. E. Peach, *Canad. J. Chem.* **47**, 1675 (1969).
(121) M. E. Peach, V. L. Tracy and T. C. Waddington, *J. Chem. Soc. A* 366 (1969).
(122) T. Surles, H. H. Hyman, L. A. Quarterman and A. I. Popov, *Inorg. Chem.* **9**, 2726 (1970).
(123) T. Surles, H. H. Hyman, L. A. Quaterman and A. I. Popov, *Inorg. Chem.* **10**, 913 (1971).
(124) R. J. Gillespie and P. Spekkens, *J. Chem. Soc. Chem. Commun.* 315 (1975).
(125) B. Frlec and J. H. Holloway, *J. Chem. Soc. Chem. Commun.* 370 (1973).
(126) V. Gutmann and E. Wychera, *Inorg. Nucl. Chem. Lett.* **2**, 257 (1966).
(127) V. Gutmann, *Coordination Chemistry in Non-Aqueous Solutions*, Springer, Vienna, 1968.
(128) A. I. Popov, *Pure Appl. Chem.* **41**, 275 (1975).
(129) E. C. Ashby, F. R. Dobbs and H. P. Hopkins, *J. Am. Chem. Soc.* **95**, 2823 (1973).
(130) J. A. Olander and M. C. Day, *J. Am. Chem. Soc.* **93**, 3584 (1971).
(131) W. F. Edgell, J. Lyford, R. Wright, W. Risen and A. Watts, *J. Am. Chem. Soc.* **92**, 2240 (1970).
(132) W. J. McKinney and A. I. Popov, *J. Phys. Chem.* **74**, 535 (1970).
(133) B. W. Maxey and A. I. Popov, *J. Inorg. Nucl. Chem.* **32**, 1029 (1970).
(134) B. W. Maxey and A. I. Popov, *J. Am. Chem. Soc.* **89**, 2230 (1967).
(135) B. W. Maxey and A. I. Popov, *J. Am. Chem. Soc.* **91**, 20 (1969).
(136) M. K. Wong, W. J. McKinney and A. I. Popov, *J. Phys. Chem.* **75**, 56 (1971).
(137) J. Borucka, J. Sadlej and Z. Kecki, *Adv. Mol. Relaxation Processes*, **5**, 253 (1973).
(138) Z. Kechi, *Adv. Mol. Relaxation Processes* **5**, 137 (1973).
(139) A. Regis and J. Corset, *J. Chim. Phys. Physiochim.* **69**, 1508 (1972).
(140) P. R. Handy and A. I. Popov, *Spectrochim. Acta A* **28**, 1545 (1972).
(141) J. L. Wuepper and A. I. Popov, *J. Amer. Chem. Soc.* **91**, 4352 (1969).
(142) M. S. Greenberg, D. M. Wied and A. I. Popov, *Spectrochim. Acta A* **29**, 1927 (1973).
(143) A. T. Tsatsas, R. W. Stearns and W. M. Risen, *J. Am. Chem. Soc.* **94**, 5247 (1972).
(144) Y. M. Cahen and A. I. Popov, *J. Solution Chem.* **4**, 599 (1975).
(145) J. M. Lehn, *Struct. Bonding (Berlin)* **16**, 1 (1973).
(146) I. S. Perelygin and M. A. Klimchuk, *Doklady Phys. Chem.* **206**, 790 (1972).
(147) A. Regis and J. Corset, *Canad. J. Chem.* **51**, 3577 (1973).
(148) M. J. French and J. L. Wood, *J. Chem. Phys.* **49**, 2358 (1968).
(149) B. S. Krumgal'z, V. M. Ryabikova, S. K. Akopyan and V. I. Borisova, *Zh. Fiz. Khim.* **48**, 2597 (1974); *Chem. Abs.* **82**, 77732r.
(150) R. E. Hester and E. Mayer, *Spectrochim. Acta A* **23**, 2218 (1967).
(151) S. G. Frankiss, F. A. Miller, H. Stammreich and T. T. Sans, *Spectrochim. Acta A* **23**, 425 (1967).

(152) D. Forster, *J. Chem. Soc. Chem. Commun.* 113 (1967).
(153) C. D. Schmulbach and I. Y. Ahmed, *J. Chem. Soc. A* 3008 (1968).
(154) T. Austad, J. Songstad and K. Åse, *Acta. Chem. Scand.* **25**, 331 (1971).
(155) J. E. D. Davies and D. A. Long, *J. Chem. Soc. A* 2054 (1968).
(156) R. W. Suter, H. C. Knachel, V. P. Petro, J. H. Howatson and S. G. Shore, *J. Amer. Chem. Soc.* **95**, 1474 (1973).
(157) P. V. Huong and B. Desbat, *Bull. Soc. Chim. France* 2631 (1972).
(158) F. P. Daly and C. W. Brown, *J. Phys. Chem.* **77**, 1859 (1973).
(159) H. J. Clase, A. M. Noble and J. M. Winfield, *Spectrochim. Acta A* **25**, 293 (1969).
(160) Y. LeDuff and R. Ouillon, *Compt. Rend.* **272B**, 757 (1971).
(161) W. Kiefer and H. J. Bernstein, *J. Raman. Spectrosc.* **1**, 417 (1973).
(162) A. J. Parker, *J. Chem. Soc.* 1328 (1961).
(163) G. Norwitz and D. E. Chasan, *J. Inorg. Nucl. Chem.* **31**, 2267 (1969).
(164) P. L. Goggin and T. G. Buick, *J. Chem. Soc. Chem. Commun.* 290 (1967).
(165) E. Kinsella, J. Chadwick and J. Coward, *J. Chem. Soc. A* 969 (1968).
(166) A. R. Davis, J. W. Macklin and R. A. Plane, *J. Chem. Phys.* **50**, 1478 (1969).
(167) T. G. Chang and D. E. Irish, *J. Solution Chem.* **3**, 161 (1974).
(168) I. S. Perelygin and M. A. Klimchuk, *Zh. Fiz. Khim.* **48**, 626 (1974); *Chem. Abs.* **81**, 7894a.
(169) E. Mayer and F. Sladky, *Inorg. Chem.* **14**, 589 (1975).
(170) C. Barker and J. Yarwood, *J. Chem. Soc. Faraday Trans. II* **71**, 1322 (1975).
(171) S. A. Al-Baldawi, M. H. Brooker, T. E. Gough and D. E. Irish, *Canad. J. Chem.* **48**, 1202 (1970).
(172) M. Chaband, C. Menard and G. Guiheneuf, *Compt. Rend.* **272C**, 253 (1971).
(173) P. G. Kirk and T. D. Smith, *J. Inorg. Nucl. Chem.* **30**, 892 (1968).
(174) G. B. Deacon, J. H. S. Green and W. Kynaston, *J. Chem. Soc. A* 158 (1967).
(175) R. A. Walton and B. J. Brisdon, *Spectrochim. Acta A* **23**, 2489 (1967).
(176) M. W. Duckworth, G. W. A. Fowles and P. T. Greene, *J. Chem. Soc. A* 1592 (1967); R. J. H. Clark and G. Natile, *Inorg. Chim. Acta* **4**, 533 (1970).
(177) C. Duboc, *Spectrochim. Acta A* **30**, 431 (1974).
(178) C. Duboc, *Spectrochim. Acta A* **30**, 441 (1974).
(179) J. L. Burmeister, R. L. Hassel and R. J. Phelan, *J. Chem. Soc. Chem. Commun.* 679 (1970).
(180) B. B. Wayland and R. F. Schraman, *Inorg. Chem.* **8**, 971 (1969).
(181) G. E. Compagnaro, I. Haque, C. E. Souter and J. L. Wood, *Spectrochim. Acta A* **30**, 517 (1974).
(182) V. P. Senthilnathan, M. Kanakavel and S. Singh, *Spectrochim. Acta A* **30**, 285 (1974).
(183) J. Yarwood, *Spectrosc. Lett.* **7**, 319 (1974).
(184) A. Szafranek, *Acta Phys. Pol. A* **46**, 621 (1974); *Chem. Abs.* **82**, 36829j.
(185) S. Badilescu, *Rev. Roum. Chim.* **19**, 1139 (1974); *Chem. Abs.* **82**, 97235j.
(186) S. Badilescu, *Rev. Roum. Chim.* **19**, 1145 (1974); *Chem. Abs.* **82**, 97236k.
(187) G. I. Baranova, P. I. Zelikman and N. G. Bakhshiev, *Opt. Spektrosk.* **36**, 73 (1974).
(188) J. Mack and C. H. Yoder, *Inorg. Chem.* **8**, 278 (1969).
(189) M. Kakimoto and T. Fujiyama, *Bull. Chem. Soc. Japan* **48**, 2258 (1975).
(190) M. P. Brown, R. W. Heseltine, P. A. Smith and P. J. Walker, *J. Chem. Soc. A* 410 (1970).
(191) K. Szczepianak and W. J. Orville-Thomas, *J. Chem. Soc. Faraday Trans. II* **70**, 1175 (1974).
(192) T. A. Weil, P. Schmidt, M. Rycheck and M. Orchin, *Inorg. Chem.* **8**, 1002 (1969).

(193) M. Aritomi, Y. Kawasaki and R. Okawara, *Inorg. Nucl. Chem. Lett.* **8**, 69 (1972).

(194) G. G. Arzoumanidis, *J. Chem. Soc. Chem. Commun.* 217 (1969).

(195) A. Kolbe and H. Pracejus, *Adv. Mol. Relaxation Processes* **5**, 65 (1973).

(196) A. P. Grinyuk, E. V. Belous and A. D. Krysenko, *Ukr. Khim. Zh.* **39**, 992 (1973); *Chem. Abs.* **80**, 8693a.

(197) R. Mierzecki, *Adv. Mol. Relaxation Processes* **5**, 129 (1973).

(198) J. LeCalvé, J. Deroualt, M. T. Forel and J. Lascombe, *Compt. Rend.* **264B**, 488 (1967).

(199) H. Wieser and P. J. Krueger, *Spectrochim. Acta A* **26**, 1349 (1970).

(200) E. Kinsella and J. Coward, *Spectrochim. Acta A* **24**, 2139 (1968).

(201) A. E. Shirk and D. F. Shriver, *J. Am. Chem. Soc.* **95**, 5904 (1973).

(202) P. N. Gates and E. F. Mooney, *J. Inorg. Nucl. Chem.* **30**, 839 (1968).

(203) J. B. Leach and J. H. Morris, *J. Chem. Soc. A* 1590 (1967).

(204) R. Mathis, M. Barthelat and F. Mathis, *Spectrochim. Acta A* **26**, 2001 (1970).

(205) T. M. Loehr and R. A. Plane, *Inorg. Chem.* **8**, 73 (1969).

(206) N. N. Greenwood, B. P. Straughan and A. E. Wilson, *J. Chem. Soc. A* 2209 (1968).

(207) N. Katsaros and J. W. George, *Inorg. Chem.* **8**, 759 (1969).

(208) J. Pola, Z. Papouskova and V. Chvalovsky, *Coll. Czech. Chem. Comm.* **38**, 1522 (1973); *Chem. Abs.* **79**, 65595y.

(209) T. Kagiya, Y. Sumida, T. Wanatabe and T. Tachi, *Bull. Chem. Soc. Japan* **44**, 923 (1971).

(210) R. A. Walton, *Inorg. Chem.* **7**, 640 (1968).

(211) J. R. Scherer, M. K. Go and S. Kint, *J. Phys. Chem.* **77**, 2108 (1973).

(212) E. Gentric, A. LeNarvor and P. Saumagne, *J. Chem. Soc. Faraday Trans. II* **70**, 1191 (1974).

(213) R. A. Bozis and B. J. McCormick, *Inorg. Chem.* **9**, 1541 (1970).

(214) R. Larsson, *Acta Chem. Scand.* **26**, 549 (1972).

(215) E. Lindner, H. Behrens and D. Uhlig, *Z. Naturforsch.* **28B**, 276 (1973).

(216) B. M. Rode, *Chem. Phys. Lett.* **32**, 38 (1975).

(217) K. C. Malhotra, O. P. Sharma and S. C. Chaudhry, *Chem. Ind.* 999 (1973).

(218) C. D. Schmulbach and R. S. Drago, *J. Amer. Chem. Soc.* **82**, 4484 (1960).

(219) G. P. Rossetti and B. P. Susz, *Helv. Chim. Acta* **47**, 289 (1964).

(220) G. P. Rossetti and B. P. Susz, *Helv. Chim. Acta* **47**, 299 (1964).

(221) D. J. Gardiner, R. B. Girling and R. E. Hester, *J. Chem. Soc. Faraday Trans. II* **71**, 709 (1975).

(222) J. Emsley, *J. Chem. Soc. A* 2702 (1971).

(223) P. Klaboe, *J. Amer. Chem. Soc.* **89**, 3667 (1967).

(224) I. Haque and J. L. Wood, *Spectrochim. Acta A* **23**, 959 (1967).

(225) I. Haque and J. L. Wood, *Spectrochim. Acta A* **23**, 2523 (1967).

(226) J. Jander, L. Bayesdorfer and K. Höhne, *Z. Anorg. Chem.* **357**, 215 (1968).

(227) H. Touhara, H. Shimoda, K. Nakinishi and N. Watanabe, *J. Phys. Chem.* **75**, 2222 (1971).

Chapter 6

RAMAN MEASUREMENTS ON FLAMES

M. Lapp and C. M. Penney

*General Electric Company, Corporate Research and Development, Schenectady,
New York 12301, U.S.A.*

1   INTRODUCTION

From the time of its discovery in 1928 until a few years ago, Raman scattering
was used primarily as a source of information about fundamental molecular
properties, and for laboratory spectroscopic analyses. However, the on-going
development of laser sources has increased the sensitivity, ease of use, and availability of instrumentation for Raman scattering; the technique is now being used
to obtain data from distant points in the presence of substantial background
luminosity.

The primary advantage of Raman scattering as a probe of combustion
systems is its provision of easily interpreted measurements of temperature and
the densities of major individual constituents with precise space and time
resolution. The overall quality of this information can be much greater than that
available from other well-established probe techniques, to the point, for example,
where the effects of turbulence in combustion can be studied in greater detail
than previously. The impact of such improved information about combustion
and fluid-mechanical properties can be profound for modern power generation
and industrial processes, most prominently today from the competing demands
of increased fuel efficiency and increasingly stringent emission controls.

Thus, the study of flames with newly-developed physical probes has received
increasing attention such as, for example, during a recent study sponsored by
the American Physical Society[1,2] on the application of physics to problems in
combustion. Raman scattering has emerged from these studies as a prime
candidate for use in advanced measurements. We present here an analysis and
evaluation of this relatively new technique, its accomplishments to date, its
capabilities and potential limitations.

2 REVIEW OF COMBUSTION-MEASUREMENT METHODS

In order to obtain some perspective concerning the relationship of Raman-scattering measurements to other methods used for studying combustion probes, we categorize them into (1) non-perturbing, (2) perturbing (non-purposeful), and (3) perturbing (purposeful).[1-3] Here, we utilize the term 'non-purposely perturbing' to imply that the system under study is altered inadvertently to a measurable degree by application of the method. Correspondingly, 'purposely perturbing' implies that a minor perturbation is produced intentionally in a system in order to obtain a response signal which can then be monitored in order to obtain a measure of desired system properties. A representative outline of combustion diagnostic methods is given in Table 1.

TABLE 1
Outline of representative combustion-measurement methods[1-3]

Perturbing		*Non-perturbing*
Non-purposeful—solid probes such as		Optical Absorption/Emission
	thermocouples and sampling	Interferometry
	techniques	Scattering—Laser Doppler
Purposeful	—optically excited	velocimetry (LDV)
	—acoustically excited	Laser Raman Scattering
	—radioactive tracers	(RS)
	—isotopic tracers	Resonance RS
	—optical emission tracers	Coherent Anti-Stokes
		RS (CARS)
		Laser Fluorescence
		Image Particle Scattering
		Forming— Optical Emission
		Holography
		Radiography
		Ramanography
		CARS

Solid probes and sampling techniques have provided a wealth of information on combustion processes, and have been well-documented in the literature. Their limitations are largely related to perturbations of the system under study, to an inability to survive under severe experimental conditions, and in some instances to difficulties in relating the measured variables to properties of interest. Their principal advantages are relative simplicity of construction and operation, coupled with a long history of use, which provides sufficient experience and faith in these measuring systems that they are widely used with confidence by a great many workers.

Purposely perturbing probes are potentially important for analysis of combustion systems, but have not yet been utilized to a substantial degree. Among the possible methods, optical excitation of a chemical species by the strong monochromatic energy of a laser beam appears to be a promising technique for use in monitoring the course of a chemical reaction, and perhaps even for use in significantly altering the course of the reaction in the combustion system. Examples of laser-induced chemical changes already exist in other areas of research, most prominently in some laser chemistry studies leading to prototype laser isotope-separation schemes.

Within the framework of non-perturbing techniques, a wide variety of methods have been explored to measure state properties of the combustion systems as well as to image the actual system itself in a detailed fashion. It is our belief that most of these techniques are, in fact, not so much competitive as complementary, and that the best-studied advanced combustion systems will be those for which a combination of these methods is utilized. Thus, for example, sensitive measurement techniques for species concentrations can be based upon optical emission and absorption. These methods are often useful for trace as well as major constituents, but with limitations in spatial resolution, in the influence of the surrounding gaseous medium, and in the frequently severe spectral inter-ferences. Fluorescence measurements can also be very sensitive, with good spatial resolution, but can suffer from the substantial influence of quenching by the surrounding gases. This problem is made all the more difficult by the fact that the exact composition of the combustion system is often not well known and that, in turn, the specific values of fluorescence-quenching cross-sections are also not well determined.

However, other concentration-measurement techniques are not sufficiently sensitive for trace-constituent measurements (with the potential exception of coherent anti-Stokes Raman scattering (CARS) and, possibly, resonance Raman scattering, which are still in developmental stages for application to flame studies). Therefore, optical absorption, emission, and fluorescence currently are methods of choice by combustion workers for minor species detection. Laser Doppler Velocimetry (LDV) is the advantageous method for gas-velocity determinations, and various image-forming techniques (including Ramanography, as named by Hartley[4]) are essential for such tasks as visualiz-ing shock-wave structures, concentration zones of particular species, droplet phenomena, etc. In this scheme of things, vibrational Raman scattering would then provide measures of temperature and of major-species concentrations. Clearly, a combination of measurement techniques is needed in order to deter-mine the large number of variables that characterize combustion systems; these are multi-component systems which are hot, chemically reacting, and usually turbulent.

We wish to emphasize here that the optical techniques which we have just mentioned are mutually compatible, in the sense that optical access to the com-bustion system can often be shared, common or compatible laser sources can be used for the 'active' laser-based probes, etc. Consider, for example, the problems requiring the measurement of state properties of gases in high-temperature combustion systems. In this case, we would choose methods from among the various possible non-perturbing, non-image-forming optical techniques, beginning with the combination of Raman scattering and LDV, in order to determine the most fundamentally needed state properties viz. temperature, major-species concentrations, and gas velocity. If we add to this measurement system the capability to determine minor- and trace-species concentrations (with, currently, tunable-i.r.-laser absorption or fluorescence and, eventually, with CARS) we would then have a relatively complete description of the system under investigation.

3 DESCRIPTIONS AND COMPARISONS OF LIGHT-SCATTERING TECHNIQUES FOR MEASUREMENTS OF TEMPERATURE AND SPECIES CONCENTRATIONS

We discuss here the basic characteristics of light scattering, how these characteristics lead to advantages for combustion probe applications, and to what extent the advantages must be qualified. This discussion is, of necessity, brief, and the reader is advised to refer to a number of recent books in the field for more detail. (See, for example, Refs 5–7.)

Molecular light scattering is generally a weak process, requiring the intense beam provided by a laser source for its implementation in diagnostic probe methods. A basic configuration for a light-scattering probe is shown in Fig. 1. An incident laser beam with diameter typically between 0.01 and 1 cm is projected through the region to be observed. Light scattered from gas molecules in a portion of this beam is collected and analyzed to obtain the desired information. The spatial resolution is defined by the diameter of the incident beam and the length of this beam that falls within the field of view of the light collection optics. Excellent spatial resolution, to measurement volumes smaller than 1 mm^3,

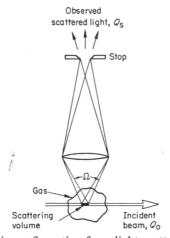

Fig. 1. Basic configuration for a light-scattering probe.

TABLE 2
Types of light scattering observed from gas systems

	SCATTERING FROM PARTICLES
Tyndall (Mie) scattering	—Unshifted spectrum can be strong, because of constructive interference of scattering from different molecules in the particle. Provides partial information about particle-number densities and size distributions.[a]
Raman scattering	—Characteristic spectral shifts, but usually too weak to be useful because of small amount of material in particle form and lack, except occasionally under resonance conditions, of augmentation by constructive interference.
Fluorescence	—Possibly characteristic spectrum. Can be strong. Should provide some useful information about particles and adsorbed gases. More easily used for obtaining qualitative rather than quantitative data for hot combustion gases.
	SCATTERING FROM MOLECULES
Rayleigh scattering	—Fairly strong. Unshifted spectrum. Very difficult to separate from Mie scattering. Can provide useful density and temperature measurements in system with roughly known constitution and no particles.
Raman scattering	—Characteristic spectral shifts. About 100 to 1000 times weaker than Rayleigh scattering, but contains extensive accessible information. Can provide temperatures and major-constituent densities in practical applications, but can be limited by lack of sufficient optical access.
Fluorescence	—Characteristic spectrum. Many orders of magnitude stronger than Rayleigh scattering, but spectrum and intensity per molecule depend on gas pressure and composition. Best for observation of minor (p.p.m.) constituents; e.g. OH, C_2, etc. Better potential for qualitative data than for quantitative data relating to hot combustion gases, but possibilities do exist for obtaining quantitative data.
Coherent anti-Stokes Raman spectroscopy	—Very strong. Essentially in-line optical process for gases. Can measure both composition and temperature. Can measure low density of pure gas, but is limited somewhat by background gas in partial density measurements. Possible limitations may exist for application to strong turbulence measurements.

[a] Although often used in a general sense, the term Mie scattering refers to a classical analysis of scattering by spherical particles.

is obtainable with this configuration. Pulsed lasers can provide time resolution to better than 1 μs in combination with this spatial resolution.

The information obtained about an observed medium in a light-scattering experiment depends upon the type of scattering that is observed. Various scattering processes which can be observed in a combustion system are listed in Table 2. The complementary character for combinations of many of the scattering measurement schemes can be seen by inspection of the table.

3.1   Raman-Scattering Characteristics

Perhaps the primary question to ask concerning the application of Raman scattering techniques to flame measurements is: Why use such a weak optical process for these measurements at all? The answer to this question lies in an appreciation of the advantages of the technique, when compared with presently-used methods, for obtaining data on samples for which other means of temperature measurement is difficult. A description of the characteristics of the technique[7,8] is repeated here in order to show clearly these advantages.

(a) *Specificity*. The spectral shift of Raman scattered light is equal to a vibrational or rotational frequency of the observed molecule (ignoring electronic effects). Since these frequencies are different for different molecules, and change with their level of molecular excitation, it is possible to identify each component of a Raman spectrum with a particular type of molecule *and* its level of excitation.

(b) *Relative lack of interference*. The vibrational Raman bands of many molecules are well separated. In some cases interferences do exist, e.g. the band of CO is obscured by that of N_2 when the former is at very low relative concentrations.

(c) *Well-determined and independent response*. The intensity of a Raman-scattered line is directly proportional to the number density of the scattering molecules and is independent of the density of other molecules. Experimental and theoretical evidence has supported these conclusions for wide ranges of gas pressure and temperature.

(d) *Three-dimensional spatial resolution*. On a laboratory scale, three-dimensional zones, with each dimension smaller than 1 mm, can be resolved. Furthermore, because Raman scattering is effectively instantaneous, the time dependence of the observed scattering can be used to provide range resolution. This so-called lidar technique, which is analogous to that employed in radar, has been especially useful on a field scale, particularly in atmospheric measurements.

(e) *Instantaneous time resolution*. In favorable cases, information can be time-resolved to the nanosecond, or even shorter, time ranges using pulsed lasers. With suitable signal analysis this information can be displayed on-line in real time.

(f) *Non-perturbing nature*. The coupling interactions between optical radiation and non-absorbing gases are extremely weak. Consequently, over a wide range of experimental conditions, the state of the observed gas is not perturbed significantly by scattering probes. Exceptions can occur when a short energetic pulse is focused tightly, producing a non-linear optical response or gas breakdown, or when the normally non-absorbing gas possesses a very weak (possibly forbidden) absorption feature which becomes of importance for extremely strong exciting pulses of the probe beam.

(g) *Remote* in-situ *capability*. In general, light-scattering measurements do not require hardware near the measurement point and can be applied to any system allowing optical access of moderate-to-good quality.

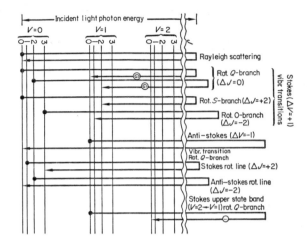

Fig. 2. Diagram illustrating some molecular transitions that contribute to Raman and Rayleigh scattering.

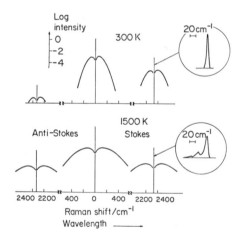

Fig. 3. Raman and Rayleigh scattering from N_2 at ambient (300 K) and elevated (1500 K) temperatures for an exciting laser line in the mid-visible region (≈ 500 nm). The unshifted lines representing the intensity of Rayleigh scattering are flanked by rotational Raman scattering represented here by wings showing the peak intensities of the rotational lines. Similar wings surround the Stokes and anti-Stokes vibrational Q-branch Raman bands, which are shown at Raman shifts of approximately 2331 cm⁻¹. (Note the large breaks in the wavenumber axis.) The various forms of scattering are shown in accurate quantitative relationships on a log scale of integrated intensity for each line or band. The spectral shapes of the vibrational bands at the two temperatures are shown in the encircled inserts on a linear scale, convoluted with a triangular monochromator spectral-slit function with 6.00 cm⁻¹ (≈ 0.18 nm) full width at half-maximum (f.w.h.m.).

(h) *Accessibility of temperature information.* For gases in thermal equilibrium, the Raman spectrum depends on both density and temperature. However, the temperature dependence is independent of density and is sufficiently strong in appropriate spectral regions to allow sensitive temperature measurements from cryogenic to combustion and gas-discharge temperatures.

(i) *Accessibility of density information.* Density information from vibrational Raman scattering is effectively independent of temperature at temperatures below that at which appreciable vibrational excitation occurs in the observed species. Even at higher temperatures, the temperature correction to an appropriate density measurement can be moderate, such that extremely accurate temperature measurements are not required for useful density information over wide ranges of experimental conditions.

(j) *Capability to probe systems not in equilibrium.* Information determining composition and levels of internal-mode excitation is readily accessible in non-equilibrium systems.

(k) *Simultaneous multiplicity of information.* Numerous different components in a gas can be observed simultaneously.

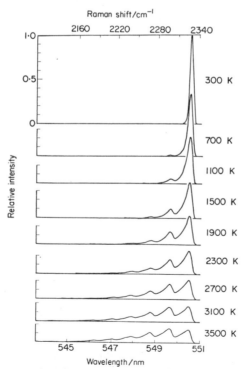

Fig. 4. Calculated Stokes vibrational Raman scattering for N_2 from 300 K to 3500 K, for a 488 nm laser source and a triangular spectral-slit function with 0.150 nm (≈ 5.0 cm^{-1}) f.w.h.m.

(l) *Wide applicability.* Each molecule has at least one allowed Raman band, whereas some molecules without a permanent dipole moment (such as N_2 and O_2) do not have an allowed infrared band.

Typical Raman (and Rayleigh) scattering processes are identified on a schematic molecular energy-level diagram in Fig. 2. For application of Raman methods to both temperature *and* density measurements, as described in subsequent sections, it is important to visualize the effect of temperature changes

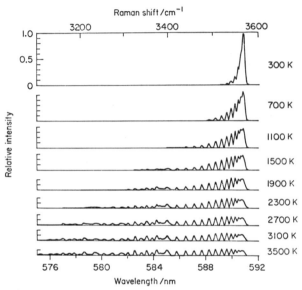

Fig. 5. Calculated Stokes vibrational Raman scattering for OH from 300 K to 3500 K, for a 488 nm laser source and a triangular spectral-slit function with 0.163 nm (≈ 4.8 cm^{-1}) f.w.h.m.

on the observed Raman contours of representative flame molecules. We first show in Fig. 3 a schematic of the vibrational Q-branch and rotational scattering for N_2 at ambient temperature and 1500 K. In Fig. 4, we show in more detail the calculated vibrational Q-branch contours for N_2 from 300 to 3500 K, while in Fig. 5, calculated contours for the radical OH are given. Presence of the hydrogen atom in this latter species causes the spectral profile to be considerably more spread-out, which is an advantage for contour analysis. However, such spread-out spectra also present greater associated difficulties in many experimental measurements because of a lower intensity per unit of spectral interval.

The intensity of each Raman line is proportional to the number density of molecules in the initial state(s) corresponding to that line. Thus, for example, the overall shape of the saw-tooth band structure exhibited by many vibrational Q-branches of diatomic molecules will be significantly influenced by the vibrational energy-level spacings as the temperature is changed. In Fig. 6, we see

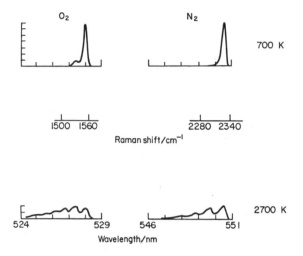

Fig. 6. Calculated Stokes vibrational Raman bands of O_2 and N_2 at low (700 K) and high (2700 K) temperatures for an exciting line at 488 nm and a triangular spectral-slit function with 6.00 cm^{-1} (≈ 0.17 nm for O_2 and 0.18 nm for N_2) f.w.h.m.

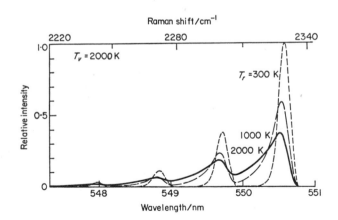

Fig. 7. Calculated Stokes vibrational Raman scattering for N_2 with vibrational temperature T_v (associated with a vibrational internal mode) fixed at 2000 K and rotational temperature T_r (associated with a rotational internal mode) at 2000 K, 1000 K, and 300 K. The relative intensities of the three curves are in correct proportion to each other. The profiles correspond to an exciting line at 488 nm and a triangular spectral-slit function with 0.150 nm (≈ 5.0 cm^{-1}) f.w.h.m.

such profiles for O_2 and N_2 compared at low and high temperatures. Note that the smaller vibrational energy-level spacings for O_2, coupled with the fact that upper state or hot-band Raman intensities increase in magnitude according to the factor $(1+v)$, where v is the lower level vibrational quantum number, cause the overall O_2 contour to peak in intensity for a hot band, while that for N_2 at the same temperature still peaks for the ground state band ($v = 0$).

In thermal equilibrium the ratio of densities in different states is determined by the temperature. Therefore, not only density, but also temperature can be determined from measurements of Raman scattering. It is important to note that an assumption of thermal equilibrium is not required to analyze Raman data. Thus, non-equilibrium systems can also be probed quantitatively. This fact is illustrated in Fig. 7, which shows the variation in N_2 vibrational Q-branch contour for 'frozen' vibrational conditions (corresponding to a 'vibrational' temperature T_v of 2000 K, defined by the ratio of adjacent vibrational energy-level populations) and for variable rotational conditions.

3.2   Temperature Measurements from Rotational Raman Scattering

Both rotational- and vibrational-Raman scattering can be useful in gas measurements. We first consider rotational Raman scattering (rotational RS), for which, as illustrated in Fig. 3, the envelope of rotational RS line intensities has a distinct and fairly sensitive temperature dependence. Temperature measurements can be obtained by measuring the intensity ratio of two lines or two groups of lines within the band, by fitting the overall band-contour envelope, by measuring the spectral interval between the peaks of the two branches of the band (for a simple molecule), and by an interferometric technique to be discussed shortly which relies upon the regularity of rotational line spacing.

The spectral extent and overall temperature dependence of rotational RS is different for different molecules. In principle, rotational lines from a single gas can be separated spectrally. However, the rotational lines are numerous and closely spaced, so that such spectral separation is often not practicable in a mixture. Consequently, it is difficult to use rotational RS for density or temperature measurements in a multi-component gas system unless the relative densities are known. In that case, the theoretical profile for the mixture can be calculated and it is not necessary to resolve separate lines.

Rotational Raman scattering is most useful for temperature measurements in the low to moderate range (say, 20–500 K). At higher temperatures the rotational line envelope becomes very wide. As a result, the intensity in convenient bands falls off relative to background noise and the temperature sensitivity decreases. For this reason, as well as the problems already mentioned concerning overlapping spectral features for hot multi-component gases, rotational RS line-ratio techniques do not appear promising for high-temperature combustion measurements. They may, however, be of some use for measurements on cooler portions of the flow field. An interferometric technique developed by Barratt et al.,[9,10] to be described in the next section on density, may have greater potential for rotational RS temperature diagnostics on flames, although practical implementation has not yet been accomplished.

The potential accuracy of rotational RS temperature measurements using line or band ratio techniques for low to moderate temperature applications has been analyzed by Lapp et al.[11] Experimental data for atmospheric pressure flows of N_2 have been obtained by Hickman and Liang,[12] with encouraging results. Salzmann et al.,[13-15] and Cooney et al.[16,17] have presented analyses of atmospheric-temperature measurements using this process along with results of extensive laboratory and field-test data. Accuracies of $\pm(2-5)\%$ can be expected for ranges of up to several kilometers. Even better accuracies should be obtainable at close range in pure gases or mixtures with known concentrations.

3.3 Density Measurements from Rotational Raman Scattering

Density information is mixed with temperature information in rotational Raman scattering; that is, in general, it is necessary to know the temperature before one can calculate the density. However, it is possible to pick bands whose temperature sensitivity is very weak over a substantial temperature range; furthermore, a simultaneous temperature measurement is available from rotational RS data. Therefore, temperature sensitivity is not a serious handicap for implementation of rotational RS density measurements.

Besides monitoring gas density by use of a monochromator or interference filters to discriminate between rotational RS signals, another technique is possible based upon use of an interferometer. Barratt et al.[9,10] have developed this latter mode of spectral analysis for rotational RS, which shows promise of being far more efficient in many cases, permitting measurements to greater accuracy and/or at lower density. It may even be possible to apply it to measurements in gas mixtures with unknown concentrations. In this method, the comb-like passband of a Fabry-Perot interferometer is matched to the rotational RS spectra by setting the interferometer free-spectral-range equal to the (nearly constant) rotational line spacing. As a result, a large number of rotational RS lines can be viewed simultaneously. Furthermore, a Fabry-Perot interferometer is very efficient in light collection. Consequently, a gain in sensitivity approaching a factor of 10–100 over that obtainable with a spectrometer can be obtained. In effect, this technique combines the comb-like rotational RS spectrum of each gas into a single line, which is seen when the plate spacing of the interferometer is at just the right value to produce a free spectral range matching the rotational line spacing for that gas.

The principal problem with this technique is that it requires an extremely stable interferometer, whose plates can be held to a demanding alignment requirement as their separation is swept over a substantial range. Barratt has solved this problem, but his super-stable interferometer probably would have difficulty outside a carefully controlled laboratory environment. However, research aimed at replacing the interferometer with a more rugged instrument appears very promising. For example, the spectral image from a small, fast spectrometer could be digitized by recording the image with a sensitive TV camera tube, and the spatial frequencies analyzed using a computer. This refinement provides a double multiplex advantage: that of viewing many rotational lines and multiple species simultaneously. It also enables single-pulse time-response ($\leqslant 1 \mu s$) which the previously described approach to the basic interferometer cannot provide. However, it probably shares the general limitation of rotational RS measurements to low and moderate temperatures (less than, say, 800 K). Furthermore, because they depend on the resolution of single lines, interferometric and other techniques based upon ideal spectral line-separations may not work well for complex and/or heavy molecules, because their rotational lines are very closely spaced.

3.4 Temperature Measurements from Vibrational Raman Scattering

The basic vibrational Raman scattering (VRS) spectrum for a diatomic molecule is composed of a strong narrow band, the Q-branch, with weak rotational wings. For polyatomic molecules, several VRS bands usually exist, corresponding to the number of Raman-active normal modes of vibration. However, those bands which correspond to the totally symmetric modes are usually strong and also distinctly polarized. For complex molecules (e.g. higher hydrocarbons) individual bands can often be associated with characteristic parts of a molecule, such as a CH bond, an OH group or a benzene ring.

Temperature measurements are best obtained on simple molecules present at high concentrations in the gas, because for these molecules the theory is adequately developed to allow accurate calculation of temperature from the observed spectral contours, and the contours themselves can be determined with sufficient experimental accuracy to provide meaningful results. Excellent candidate molecules are N_2, O_2, H_2, CO, CO_2, and H_2O.

Three approaches to VRS temperature measurements have received the most substantial study: determination of the Stokes/anti-Stokes band intensity-ratio (SAS approach); fitting the Stokes (or anti-Stokes) band series contour to a theoretical prediction; and determining the ratio of scattered intensity from a hot band to that from the ground-state band (termed the band area method, BAM). Additional possible methods for measuring temperature based upon VRS include measuring the shift of the Q-branch ($\Delta J = 0$) band peak, the, spectral spacing between the vibrational–rotational wings (O- and S-branches, corresponding to $\Delta J = -2$ and $+2$), and the width of specific Q-branch bands such as the ground-state band.

Stokes and anti-Stokes bands are spaced equidistantly on either side of the incident wavelength, as illustrated in Fig. 3. The SAS approach is based on the fact that the ratio R_{SAS} of the intensity of the anti-Stokes band to that of the

Stokes band is proportional to $\exp[-\theta_v/T]$, where $\theta_v = (hc/k)G_0(1)$ is termed the characteristic temperature of the vibrational band. Here h is Planck's constant, c is the speed of light, k is Boltzmann's constant, and $G_0(1)$ is the vibrational energy-level term-value of the first excited level. To give some examples, θ_v is 3354 K for N_2, while it is 2239 K for O_2 and, as an extreme value, 5986 K for H_2. The ratio R_{SAS} varies sensitively with temperature for temperatures $\leqslant \theta_v$; its value is sufficiently large for measurement purposes at temperatures greater than roughly $\theta_v/4$. This range of usefulness is appropriate for flame studies.

As with the SAS method, BAM measurements for the Stokes Q-branch are based on the fact that the ratio of the intensity of the first upper-state band to that of the ground-state band is also proportional to the factor $\exp[-\theta_v/T]$. Clearly, the BAM approach to temperature measurements can be implemented with either the Stokes or anti-Stokes band.

A possible problem with the SAS approach is that the Stokes and anti-Stokes bands are separated by a large wavenumber interval (*ca.* 4660 cm^{-1}) for N_2. Accurate corrections for differences in absorption, sensitivity, and background over this interval can be difficult, especially under changing gas conditions. This problem is greatly reduced in BAM measurements because the wavenumber intervals between the ground-state and hot bands of VRS are much smaller.

Both the SAS and BAM approaches have been used for temperature measurements. Detailed calculations have shown that the attainable accuracies are roughly equal for these schemes. Our experience has been with the latter approach,[18] which we find preferable to SAS because of the very much smaller wavelength span in BAM, as well as the fact that the BAM measurements can be made entirely on the anti-Stokes side in cases where fluorescence would mask the Raman signal on the Stokes side. Our experimental work has involved average temperature measurements in a 5 mm × 0.1 mm diameter resolution zone in hydrogen/air flames, using monochromator data for Q-branch profile fits as well as for ratios of the peak intensity of the hot band to that of the ground-state band.[18,19] Comparison of the Raman spectral and thermocouple measurements, as well as intercomparison of the two types of Raman measurement, indicate agreement to within several per cent in these 'proof of principle' experiments. Ultimate capabilities appear to be substantially better, based on reasonable extensions of these results that we describe subsequently. For example, it should be possible to obtain temperature measurements from N_2 in a fuel/air flame with time resolution of one microsecond to within several per cent accuracy. The spatial resolution for such a measurement should be better than 1 mm^3 for a clean flame (e.g. hydrogen/air to propane/air) to 1 cm^3 for a rich flame fueled by heavy hydrocarbons.

3.5 Density Measurements from Vibrational Raman Scattering

The intensity of VRS in any particular band is directly proportional to the density of the molecules responsible for that band. Thus, density measurements can be obtained by comparison of a band intensity to a standard intensity measured, for example, in room air. At temperatures such that only a small fraction of the molecules are vibrationally excited, density and temperature information from VRS are independent. At higher temperatures, a weak-to-moderate temperature correction to the density measurement may be required.

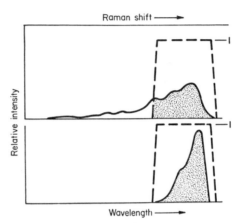

Fig. 8. Schematic representation of a vibrational Raman spectrum for a gas at high temperature (top) and at low temperature (bottom). The dashed trapezoids represent a wide monochromator spectral-slit function, with the exit slit broader than the entrance slit, or, alternatively, an idealized interference-filter band-pass.

This correction arises because the VRS from molecules in the vibrational state v (i.e. hot bands) is stronger by a factor of $(1 + v)$ than that from molecules in the vibrational ground state. The correction is easily applied for molecules of simple symmetry,† but is more difficult for more complicated molecules, such as asymmetric tops, because their energy-level structure is more complex. Therefore, their spectra are more difficult to calculate as a function of temperature.

In order to illustrate the effect of temperature on vibrational Raman density measurements, we show in Fig. 8 an idealized schematic of a band contour at low and high temperatures, together with an assumed trapezoidal monochromator band-pass.[20] If the band-pass encompasses the contour at the lowest temperature, as is assumed here, then increasing amounts of the contour fall outside this band-pass as the temperature is raised, requiring either experimental or theoretical knowledge of the *spectral* cross-section variation with temperature

† The sum of the vibrational Raman intensity terms over all v is equal to the vibrational partition function in the harmonic oscillator and rigid-rotator approximation. This is an excellent approximation for simple diatomic molecules such as N_2 at low to moderate temperatures, and still a reasonably good approximation at the highest temperatures encountered in flames.[18]

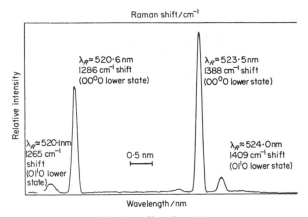

Fig. 9. Experimentally observed Stokes vibrational Raman spectrum of CO_2 at 795 K and 725 Torr, obtained through use of a 1.2 W 488 nm argon ion laser and a triangular spectral-slit function with 0.163 nm (≈ 6.0 cm^{-1}) f.w.h.m. The CO_2 was contained in a glass test cell. Here the wavelength λ_R corresponds to the spectral position within each vibrational band for $J = 0$, where J is the rotational quantum number.

in order to utilize such data quantitatively for density measurements. On the other hand, if the monochromator band-pass is made sufficiently broad to encompass the entire signature at the highest temperature encountered (thus simplifying the density measurements), the band-pass is likely to be so broad that undue sensitivity to background would occur at the lowest temperatures, resulting in density data possessing an inferior signal-to-noise ratio than otherwise.

To give examples of some of these spectra, we show in Fig. 9 the vibrational contour of CO_2 at ambient conditions,[18] while in Fig. 10 this same spectrum

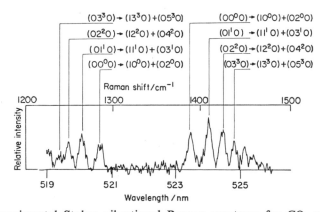

Fig. 10. Experimental Stokes vibrational Raman spectrum for CO_2 seeded into a stoichiometric H_2/air flame at about 1565 K, and at a partial pressure of about 1/3 atm. The data were obtained through use of a 1.1 W 488 nm argon ion laser and a triangular spectral-slit function with 0.163 nm (≈ 6.0 cm^{-1}) f.w.h.m.

is repeated under flame conditions at about 1565 K. The spectrum expands substantially due to increased population of the vibrational 'ladder', as can be seen from the energy level diagram[21] shown in Fig. 11. However, the molecular structure is sufficiently simple that reasonable analytical calculations of contour are possible for diagnostic purposes.

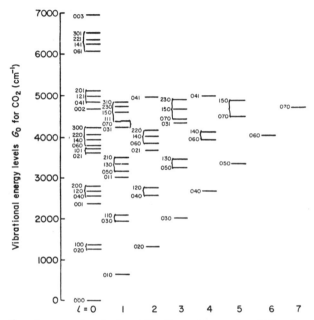

Fig. 11. Vibrational energy levels for CO_2, from the work of Tourin and Henry.[21] Here, G_0 represents the vibrational energy-level term-values relative to the lowest vibrational level for each set of vibrational quantum numbers, $v_1 v_2 v_3$ (shown next to each level, and corresponding to the normal modes of CO_2) and each value of the angular momentum quantum number l about the symmetry axis of the v_2 bending mode. (Levels perturbed by Fermi resonance are grouped together by brackets.)

As another example, the temperature dependence of the water-vapor vibrational Raman band-contour has recently been reported by Bribes et al.[22] (see Fig. 12) with sufficient accuracy to suggest the possibility of successful calculations at elevated temperatures. In Fig. 13 we show a composite of the theoretically-predicted low-temperature contours, in order to indicate that a spectral regime exists for this contour (centered about an 11.5 cm^{-1} displacement) for which the intensity remains relatively constant with temperature. Locating such spectral regimes can be of importance for temperature-independent measurements of density for molecules with spectral profiles inconveniently broad for accurate integrated intensity measurements. (See also Leonard.[23])

In Fig. 14 we show a portion of the high temperature (≈ 1500 K) water vapor spectrum found in flame experiments,[20] in order to indicate the substantial

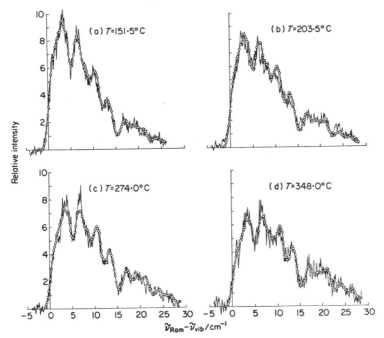

Fig. 12. Vibrational Raman-scattering ν_1 band contour for water vapor at four temperatures, for triangular spectral-slit function with 1.6 cm⁻¹ f.w.h.m. (a) 151.5°C; (b) 203.5°C; (c) 274.0°C; (d) 348.0°C. Here, $\tilde{\nu}_{Ram} - \tilde{\nu}_{vib}$ is the wavenumber displacement (in cm⁻¹) referred to the band origin. (Note that this spectrum and that in Fig. 13 are plotted in the opposite sense to all other spectra presented here.) The solid jagged curves are experimental data, obtained for spectral intervals of approximately 10^{-3} nm, and subjected to computer signal-processing. The smoother and heavier solid curves containing circular data points correspond to the theoretical calculations, with the points indicating theoretical spectral intensities contained within successive 0.2 cm⁻¹ intervals. The relative intensity scales for each temperature have been normalized to make the curves shown in parts (a)–(d) comparable on a 'per molecule' basis.

expansion of this relatively complicated profile at elevated temperatures. It is likely, for example, that the tail of this contour (not shown in Fig. 14) falls in the same region as the OH vibrational profile, so that careful analysis of the H_2O contour is necessary before definitive OH spectra from flames can be established.

Because VRS cross-sections are very small, a practical lower limit exists to the observable molecule densities for VRS techniques. The fundamental datum in a density measurement is the number of photons detected during the measurement. This number is given by:

$$N = \frac{Q\rho\sigma L\Omega\varepsilon\eta}{E_\lambda} \qquad (1)$$

where Q = Energy produced in the incident light beam during a measurement;

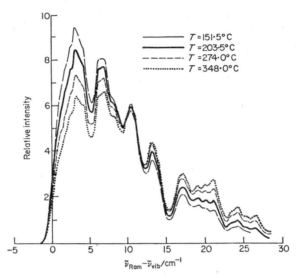

Fig. 13. Theoretical calculations of the vibrational Raman scattering ν_1 band contour for water vapor at four temperatures, for a triangular spectral slit function with 1.6 cm^{-1} f.w.h.m. Here, $\tilde{v}_{\text{Ram}} - \tilde{v}_{\text{vib}}$ is the wavenumber displacement (in cm^{-1}) referred to the band origin. (Note that this spectrum and that in Fig. 12 are plotted in the opposite sense to all other spectra presented here.)

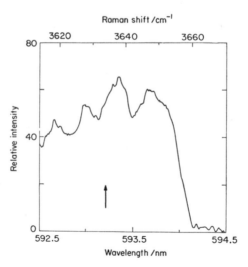

Fig. 14. Experimentally observed Stokes vibrational Raman spectrum of water vapor (ν_1-band contour) from a hydrogen/oxygen flame at roughly 1500 K, for a 488 nm laser source and a triangular spectral-slit function with 0.162 nm (≈ 4.6 cm^{-1}) f.w.h.m. The vertical arrow in the figure corresponds to the spectral vicinity in which the first upper-state vibrational band is expected.

ρ = Number density of the observed molecules; σ = Differential cross-section per steradian per molecule for the observed scattering; L = Length of the observed segment of the incident beam; Ω = Solid angle over which scattered light is collected; ε = Transmission of the receiving optics; η = Quantum efficiency of the detector; E_λ = Energy of a scattered light photon, equal to hc/λ, where h is Planck's constant, c is the speed of light, and λ is the wavelength of the scattered light.

To make a density measurement, we determine that part of eqn. (1) which remains constant (i.e. cross-section, geometry, detection-electronics characteristics, etc.) by an auxiliary measurement of a known density; e.g. nitrogen in laboratory air. This step yields a value of K in the equation [equivalent to eqn. (1)]:

$$N = KQ\rho. \tag{2}$$

Thus, the number density ρ is obtained from a measurement of the number N of detected photons corresponding to a particular value of the incident laser energy. It is on this basis that most Raman scattering density-measurements have been obtained in practice.

3.6 Error Analysis for Vibrational Raman Scattering

The fundamental limit on measurement accuracy arises because the scattering and detection of photons are statistical processes. Thus, if the average number of photons that would be detected in a series of identical measurements is $\overline{N}$, the minimum standard deviation of these measurements resulting from the statistical fluctuations of light scattering and detection, is:

$$\Delta N = \sqrt{\overline{N}}.$$

The resulting relative standard deviation (r.s.d.) of a density measurement is:

$$\frac{\Delta\rho}{\rho} = (\overline{N})^{-1/2}. \tag{3}$$

The r.s.d. has the following meaning: if the only significant source of error is photon statistics, then 67% of the individual measurements will be within $\pm\Delta\rho$ about the true value, and 95% within $\pm 2\Delta\rho$. The r.s.d. expresses this error characterization in terms of a fraction of the true value. Thus, 100 photons must be detected for an r.s.d. of 10%, and 1000 for 3%. In practice other sources of error (e.g. amplification noise) can be significant; however, with care, the performance predicted by eqn. (3) can be approached closely.

In order to illustrate the practical implications of this result, we introduce a 'standard example' with optical parameters corresponding to a measurement of a major flame species in the mid-visible region (at a scattering wavelength of, say, 500 nm), with good spatial resolution in hot combustion gases: $Q = 3J$; $\rho = 3 \times 10^{18}$ molecule cm^{-3}; $\sigma = 8 \times 10^{-31}$ cm^2 sr^{-1}; $L = 0.1$ cm; $\Omega = 0.1$ sr; $\varepsilon = 0.2$; $\eta - 0.2$; $E_\lambda = 4 \times 10^{-19}$ J. Then from eqn. (1), $N = 7 \times 10^3$ detected photons, and from eqn. (3), the measurement error is characterized by an r.s.d. of 1.2%.

If we define the minimum measurable density ρ_{min} to be that density measurable to 10% accuracy (i.e. $N = 100$), then for the laser pulse and optical parameters quoted in this example

$$\rho_{min} = 4 \times 10^{16} \text{ molecule cm}^{-3},$$

or about two parts-per-thousand at s.t.p. Before we draw any conclusions from this result, it should be noted that:

(i) The minimum measurable density can be decreased by increasing L, i.e. by decreasing spatial resolution. However, practical limits exist for the product $L\Omega$, of the order of 0.1–1 cm sr, imposed by optical access considerations and criteria for matching to a spectrometer for the desired spectral resolution.

(ii) Multiple reflection techniques can increase the effective energy of the incident light pulse and the collection angle.

(iii) Cross-sections for polyatomic molecules are larger than the assumed value. In fact, these cross-sections increase roughly as the square of the number of atoms. But measurement difficulties also increase for polyatomic molecules, because the Raman spectra become more complicated and VRS bandwidths increase. These changes make discrimination against other species and background more difficult, roughly compensating for the increase in cross-section.

(iv) The number of detected photons per joule of excitation energy usually increases substantially as the exciting wavelength is shortened, since $\sigma_\lambda / E_\lambda$ is proportional to λ^{-3}, and the detector quantum efficiency η_λ also typically increases to the blue. This effect is, however, somewhat lessened, since available laser energy decreases to the blue, and fluorescence background increases.

(v) Measurement of the very low scattering intensities produced by minor constituents, with densities in the p.p.m. range, can be masked by background interference from gas fluorescence or emission, particle scattering luminescence or fluorescence, and scattering by optical components; additionally, weak Raman scattering (e.g. rotational and rotational-vibrational wings) occurs from major constituents.

These factors, which are discussed in more detail in the subsequent text, lead to the conclusion that VRS is convenient for measurements with good spatial resolution (*ca.* 0.1 cm) of constituents with densities down to several parts-per-thousand in combustion gases. Consequently, we expect useful measurements of species such as N_2, O_2, CO, CO_2, H_2O, and unburned fuel fragments in combustion products. On the other hand, minor species in the p.p.m. range have been and probably will continue to be quite difficult to measure by VRS.

3.7 Measurements from Rayleigh Scattering

Rayleigh scattering, which is essentially elastic, can provide excellent measurements of gas density when the relative abundance of strong scatterers is known.[24] Since the Rayleigh scattering from each type of molecule falls in the same spectral region, unshifted from the incident beam, and since the Rayleigh scattering cross-sections of different molecules can vary considerably, it cannot in general be used to determine the relative abundance of different molecules in a mixture of gases. However, total gas density can be measured if the composition is already roughly known, or the cross-sections for the particular species present are close in magnitude. (For large air dilution, the latter assumption may be adequate for probing systems containing molecules similar to N_2.)

Temperature information has been obtained from Rayleigh scattering,[24] although this type of line-width measurement requires high spectral resolution with concomitant expense and delicacy. However, since Rayleigh scattering is a stronger process than Raman scattering, it is possible that it can be applied to situations for which Raman scattering produces too weak a signal.

Particle (often termed, Mie) scattering arises from the coherent addition of light scattered elastically from the separate molecules in a particle. Therefore, Mie scattering also falls in the same spectral region as Rayleigh scattering. For very small particles (much smaller than the light wavelength), the intensity of scattered light is proportional to the square of the number of molecules in the particle. Thus the intensity of Mie scattering can be very strong relative to Rayleigh scattering, even when only a small fraction of the total system mass is in particle form. For use of Rayleigh scattering in realistic combustion environments, care must be taken either to avoid the presence of particle scattering, or to correct for strong potential distortions of the data.

Rayleigh and Mie scattering can, in principle, be separated from each other spectrally since the Mie signal is essentially a very sharp spike at the center of the Rayleigh profile. This type of separation requires the same difficult high spectral resolution as a temperature measurement, and thus is not practicable for many applications. In some cases, these two types of scattering can be separated by analyzing the time dependence and/or the polarization of scattering. Individual pulses of fairly large particles (>1 μm) at low density, occurring as they pass through a tightly focused beam, can be separated, as can the highly depolarized scattering from anisotropic particles.

3.8 Stronger Processes: Fluorescence, Resonance Raman Scattering, and Coherent Anti-Stokes Raman Spectroscopy

We have considered to this point ordinary Raman and Rayleigh scattering measurement-techniques for density and temperature. Because of its particular attributes, vibrational Raman scattering has shown the greatest promise for combustion measurements, despite its weak intensity. However, circumstances exist where this weakness prohibits VRS from providing useful data, as, for example, in the measurement of low density species, or for general measurement applications with very poor optical access. For this reason, we wish to explore other stronger diagnostic schemes which (hopefully) avoid some of the pitfalls of rotational Raman scattering and Rayleigh scattering without (also, hopefully) introducing other serious experimental or interpretative problems. To this end, we discuss briefly in this section (1) fluorescence, (2) resonance Raman scattering, and (3) coherent anti-Stokes Raman spectroscopy (CARS).

The strongest of the processes we now consider is *fluorescence*, which can be up to roughly 10^{14} times more intense for an atomic species such as Na than typical molecular VRS. However, unlike VRS, fluorescence intensities per molecule have a dependence on gas pressure, composition, and temperature because of collisional quenching phenomena. Therefore, fluorescence data can be substantially more difficult to interpret for density (or temperature) information. Furthermore, the strongest types of fluorescence result from excitation into individual lines, such as those of Na (Jyumonji et al.[25]) or OH (Wang et al.[26-28]); this requires precise control of wavelength if a laser source is used. Other molecular species providing data of interest to combustion studies include, e.g. NO_2 (Birnbaum et al.[29]), SO_2 (Penney et al.[30]), or the radicals C_2 (Vear et al.[31] and Hendra et al.[32]), and CH (Barnes et al.[33]). Yet even at s.t.p. fluorescence can be 10^3–10^4 times stronger than ordinary VRS, allowing measurements down to the parts-per-million range. These measurements can be quantitatively accurate if the effects of the primary quenchers can be calculated or measured with good accuracy. Thus, atmospheric SO_2 can be measured to 100 p.p.b. if the quenching effects of N_2, O_2 and perhaps CO_2 and H_2O are determined.

There are several scattering-like processes that lie between ordinary Raman scattering and fluorescence in intensity, and possess desirable scattering-like insensitivity to quenching. (See, for example, Fouche and Chang,[34] St. Peters et al.,[35] and Holzer et al.[36]) The most important of these appears to be the type of *resonance Raman scattering* that results from excitation into a dissociation continuum. This process has been observed from I_2 and other halogen vapors,[36] and from O_3,[30] leading to cross-sections several hundred times larger than that for N_2 VRS. However, the number of molecules for which this process can be observed practically, within the limits of reasonable laser technology, is quite limited. Furthermore, the enhancement in sensitivity is quite modest, considering the difficulties of implementation.

Coherent anti-Stokes Raman scattering (CARS) is a non-linear optics process (sometimes called three- or four-wave mixing) that was first investigated over ten years ago.[37] However, its use as a gas probe has developed only recently, pioneered by Taran and co-workers[38-42] at ONERA (Chatillon, France). This group demonstrated that CARS provides scattered light signals that are stronger than ordinary Raman scattering by many orders of magnitude (5–10) for gas densities near s.t.p. Furthermore, this strong scattered light is collimated into a narrow beam. These characteristics are very favorable for light detection and discrimination against background, including fluorescence. Consequently, several groups are now investigating the application of CARS to combustion diagnostics. Among these groups (in addition to ONERA) are the Naval Research Laboratory, Stanford University, Allied Chemical Corp., AVCO Everett Research Laboratory, Air Force Aero Propulsion Laboratory, Instituto de Fisica Gleb Wataghin (Campinas, Brazil), etc. Representative indications of the work from some of these locations are given by Begley et al.,[43,44] Harvey et al.,[45] Barrett and Begley,[46] Itzkan and Leonard,[47] Moore and Fraas,[48] and Roh et al.[94]

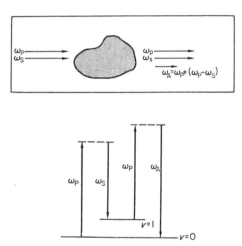

Fig. 15. Schematic representation of the physical configuration and energy-level diagram characteristic of coherent anti-Stokes Raman scattering (CARS). The dashed lines in the energy-level diagram indicate virtual levels involved in the CARS process.

The CARS process can be visualized with the help of Fig. 15 (although a literal interpretation of a step-wise procedure from this energy-level schematic is *not* implied). This process requires two incident light sources, called the pump (ω_P) and Stokes (ω_S) beams, focused colinearly (or nearly so) within the measurement volume. When one of these beams is tuned spectrally such that the frequency difference between the beams is equal to a Raman shift ($v = 0 \rightarrow v = 1$) for a gas in the measurement volume, a third beam, the coherent anti-Stokes Raman scattering (ω_A), is produced along a line nearly parallel to the incident beams. Since this beam is shifted to the blue from the pump beam by the Raman frequency, and to the blue from the Stokes beam by twice the Raman frequency, it can be separated from the incident beams by filtering.

Both incident beams can be of fixed frequency (with the Stokes beam generated by stimulated Raman scattering from an appropriate gas through which the pump beam passes). A more flexible arrangement utilizes a tunable dye laser for the Stokes beam, or two tunable lasers. The incident beams must be of high power, as well as spectrally narrow. Moya et al.,[42] for example, have used a 1–5 MW ruby laser of 10^{-2} cm^{-1} line width in combination with a dye laser pumped with 50% of the ruby laser power that is split off and doubled, giving a diffraction-limited beam of 50–100 kW with a line width of 1–0.2 cm^{-1}.

The intensity of a CARS signal is proportional to:

(observed molecular number density)^2,
(ordinary VRS cross-section)^2/(Raman line width)^2, and
(pump laser power)^2 × (Stokes laser power),

where we have assumed that the line widths of the pump and stimulating beams are narrow in comparison to the Raman line width and are precisely tuned to the center Raman shift.

Spatial resolution is obtained in CARS by focusing, which limits the effective response to a small region because of the strong non-linear intensity dependence. However, the intensity of the CARS signal is independent of the focusing geometry and of the focal length of the lens used, at least for diffraction-limited beams.[42] The CARS process leads to diagnostic data which provide excellent discrimination against background fluorescence because of the strength and collimation of the anti-Stokes signal.

However, as a counterbalance to the many strong advantages of CARS, certain important disadvantages must also be understood and overcome. Among these are:

(i) The demanding line-width and stability requirements for the pump and Stokes beams, along with the overall experimental delicacy required. An important step toward reduction of this difficulty has been described recently by Roh et al.,[94] who used a broad-band Stokes beam to observe the full contour of the hydrogen Q-branch at high pressure and ambient temperature with one laser pulse. If such a broad-band Stokes beam can be used successfully in typical combustion environments, the experimental delicacy required for such measurements will be greatly relaxed.

(ii) Possible effects of turbulence on the CARS signal intensity, caused by combination of the non-linear intensity dependence and laser beam defocusing and wandering.

(iii) Strong dependence on line width, which depends upon gas composition, density and temperature.

(iv) Although relatively low pure-gas densities can be probed with CARS, the measurement of that same small concentration of a given species in a large concentration of another species may not be successful because of the background signal provided by the electronic susceptibility of the major species.

4   POTENTIAL EXPERIMENTAL LIMITATIONS

For the application of Raman scattering measurement-techniques to flames, several important experimental difficulties must be anticipated and resolved—particularly when optimized diagnostics are sought for complex and/or highly luminous combustion systems. Those difficulties of primary concern involve background interference (caused by the incident laser beam and also independent of the incident beam), and the factors related to spatial resolution, and low-concentration measurements.

4.1   Background

All light other than Raman scattering seen by the detector is considered here to be background. When it is significant in comparison to the scattering, background unavoidably increases measurement errors, even if the background rate is known precisely, because of the statistical fluctuations inherent in any small light signal. For example, suppose that a total signal (photon count) corresponding to the average of a series of identical experiments is $\bar{T}$, made up of $\bar{N}$ Raman counts and $\bar{B}$ background counts, and that $\bar{B}$ has been determined precisely from auxiliary measurements. Then the Raman count N in any particular measurement is calculated from the total count for that measurement T according to:

$$N = T - \bar{B}.$$

But the statistical error is now:

$$\frac{\Delta N}{N} = \frac{\sqrt{T}}{T - \bar{B}} = \frac{\sqrt{(N + \bar{B})}}{N}.$$

Thus, if the background count equals the Raman count, the statistical error will be larger by a factor $\sqrt{2}$ than it would be in the absence of background.

Background sources can be divided into those that are caused by the incident beam, such as fluorescence, and those that are independent of this beam, such as ambient light. The division is significant, because use of high-power pulsed lasers can reduce interference from the latter significantly.

4.2   Background Caused by the Incident Beam

Incoherent light emitted by the laser can provide significant background, even though it is much weaker than the primary beam, when there is strong scattering from particles or cell walls. This background is particularly likely to cause measurement errors when it contains line structures such as that from an argon laser. For example, in Fig. 2 of the work of Aeschliman and Setchell,[49] data are shown concerning fluorescence limitations to RS spectra of CO_2 and O_2 in the exhaust of a gasoline engine. Along with direct fluorescence from hydrocarbon aerosols and Mie-scattering-induced fluorescence of optical components, an argon plasma line is seen to be in near-coincidence with the O_2 vibrational Raman band. Thus, in the presence of aerosols or particles, an elastically-scattered signal can be obtained from this plasma line which could mask a desired Raman signal. These spurious signals can be greatly reduced,

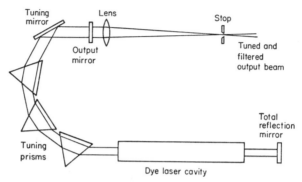

Fig. 16. Diagram of a dye-laser cavity for use as a light source for temperature and density measurements. The tuning prisms disperse the incoherent emission away from the primary laser beam.

when necessary, by a narrow line filter on the laser, but use of such a filter reduces laser power, and care is required to avoid burning the filter. Interference filters we have used fail at continuous power densities of 10–100 W cm^{-2} and pulse ($\approx 1\ \mu$s) energy densities of 1–100 J cm^{-2}. Beams with higher power or energy density can be expanded, or a low-loss prism/stop combination can be used for filtering. In Fig. 16 we show a conceptual drawing of such a scheme, in which the laser beam is shown deflected through approximately 180° by three Brewster's angle prisms. The beam is then focused through a small stop to complete the spectral filtering.

4.2.1 Laser beam heating of particles

When a pulsed laser is used, absorption of light from the laser beam by particles entrained in the gas can raise the particle temperature to the vaporization point, increasing thermal radiation from the particles. Eckbreth[50] has studied this problem in detail, and found a substantial background interference in measurements on a hydrocarbon flame using a pulsed dye laser (pulse length $\approx 1\ \mu$s). The interference can be reduced by using a shorter pulse and synchronized gated detector. The particles do not get much brighter in the shorter pulse because they remain near their normal vaporization temperature. However, the shorter open-gate on the detector allows less of their radiation to be observed. Thus, the method used by Lederman[51–54], in his measurements employing a Q-switched ruby laser with a pulse half-width of less than 20 ns, is to be preferred for particle-laden flows.

This type of interference can be reduced also by observing RS at shorter wavelengths, because the Raman intensity (for equal laser pulse energy) increases rapidly to the blue, while black-body emission falls off to the blue.

For combustion systems for which particles are not anticipated to be a prime problem, a short-pulse dye laser (pulse length $\approx 0.5 \mu s$) is particularly well suited as a source. Here, a reasonable approach would be to observe Stokes and anti-Stokes scattering from a blue beam ($\lambda \approx 470$ nm) or anti-Stokes scattering from a red beam ($\lambda \approx 620$ nm). These choices should reduce interference from any laser-heated particles by a factor of 3–10 in comparison to that encountered in Eckbreth's experiments.

4.2.2 Fluorescence

Fluorescence occurs when one or more constituents of the observed system absorb part of the incident light, and then emit some of this absorbed energy. The fluorescence emission per molecule can be many orders of magnitude stronger than RS. Thus, fluorescence from minor constituents can provide severe background interference to RS measurements. In measurements on combustion systems, fluorescence has been attributed to absorption by fuel constituents by Leonard and Rubins[55] (primarily in aerosol form, Aeschliman and Setchell[49]), free radicals (Vear et al.[31] and Hendra et al.;[32] Barnes et al.[33]), materials adsorbed on smoke particles, etc. The observed fluorescence intensity in gasoline-engine exhaust studies, for example, has been shown to vary from a rather small contribution in suitably preconditioned experiments (by optical filtering, exhaust drying, exhaust heating, etc.) to a huge contribution in the absence of any preconditioning, †Aeschliman and Setchell.[49]

A number of methods, listed below, have been proposed to reduce the effect of fluorescent background to manageable levels in applications where it provides significant interference with RS data:

(a) Determine the fluorescence background in spectral regions adjacent to Raman bands, and subtract it from the total signal to get the Raman signal.

(b) Choose a laser wavelength in a region of low absorption. This approach is becoming more practicable as tunable lasers develop. It has the added

---

† We are dealing here with fluorescence as a background interference to the Raman signal, but emphasize that this process is not always to be avoided; it provides a useful probe for minor species concentrations, utilizing the same general type of instrumentation employed for Raman scattering. The major difficulty with utilization of fluorescence for quantitative measurements is the lack of knowledge of appropriate quenching cross-sections (as well as a lack of knowledge of the detailed composition of quenchers). The best method to circumvent this problem would be to make *in situ* measurements of 'effective' quenching cross-sections for the flame species and conditions. Temperature measurements from fluorescence experiments are usually more difficult than density measurements, requiring observation of the temperature-sensitive internal-mode structure following optical excitation and the subsequent redistribution of energy among excited molecular states.

advantage of reducing the possibility of gas perturbations through absorption.

(c) Confine observation to the anti-Stokes side of the exciting line. Anti-Stokes fluorescence falls off much faster than anti-Stokes RS. At elevated temperatures both density and temperature can be measured from anti-Stokes RS.

(d) Use a polarization filter. Broad band fluorescence is usually depolarized, whereas many Raman bands are strongly polarized. Thus a polarization filter can reduce the observed fluorescence relative to scattering by a factor of up to 2.

(e) Reduce the spectral band-pass. The band-pass can be reduced advantageously down to the spectral width of the Raman bands. These bands have widths on the order of 1–2 nm in the visible at elevated temperatures for many simple molecules, but can be wider for some species—especially molecules with light atoms that also lack symmetry (such as water vapor which displays significant intensity over 4–5 nm at flame temperatures).

(f) Observe resonance RS. This form of RS is much stronger but appears to be useful only in a few special cases.

(g) Reduce the measurement time. At low pressure, fluorescence persists for 10^{-8}–10^{-6} s, whereas RS persists only over the laser pulse. At higher pressures collisions quench the fluorescence in a shorter time, $\approx 10^{-9}$ s. Nevertheless, mode-locked laser pulses with durations on the order of 10^{-11} s and fast gated detection offer some promise in discrimination against fluorescence. However, this combination of techniques is difficult to implement for practical measurements.

(h) Increase the incident spectral power density to well beyond the level where fluorescence saturates. Saturation occurs when the number of molecules in those initial states that are excited by the laser is reduced substantially because of the laser irradiation. Tighter focusing of the incident laser beam then results in diminished fluorescence relative to the Raman scattering. This approach is, however, untested for flame situations. For its application in this instance, it is not clear that the RS signal will, in fact exceed the diminished fluorescence signal before severe laser-induced perturbations occur in the system.

(i) Observe coherent anti-Stokes Raman scattering (CARS). This non-linear process offers very strong discrimination against fluorescence. Currently it is being investigated by several groups for practical diagnostic applications. However, for many experimental situations, it is difficult to implement as presently envisaged, and questions still exist regarding the quantitative interpretation of the data for hot, turbulent, multi-component flows.

(j) Make the physical observation conditions more favorable, where possible. For example, observe flames at high pressures where collisional quenching drastically reduces the fluorescence. This condition is favorable for discriminating against gas fluorescence, but probably does not reduce fluorescence from particles or aerosols. Where measurements are to be made on exhaust gases and preconditioning is feasible, problems arising from aerosols can be ameliorated by drying or heating techniques.

4.3 Background Independent of the Incident Beam

4.3.1 Detector noise

Photomultipliers are still the detectors providing lowest noise for very low-level light signals in the range from the u.v. through to about 850 nm. Optimally cooled and shielded photomultipliers with sensitive areas of the order of 4 cm diameter can contribute as low as 5–15 count s^{-1} detector noise in the photon counting mode. This level is insignificant in most combustion measurements using pulsed lasers.

Another type of detector, which offers an important advantage over a photo-multiplier in data-handling capability, is composed of a combination of one or more optical image-intensifiers and a two-dimensional transducer such as a vidicon or diode array. We discuss subsequently how this type of multi-channel detector can be used to provide simultaneous measurements of the Raman scattering spectral distribution at many spatial points during a single laser pulse, thereby greatly reducing the overall experimental time and laser energy needed to obtain a given amount of information, and providing the data necessary to determine spatial correlation functions. Commercial versions of this instrument, such as the Optical Multichannel Analyzer (OMA® detector†) are now available, offering photon counting sensitivity and adequate dynamic range ($\geqslant 100$). Noise levels are low, because of the small photosensitive area associated with each channel. In particular, these detectors can be gated to respond only within a short ($\leqslant 1$ μs) laser pulse, in which case photon counts arising from detector noise can be much smaller than one count per channel.

4.3.2 Flame luminosity

Background interference from flame luminosity is most likely to be severe when a continuous wave (c.w.) laser is used as the source, because then the background must be viewed continuously along with the RS. Nevertheless, good measurements have been obtained from pre-mixed H_2/air flames using a c.w. argon ion laser with an output beam of approximately 1 W in the visible, in subdued incandescent room light, with a black target intercepting the detector field of view behind the flame. (See, for example, Lapp.[19,20]) These H_2/air flames have low gas luminosity, and contain few particles to emit thermal radiation or scatter ambient light towards the detector. By using an acousto-optic modulator and synchronous gated detection with a c.w. argon ion laser and a multiple-reflection laser-beam mirror system, Setchell[56] obtained Raman data

† OMA® is a registered trademark of Princeton Applied Research Corporation, Princeton, New Jersey.

from the more luminous H_2/air turbulent diffusion flames. Brighter and/or particle-laden flames pose more difficult background problems. In such cases it is usually necessary to use a pulsed laser. The detector or subsequent electronics can be gated to observe the scattering region only during the laser pulse.

An extreme case of interference from flame luminosity can be examined by comparing RS intensity and black-body emission at the anticipated temperature of the observed system. The black-body spectral radiance† is given by:

$$I_B(\lambda, T) = \frac{J(\lambda, T)}{\pi} \qquad (6)$$

in typical units of $W \, cm^{-2} \, nm^{-1} \, sr^{-1}$, where $J(\lambda, T)$ is the black-body radiant flux emitted per unit area and unit wavelength into a solid angle of 2π steradians. Resulting values of I_B for temperatures of 1000–3000 K are plotted in Fig. 17.

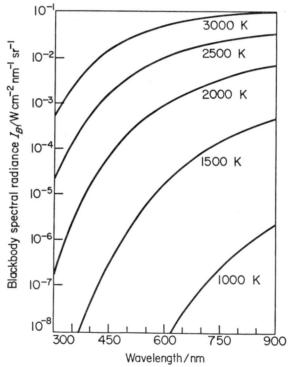

Fig. 17. Values of black-body spectral radiance I_B as a function of wavelength for temperatures of 1000–3000 K.

† This term is adapted here from the definition of radiance given by the Illuminating Engineering Society Lighting Handbook[95] as the radiant flux leaving a surface element per unit solid angle per unit of projected area of the emitter surface on a plane normal to the observation direction. Here, since we are also concerned with the radiant flux emitted per unit wavelength interval, we form the term spectral radiance.

The equivalent RS intensity, averaged over the diameter d of the incident beam, the spectral bandpass $\Delta\lambda$, and the observation time Δt is:

$$I_R = \frac{Q\rho\sigma}{d\Delta\lambda\Delta t} \tag{7}$$

provided that d, $\Delta\lambda$, and Δt are greater than the width of the observed incident beam, the spectral width of the RS, and the duration of the pulse, respectively. Here we consider an example that corresponds to measurement of the concentration of a major species (N_2) in a hydrocarbon flame. Let $Q = 3J$; $\rho = 3 \times 10^{18}$ molecule cm^{-3} (N_2 at 60% relative abundance at 1500 K); $\sigma = 8 \times 10^{-31}$ cm^2 sr^{-1} (N_2 VRS at 500 nm[57]); $d = 0.1$ cm; $\Delta\lambda = 1$ nm; $\Delta t = 10^{-6}$ s. Then $I_R = 7 \times 10^{-5}$ W cm^{-2} nm^{-1} sr^{-1}. Comparison with Fig. 17 indicates that, for example, the RS at 500 nm will be well over an order of magnitude more intense than 1500 K black-body emission.

This comparison, although favorable in the present example, suggests that thermal luminescence can provide serious interference to Raman measurements of major species at many temperatures and wavelengths, and in particular those toward the red. Furthermore, it raises a question about the flame luminosity interference in temperature measurements, because these require observation of two Raman bands of which the weaker (upper state) contribution for N_2 is typically only 20–40% as intense as the ground state band of the fundamental band series ($\Delta v = +1$). Finally, the comparison does not encourage measurements of intermediate and minor species at elevated temperatures.

The equivalent RS intensity cannot be increased at will. Laser/gas perturbations impose a limit on $Q/\Delta t$ in eqn. (7) (for a given beam cross-sectional area); d cannot be made arbitrarily small because optical focusing limitations and fluctuations of the refractive index of the gas exist; and $\Delta\lambda$ is characteristically 1 nm or more for hot combustion gases. Furthermore, taking advantage of the decrease in black-body emission toward the blue (Fig. 17)—i.e. using a shorter wavelength laser source—is not always advisable in combustion systems, because of potentially increased competition from other background processes (recombination continuum emission, elastic scattering processes, fluorescence, etc.).

On the other hand, full black-body emission in the visible from combustion gases is unlikely unless the observed pathlength through the flame is very long and/or the particle loading is heavy. For example, estimates presented by Hottel and Sarofim[58] suggest an emissivity of a few tenths for a several-meter-diameter fuel-oil flame containing porous coke particles. Consequently, we believe that thermal background will not provide serious interference for a wide variety of experimental measurements. For example, this expectation is supported by the success of Lederman's measurements on a natural gas/air flame.[51-54]

4.4 Limits to Spatial Resolution

A major experimental goal for Raman studies of flames is to obtain measurements with as precise spatial resolution as possible, especially in studies exploring such phenomena as turbulence and flame-front structure. In RS diagnostics, spatial resolution is defined by the intersection of the incident beam and the field-of-view of the receiver optics. In practice, resolution volumes smaller than a millimeter cube can be obtained. Here, in support of this statement, we discuss experimental conditions that limit spatial resolution; i.e. refractive index fluctuations, light economy, and laser/gas perturbations.

4.4.1 Refractive index fluctuations

Variations in gas density associated with turbulence cause commensurate spatial variations in refractive index n that can shift the optical axes of the incident beam and receiver significantly as a function of time, thus changing the

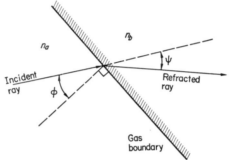

Fig. 18. Bending of a light ray at a boundary between gas regions with different refractive indices.

measurement point. The magnitude of these shifts depends upon the angle ψ through which a light beam is bent at a boundary between gas regions with different refractive indices, $n_a > n_b$. For the simple case illustrated in Fig. 18, this angle is given by Snell's Law, which yields

$$\psi \approx \frac{n_a - n_b}{n_b} \tan \phi. \tag{8}$$

Typical values for refractive indices for gases at s.t.p. are:

Air	1.000 293
Hydrogen	1.000 140
Methane	1.000 444
Carbon Dioxide	1.000 448

Of course, at higher temperatures gases generally have lower refractive indices. Thus we conclude that $(n_a - n_b)/n_b$ is not likely to be larger than roughly 0.001. In this case the optical axis must nearly graze the boundary ($\phi = 84°$) before it is bent by as much as 10 mrad, corresponding to a shift of 1 mm at a distance of 10 cm.

At angles even closer to grazing, if the optical axis passes from higher to lower refractive index, total internal reflection will occur, producing larger bends than predicted by eqn. 8. This phenomenon appears when $\phi \geqslant \phi_c$, where ϕ_c is the critical angle

$$\phi_c = \arcsin (n_b/n_a).$$

For example, if $n_b/n_a = 0.999$, $\phi_c = 87.4°$. For angles between the critical angle and 90° eqn. 8 is replaced by

$$\psi = 2(90° - \phi).$$

In this case, for $n_b/n_a = 0.999$, angular bends as large as $\psi = 5.2°$, or 91 mrad can occur.

Any boundary between gases with different properties is likely to be irregular, and at near-grazing angles part of the beam is likely to be reflected, and thus deflected significantly. However, we conclude, in a conservative estimate, that shifts in the measurement point produced by turbulent fluctuations are unlikely to be significant unless the optical paths through the combustion zone are much greater than 100 times the desired resolution, or the experimental features involve grazing angles between the beams and boundaries of different regions in the gas.

4.4.2 Light economy

Spatial resolution is determined by the cross-section of the incident beam and the length L of the incident beam observed by the detector optics. But according to eqn. 1, the number of detected photons in a measurement is also proportional to L and, thus, from eqns. 1 and 3, the relative error in a density measurement is proportional to $L^{-1/2}$.

In order to illustrate the significance of this limitation, consider an example for which the error corresponding to a spatial resolution of 0.05 cm is about 2%, values which are attainable with present apparatus. For a spatial resolution of 0.01 cm, this error becomes only about 5%. Thus light economy does not provide a severe limitation for major species density and temperature measurements in the range of present interest. In fact, it is likely that the ultimate limit to spatial resolution for measurements that are accomplished in single short pulses is reached when the power or energy density in the incident beam is sufficient to perturb the gas in such a way that measured values of density or temperature are also perturbed.

4.4.3 Laser/gas absorption perturbations

The range of optical parameters for which ordinary absorption can produce significant heating depends on the fraction of the incident beam energy absorbed (and eventually converted into thermal energy) within the probed zone. However, the relevant question regarding laser measurement perturbations is: What is the threshold for significant *RS measurement perturbations* for short laser pulses relative to the threshold for an *absorption-induced perturbation* for some specific flame species? This absorption-induced perturbation can result in some species being raised to temperatures significantly above those otherwise present in the flame, or to non-thermal equilibrium; the RS measurement perturbations will only occur if the effect of the absorption-induced perturbation can be transferred to the Raman-observed molecule *during the laser pulse*. (Typically, such observed molecules are N_2 for temperature measurements, major product gases, unburned fuel and oxidant species, and, hopefully, some important intermediate molecules and radicals.)

This question, in its general form, has not yet received sufficient attention to be answered with any completeness. That RS measurement perturbations can occur for situations wherein gas-phase absorption of the incident laser beam occurs has been well-documented. (See, for example, the observations of Holzer et al.[36] for halogen gases with visible irradiation.) However, major flame species such as N_2, O_2, H_2, CO, CO_2, etc. have no absorption bands near the commonly-used visible laser wavelengths, and known weak resonance absorptions due to other species (such as weak vibrational-rotational lines in the visible for major species such as H_2O, or stronger absorptions for minority species such as C_2) can be avoided by use of a tunable laser source. The major problem with this argument, of course, is that fortuitous absorptions that are not anticipated (or perhaps not even known) for some minor species can possibly become a significant problem. Furthermore, absorption of laser energy by particles with ensuing vaporization of material[50] can produce additional species which, in addition to simply providing sources of excess of thermal energy in collision with Raman-observed molecules, can perhaps themselves absorb (and then also transfer) significant additional amounts of laser energy.

4.4.4 Laser/gas breakdown perturbations

The power density in a tightly focused laser pulse can be very great. For example, a 1 J, 30 ns pulse focused into a circular beam of 0.1 mm radius will produce a radiant flux per unit area greater than 10^{11} W cm^{-2}. Such beams can cause gas perturbations ranging from simple absorption heating to the extreme case of laser-induced gas breakdown. There is little question but that the runaway type of perturbations characteristic of laser-induced breakdown will prevent accurate measurement if they occur. Accordingly, we shall assume that the onset of breakdown establishes an upper limit on the allowable focusing of the incident beam. Here we qualitatively discuss this limitation, and, in the next section, describe the resulting trade-off that develops between measurement accuracy and spatial resolution.

The controlling mechanism of plasma breakdown is usually an ionization avalanche excited by inverse bremmstrahlung absorption of the incident beam. As discussed by Boni and Meskan,[59] in the case of very short pulses ($< 10^{-9}$ s) the breakdown threshold is determined by the energy density of the pulse, because loss mechanisms such as recombination and diffusion are too slow to affect the electron density build-up in this time regime. A typical short-pulse threshold in a clean gas (no particles) for incident light in the mid-visible region (500 nm) is between 10^3 and 10^4 J cm^{-2}. For long pulses ($> 10^{-8}$ s) the threshold is determined by power density because a balance is reached between free electron generation and losses.

The breakdown threshold is reduced by the presence of particles in the gas for pulse lengths in excess of about 10^{-9} s. As the diameter of the particles increases, the threshold power density decreases (for a given pulse length) to the apparent limit obtained by extrapolation of the short pulse threshold. No dependence on the particle composition is as yet evident.

For very small beam diameters, electron-diffusion losses can become important, increasing the breakdown threshold; furthermore, this threshold varies as λ^{-2}, because of the wavelength dependence of the inverse bremmstrahlung mechanism, and is therefore much higher in the visible than in the infrared (where the experimental data presented by Boni and Meskan were obtained). The threshold varies inversely with the electron-neutral molecule collision frequency,[60] and therefore also with the gas density.

To our knowledge, no definitive measurements of laser-breakdown characteristics in flames have been published to date. However, we can speculate as follows. In a flame at atmospheric pressure, as compared to clean gas at standard temperature, the threshold will tend to:

(a) *Increase* because the collision frequency is smaller.[60]

(b) *Decrease* to the extent that photo-ionization of excited species is important.

(c) *Decrease* if particles are present.

(d) *Decrease* to the extent that the initial ionization (starting point for the avalanche) is larger.†

The net effect cannot be estimated very well at this time because of a lack of experimental data. However, a one or two order-of-magnitude decrease in the energy density threshold appears reasonable for 1 μs pulses in a moderately clean hydrocarbon flame. On the other hand, in a hydrogen/air flame the threshold may be even larger than that for air at s.t.p.

---

† This comment is suggested by the experimental work of Brown and Smith[96] and the theoretical calculations of Nielsen and Canavan [97] for preionized helium. The level of ionization in pure equilibrium flame gases [61] is low, with NO contributing substantially because of its relatively low ionization potential. Thus, an electron density of about 1.5×10^7 cm^{-3} would result from 1% of NO at 2000 K. This level of ionization can be substantially increased, however, by normally-encountered small concentrations of impurity species such as Ca, K or Na. Furthermore, ionization in hydrocarbon flames, above the reaction zone as well as in the zone, is several orders of magnitude higher than is predicted by thermal equilibrium calculations. (This latter comment is not the case for hydrogen/air flames.) Ionization levels of 10^{12} cm^{-3} are not uncommon for organic flames, and are, for example, well within the range of pre-ionization electron densities present in the helium work.[96,97]

4.4.5 Trade-off between accuracy and resolution

The energy density threshold for significant measurement perturbation establishes an important trade-off between measurement accuracy and spatial resolution for measurements obtained during a single laser pulse. To determine this trade-off, we substitute $Q = Q^*s^2$ into eqn. (1), where Q^* is the energy density threshold, measured, say, in units of J cm^{-2}, and s is the incident beam diameter. If the spatial resolution is to be a cube of side s, then the observed length of the incident beam, represented by L in eqn. (1), must be set equal to s. Consequently, we obtain an expression for the maximum number of photons that can be detected from this resolution volume during a single pulse without significant measurement perturbation:

$$N_{max} = zQ^*s^3,$$

where the proportionality factor is defined as:

$$z \equiv \frac{\rho\sigma\Omega\varepsilon\eta}{E_\lambda}.$$

The resulting limit to relative accuracy $(\Delta\rho/\rho)_{min}$ in a density measurement is given by eqn. (3); i.e.

$$\left(\frac{\Delta\rho}{\rho}\right)_{min} = (N_{max})^{-1/2} = (zQ^*s^3)^{-1/2}. \tag{9}$$

Equation (9) expresses the trade-off between measurement accuracy and spatial resolution. For the relevant optical parameters for Raman scattering detection at 500 nm given in Section 3.6, the value $z = 2.4 \times 10^4$ cm J^{-1} is obtained. We recall that this case is characteristic of measurements of major species in a flame. In a *hydrogen/air flame* there are few absorbing species in the visible and thus the threshold is probably determined by breakdown. The breakdown threshold may even be higher than that in clean air, because gas densities are lower and ionization levels are not increased above those corresponding to thermal equilibrium. The optimum laser pulse length is *ca.* 1 μs, providing sufficient time resolution and discrimination against flame luminous background. We estimate that the measurement perturbation threshold for a 1 μs pulse in the visible is of the order of 10^4–10^5 J cm^{-2}, allowing spatial resolution to be about 0.1 mm for the example just mentioned. (See Table 3.)

In a *hydrocarbon flame* the limiting threshold can be substantially different because of the presence of particles, other absorbing species, and high initial degrees of ionization. Very short laser pulses ($\ll 1\ \mu$s) are advantageous because:

(a) Flame luminous background must be overcome.
(b) Additional luminescence from laser-heated particles must be overcome (which can be a severe problem for pulses longer than about 1 μs[50]).
(c) Short measurement times are desirable to prevent any possible absorption-induced perturbations to measured quantities.

The optimum choice to meet these criteria in a 'dirty' hydrocarbon flame is probably a laser providing very short ($ca.$ 10^{-8} s) bright pulses, such as a Q-switched laser. If the output is in the red, the threshold is probably determined by plasma breakdown; in the blue, ordinary absorption processes may possibly

TABLE 3
Estimates of spatial resolution elements (s) as functions of the energy density threshold Q^* and the limiting value of relative accuracy for density measurement $(\Delta\rho/\rho)_{min}$[a]

Rough estimate of perturbation threshold	$Q^*\backslash(\Delta\rho/\rho)_{min}$	10%	3%
Hydrocarbon flames	10 J cm^{-2}	0.8 mm	2 mm
	10^2	0.4	0.8
H$_2$ flame	10^4	0.1	0.2

[a] These values of s are calculated from eqn. (9) using a proportionality factor z of 2.4×10^4 cm J^{-1}, corresponding to the relevant optical parameters for Raman scattering detection at 500 nm given in Section 3.6.

provide the limiting threshold for gas perturbation. As we have mentioned previously, published data for laser pulse breakdown in flames are lacking, but as rough estimates, we expect that the threshold for significant perturbation of hydrocarbon flames is between 10 and 10^3 J cm^{-2}. Although this threshold estimate is several orders of magnitude smaller than that for the hydrogen/air flame, the effect on spatial resolution is not severe, because for constant accuracy, s is proportional to $(Q^*)^{-1/3}$ according to eqn. 9. Thus, we estimate that single-pulse measurement resolutions down to at least a few millimeters can be obtained for this case, as indicated in Table 3.

4.5   Spectral Interference

The vibrational Raman bands of many different molecules of interest for flame studies (e.g. N$_2$, O$_2$, CO, CO$_2$, H$_2$, H$_2$O, NO, etc.) are well separated; thus independent measurements of the concentration of each of these molecules can, in principle, be obtained from Raman scattering. However, the rotational wings of the vibrational Raman scattering from one of the major constituents can interfere with the measurement of a second species at low concentration. This interference is more likely at high temperatures, when the rotational wings spread out and become more intense far from the vibrational Q-branch.

Leonard[62] investigated this type of spectral interference for small amounts of CO in the presence of excess N$_2$ during the design of a Raman probe to measure the composition of exhaust gases from a jet engine. We have also made rough estimates of the concentration of CO which would produce a vibrational Raman signal equal to that of the excess of N_2 (weak rotational wing, O-branch anti-Stokes scattering) for a particular spectral passband (24 cm^{-1} rectangular passband about the Stokes vibrational CO-line for incident ruby-laser excitation). For these estimates, we utilized unpublished rough experimental data taken in our laboratory relating the N_2 Q-branch intensity to O-branch intensities. (These data indicate that the strongest line in these vibrational–rotational wings for N_2 at room temperature has about 1% of the Q-branch intensity.)

TABLE 4
Relative cross-sections of CH stretch vibration per CH bond, from the data published by Stephenson.[64] These cross-sections are normalized to the N_2 Q-branch vibrational cross-section, which is 5.4×10^{-31} cm^2 sr^{-1} for excitation at 488 nm (Penney et al.[57]).

Molecule	Number of CH bonds	Relative values of integrated cross-section for CH stretch	Relative values of cross-section per CH bond
Methane	4	11	2.8
Ethane	6	21	3.5
Propane	8	28	3.5
n-Butane	10	32	3.2
n-Pentane	12	42.5	3.5
n-Hexane	14	46	3.3
Benzene	6	22	3.7
2,2-Dimethylpropane	12	44	3.7
Ethene	4	9.7	2.4
Propene	6	21.7	3.6
1-Butene	8	30.4	3.8
Toluene	8	29.7	3.7
Isobutene	8	32.1	4.0

At room temperature, we estimate that several hundred p.p.m. of CO produces a vibrational intensity equal to the appropriate rotational lines of N_2, while at 1250 K, roughly 5000 p.p.m. of CO is required to equal the N_2 intensity. Thus, sensitive detection of CO in air flames by vibrational Raman scattering is clearly unattractive, as would be required, for example, for lean flame studies. (However, for rich hydrocarbon/air flames, CO can be present in sufficiently large quantities to be well-determined by this method, as has been shown by Setchell[63] for rich methane/air flames.)

Another type of spectral interference is produced by more complex hydrocarbon molecules, because their Raman spectra typically contain at least several strong bands. Stephenson[64] investigated this problem to find out if the concentrations of numerous hydrocarbons can be determined independently in automobile exhaust. He obtained quantitative Raman scattering spectra for a large number of hydrocarbons which show a high degree of overlap, suggesting that the specific determination of the concentrations of different hydrocarbons will very likely be prevented by their spectral interferences.

On the other hand, all of these hydrocarbon spectra show a common feature viz. a strong narrow band arising from the CH bond. Furthermore, the strength of this band for each molecule is nearly proportional to the number of CH bonds in the molecule, as shown in Table 4 which is calculated from Stephenson's results. Therefore, observation of the CH band should provide a good measurement of the concentration of CH bonds in the gas. Furthermore, comparison of this measurement against a total hydrocarbon measurement by a different technique, such as flame ionization detection, might provide a determination of the relative concentration of carbon present in CH bonds compared with carbon in other forms.

Other types of spectral interference can arise between Raman scattering and background sources, such as fluorescence, as discussed previously. Of course, the limitations imposed by interference will be different for each environment and species. However, one form or another of interference is likely to be substantial for Raman measurements of low concentrations—say, below roughly 100 p.p.m.

5 EXPERIMENTAL CAPABILITIES AND REQUIREMENTS

In this chapter the experimental capabilities and requirements that lead to optimum choices of equipment are described. These considerations are then applied to a particular experiment.

Factors affecting the choice of a laser for an experiment are its output wavelength and average power, the time dependence of its output (c.w. or pulsed), pulse power and energy, beam polarization, beam quality, cost, and convenience of operation. Since the choice of the laser is usually the initial step when an experiment is designed, we will treat this matter first.

5.1 Laser Advantage Factor

It is useful to define a laser advantage factor (LAF) as the product of available laser average power at a typical cost (arbitrarily chosen here to be $25 000), detector sensitivity, and scattering strength. This factor is proportional to the rate at which information can be obtained from Raman scattering measurements using various lasers. It contains the factors in the scattering equation, eqn. (1), that show strong dependence on wavelength. Consequently, it is useful (though not definitive) in identification of a preferred wavelength range and selection of a laser type. The components of LAF are discussed below; resulting values are shown in Table 5.

5.1.1 Average laser power
Representative average powers of presently available lasers in the $25 000

price range are shown as a function of wavelength in Table 5. The laser selections correspond to those which have already been used for Raman scattering measurements. The development of new lasers, such as the copper-vapor laser, may well bring additional highly useful alternatives to this catalog.

TABLE 5
Laser advantage factor, LAF[a]

Laser type	λ_L/nm	P/W	λ_S/nm	$\eta_{\lambda_s}\%$	S	LAF
Argon ion	488	5	551	20	1.0	1.0
Dye	470	4	523	22	1.2	1.0
			(424)	(25)	(2.2)	(0.22)
Doubled Nd:YAG	530	5	605	15	0.76	0.57
			(472)	(20)	(1.6)	(0.16)
Pulsed N_2	337	0.5	366	30	3.4	(0.51)
			(313)	(25)	(5.5)	(0.07)
Quadrupled Nd:YAG	265	0.2	282	25	7.4	0.37
Ruby (normal pulse, ≈ 1 ms)	694	20	828	2	0.3	0.12
			(598)	(15)	(0.8)	(0.24)
Nd:YAG	1060	200	(850)	(1.6)	(0.27)	(0.09)
Doubled ruby	347	0.05	378	30	3.1	0.05
Ruby (Q-switched)	694	1	828	2	0.3	0.006
			(598)	(15)	(0.8)	(0.01)

[a] The product of laser average power P, detector quantum efficiency η, and relative scattering strength S as a function of laser output wavelength λ_L. Values of laser power are our estimates of levels provided by good quality lasers of each type commercially available for approximately $25 000. Here, S is the value of σ_λ/E_λ relative to the value for Stokes vibrational scattering from N_2 excited at 488 nm. The detector quantum efficiency and scattering strength are expressed at the wavelength λ_S of Stokes (or, for values in parentheses, anti-Stokes) vibrational Raman scattering from N_2 excited at the laser wavelength. Values of LAF for anti-Stokes scattering are multiplied by 0.1 to account approximately for the relative intensity of the N_2 Stokes and anti-Stokes lines at 1500 K.

5.1.2 Scattering strength

Among the factors in eqn. (1) which determine the strength of a Raman scattering signal, the values of L, Ω, and ε are relatively insensitive to wavelength and can be optimized by proper experimental design. However, the ratio σ_λ/E_λ, which we shall call scattering strength, varies as λ^{-3} (where λ is the scattering wavelength). Values of this ratio, normalized to 1 for Stokes vibrational scattering from N_2 excited at 488 nm, are shown in Table 5.

5.1.3 Detector sensitivity

Photomultipliers and image intensifier/multi-channel detectors are optimum for the low light levels characteristic of Raman scattering. The sensitivity of these devices when used in the photon-counting mode is determined by their quantum efficiencies η_λ. Values in Table 5 correspond to optimum values published by a representative photomultiplier manufacturer for each wavelength. At infrared wavelengths beyond 1 μm, solid state detectors give a better signal-to-noise ratio than vacuum-photoemissive devices. However, we have not included this range in our calculations because of the difficulty of using solid state detectors for the very low light levels of concern here, and because the product of detector sensitivity and scattering strength diminishes much faster than available laser power increases with wavelength in the infrared.

5.1.4 Discussion of LAF

The resulting products of power, quantum efficiency, and scattering strength indicate that the argon ion, dye (470 nm), doubled Nd:YAG, and pulsed N_2 lasers are good choices for economic gathering of information, with the remaining lasers listed in Table 5 viable as additional choices for specialized purposes. These sources span the wavelength range from 265 nm to 1.06 μm, with some wavelength advantage indicated from the u.v./blue to the green. However, other wavelength-dependent factors that we described previously as more difficult to quantify, such as minimization of fluorescence, natural background, and laser-induced gas perturbations, also assume major importance in selection of a laser. Furthermore, the time-dependence of the laser output can be extremely important when the observed medium produces a strong background light level and/or strong fluctuations. Thus, for example, a comment is in order concerning the Q-switched ruby laser. Its LAF is low compared to other lasers listed in this table, but it possesses unique qualities (i.e. very short time duration, intense pulses) which can be of significant value for some difficult systems, such as highly luminous flames. Thus, one must only use the LAF value as a rough guide; the detailed experimental requirements will finally dictate the laser choice.

5.2 Raman Measurements in Fluctuating Systems

Raman scattering has been used in a number of investigations designed to probe gas-phase systems in which the unsteady character of the flow is of dominant importance, the studies ranging from relatively slow variations to turbulence effects to shock wave phenomena. (See, for example, Setchell,[56] Lederman,[51-54] Eckbreth,[50] Hartley,[65] Boiarski,[66] Birch et al.,[67] Brown et al.,[68] etc.) Here, we will be particularly concerned with measurements of average values in strongly fluctuating systems (see, for example, Setchell[56]) and several types of time-resolved measurements which also possess good spatial resolution (see, for example, Lederman,[51-54] Birch[67]). In order to facilitate this discussion, we shall distinguish between three broad classes of lasers:

  (i) Lasers that emit a continuous wave (c.w. lasers).
  (ii) Lasers that emit large pulses (l.p. lasers). The distinguishing characteristic of l.p. lasers is that each single pulse contains sufficient light energy to

produce a Raman measurement with useful statistical accuracy. A typical l.p. laser might emit several joules per pulse in the mid-visible region, with a pulse-repetition rate of at least several pulses per minute.

(iii) Lasers that emit a series of small pulses (s.p. lasers). A typical s.p. laser might emit several millijoules per pulse in the mid-visible region with a pulse-repetition rate of several hundred pulses per second.

5.2.1 Average value measurements

Average values of species density and temperature can be obtained by observing the Raman signal excited by a c.w. or s.p. laser over an extended period. This procedure yields a time average over the spatial extent of the measurement zone, to the limit that the measured quantity is linearly proportional to the Raman signal over the temperature range encountered during the measurement. Departures from linearity in temperature measurements, as well as in high-temperature density-measurements can exist (see Sections 3.4 and 3.5) and require careful interpretation when temperature varies significantly over the spatial and/or temporal extent of the measurement.

Average values can also be obtained from continuous time-variation measurements, and from instantaneous measurements using l.p. lasers. These approaches, which are discussed subsequently, allow corrections for non-linear response, and thus provide more accurate average values in systems showing strong temperature fluctuations.

5.2.2 Continuous time-variation measurements

These measurements can be obtained from the time variation of Raman scattering excited by a c.w. or high repetition-rate s.p. laser. Resolution is limited to periods over which sufficient photons are detected to provide a measurement of useful accuracy. From eqn. (1), the average detection rate of scattered photons can be written in the form $R = AP$, where R is in photon s^{-1}, A ($= \rho \sigma L \Omega \varepsilon \eta / E_\lambda$) is in photon $W^{-1} s^{-1}$, and P ($=$ average laser power) is in W. If the optical parameters in A correspond to those given previously in Section 3.6 for the detection of a major species density in a flame, then:

$$A = 1.8 \times 10^3 \text{ photon } W^{-1} s^{-1}.$$

The average number of photons collected over a time-resolution period Δt is $N = R\Delta t = AP\Delta t$. The measurement accuracy is characterized by a relative standard deviation (r.s.d.) given by eqn. (3):

$$\text{r.s.d.} = (AP\Delta t)^{-1/2}.$$

This equation determines the average power required from the laser in terms of the parameters r.s.d. and Δt. For example, we find for the experimental case described in Section 3.6, measurements to an accuracy (r.s.d.) of $\pm 10\%$ with time resolution of ten milliseconds will require an average laser power of 6 W at $\lambda \approx 500$ nm. This power is near the maximum value provided by convenient lasers in a single visible line at the present. Of course, A is proportional to the density of the observed molecules, and consequently, it can be larger for major species at lower temperatures and higher pressures. This factor can be increased also by increasing the observed length L of the incident beam. The problem with this approach is that the spatial resolution along the incident beam is thereby

TABLE 6
Practical limits to time resolution for a continuous time-variation measurement of major-species density or temperature (r.s.d. $= 10\%$, laser average power $= 8$ W at 488 nm).[a]

Medium	Partial pressure/atm	Temp./K	Time resolution/ms
Flame	0.5	1500	10
Ambient	1	300	1
Dense gas	3	90	0.1

[a] Note that multiple reflection or laser intracavity techniques can decrease these limits to the extent that they increase effective laser power within the measurement zone.

increased, and many measurement situations require excellent time and spatial resolution simultaneously. Finally, the factor A can be increased by using laser intracavity or laser multiple-reflection techniques. This latter method, developed by Hill and Hartley,[69] has been used by Setchell[56] in flame studies. The results have been worthwhile, since care was taken in alignment to prevent undue loss of spatial resolution. In the absence of such techniques, a direct recording with time resolutions less than those shown in Table 6 for different media cannot be obtained conveniently from Raman scattering.

5.2.3 Correlation functions

Birch et al.[67] have found that time-correlation functions of fluctuating gas density from Raman measurements can be obtained using a c.w. laser with instrumentation techniques that have been applied recently with good success in laser velocimetry. The compatibility of these methods (use of same equipment) is significant because the measurement of combinations of density, temperature and velocity fluctuations is particularly valuable in combustion research.

A time-autocorrelation function of density can be defined by

$$C(\tau) = \langle \rho(t)\rho(t+\tau) \rangle$$

where the angle brackets indicate an average over time t. This function is equal to $\langle \rho^2(t) \rangle$ for $\tau = 0$, and approaches $\langle \rho(t) \rangle^2$ for times τ long compared to the density-correlation time. Typical variations resembling results obtained by Birch et al.[67] are shown in Fig. 19. The behavior of this function provides an indication of the turbulence intensity and its time scale. When the latter information is combined with velocity data, an indication of the spatial-turbulence scale is obtained.

The correlation function can be obtained from a similarly defined correlation function of the actual Raman scattering signal. The Raman correlation function can be measured over a long time to smooth statistical fluctuations. Consequently, it can provide time-resolved information to a resolution much shorter than that obtained in a continuous time-variation measurement, as illustrated by the results of Birch et al.[67]

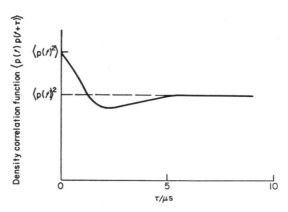

Fig. 19. Typical variation with time τ of a density correlation function $\langle \rho(t)\rho(t+\tau)\rangle$ in a turbulent system.

Two limitations of this approach must be recognized. First, the correlation function provides less information than a continuous recording. Second, it will be difficult to apply this technique to bright flames, because of the resulting high background levels.

5.2.4 Instantaneous measurements

Measurements of instantaneous values of major-species densities and temperature can be obtained with an l.p. laser. The time resolution for these measurements is determined by the laser-pulse length, of the order of 1 ms (normal pulsed ruby or neodymium laser), 1 μs (coaxial dye laser), 10 ns (Q-switched laser and pulsed N_2 laser), or 10 ps (pulse selected and amplified from mode-locked train). Measurements of different instantaneous values (e.g. oxidant and fuel densities, and temperature from Raman scattering, with velocity from laser velocimeter data) can be correlated using this technique, and probability distribution functions (p.d.f.), which indicate the fraction of time a measured value takes each value within its range, can be obtained from the instantaneous measurements, along with average values. Thus, a series of instantaneous measurements provides a wealth of information in the short time-resolution range ($\leq$1 ms). Furthermore, these measurements can be obtained with excellent spatial resolution in many cases (<1 mm), and the short energetic pulses required for these measurements also provide excellent discrimination against natural background. The potential difficulty with this technique is the possibility that perturbations of the flame gas by these laser pulses will occur and introduce significant perturbations of the measurements.

5.3   Detectors and Instrumentation

5.3.1   Photomultipliers

Photomultipliers are excellent detectors for the low light levels characteristic of Raman scattering, for scattered light wavelengths up to about 1 μm. The primary advantage of photomultipliers is their amplification, by factors on the order of 10^6, with very low noise, of electrons ejected from the photocathode (the light sensitive surface). This amplification is achieved in a vacuum by secondary emission avalanche as the current trajectory cascades down a dynode chain containing, typically, from 6 to 14 stages, through a high voltage drop.

Photomultiplier signals from very low light levels, below 10^{-11} W, are best analyzed in the photon counting mode. A level of 10^{-11} W corresponds to about 2.5×10^7 photon s^{-1}. Typical quantum efficiencies, expressing the fraction of photons detected, are of the order of 10% or better (see Table 5). Thus at 10^{-11} W, about 2.5×10^6 electrons will be ejected from the photocathode in the initial step of photon detection. The resulting amplified pulses can be seen on an oscilloscope and counted by suitable instrumentation.

Photon counting is more accurate than a direct reading of the photomultiplier current for three reasons:

(i) The detector output pulses, with statistically varying heights, are replaced by standard height pulses.

(ii) The photon counting rate can be much less sensitive to power supply voltage fluctuations than the photomultiplier output current.

(iii) Photon counting instruments do not see leakage currents.

The basic source of noise in this detection mode is the statistical fluctuation in the counting rate, which was discussed previously. A slight amount of additional noise is contributed by the variation in amplified pulse heights caused by the statistical fluctuations of secondary emission. The amplification fluctuations, which occur predominantly in the first few stages of amplification, lead to a broad pulse height distribution such as that shown in Fig. 20. In practice a discriminator is set to produce a standard height output-pulse for those photomultiplier pulses above a height represented by the vertical dotted line in the figure. This discriminator height is chosen such that it excludes very low pulses caused by current leakage in the photomultiplier and noise from the intervening circuit. In this case the additional noise (beyond the basic statistical limit) is attributable to the photon counts missed because they fall below the discriminator setting. This effect is equivalent to a reduced quantum efficiency in eqn. (1). However, the reduction can usually be made very small by proper choice of the discriminator setting.

Photon counting techniques cannot be used easily when the detection rate is above about 10^7 count s^{-1}, because at those rates it becomes difficult to resolve the closer adjacent pulses. Counting rates above 10^7 are often encountered in Raman diagnostics when pulsed lasers are used. In such cases it is necessary to use another type of signal processing. For example, the photomultiplier signal can be integrated over the pulse duration and, after any background is subtracted, the net charge q can be interpreted as arising from N photons, where

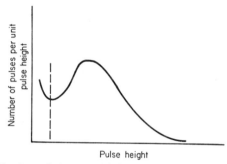

Fig. 20. Typical distribution of photomultiplier output pulses (in, for example, units of coulombs, amperes, or volts) for detection of individual photons. The vertical dashed line shows an optimum discriminator setting for photon counting.

$N = q/z$ and z is the average charge in a photomultiplier signal pulse per detected photon. This assignment is uncertain, and adds noise beyond the basic statistical uncertainty, because of statistical variation of photomultiplier amplification from shot to shot. The amount of additional noise added depends sensitively upon the photomultiplier pulse-height distribution, but a typical result is that the relative standard deviation in N is increased by roughly 30%, to $1.3 \sqrt{N}$. (See for example, Ref. 70.)

Thermal emission from the photocathode is an additional source of noise. At room temperature 10 000 count s^{-1} can be generated by thermal emission from a 4 cm diameter photocathode sensitive to the red, versus about 300 count s^{-1} from a 4 cm bi-alkali photocathode sensitive only to the u.v. and blue. Where necessary, this dark count can be lowered by cooling the photomultiplier and/or using magnetic lenses to reduce the sensitive area of the photomultiplier. A combination of both techniques (cooling to $-70°$C and reduction of sensitive area to 1 cm^2) can reduce the dark count rate of even a red-sensitive tube such as RCA's ERMA series to a few counts per second.

5.3.2 Solid state photodiodes

The quantum efficiency of a solid state photodiode can be much larger than that of a vacuum photomultiplier, approaching 70% in the red and near infrared. Diodes are more compact and rugged than photomultipliers, and do not require high voltage or careful voltage regulation. However, these devices lack the low noise amplification that is required for photon counting despite the internal amplification of avalanche photodiodes and external amplification by close-coupled electronics. Thus the best solid-state detectors fail by several orders of magnitude to equal the ability of photomultipliers to measure low light levels in the visible and u.v. For this reason photodiodes do not appear to be generally useful by themselves for combustion measurements.

5.3.3 Image intensifier vidicon tubes

As mentioned previously in Section 4.3.1, an image intensifier in front of a vidicon tube can provide sufficient amplification for photon counting sensitivity over a two-dimensional matrix. This combination is particularly useful for Raman diagnostic measurements because it enables simultaneous spatial and spectral multiplexing. For example, a grating can be used to disperse spectral information in the y-direction, while position along the incident light beam is imaged in the x-direction. In this way, one can obtain major-constituent densities and temperature along a line through a combustion zone during a single laser shot, thereby permitting extensive correlation studies. This procedure saves time, and requires significantly fewer laser pulses to obtain a given amount of information, but requires more comprehensive computer and associated electronic apparatus.

In the past few years, development of this type of detector has accelerated (see, for example, Bridoux et al.,[71,72] Smith,[73,74] Schildkraut,[75] etc.) and a commercial version that is applicable to Raman diagnostics is now available. (See Bell et al.[76] for an evaluation for remote Raman sensing.) Use of this type of detector for combustion measurements will be described more fully in Section 5.4.2 (see also Section 4.3.1).

5.4 Prototype Experiment

In this section we describe the equipment selection for an illustrative experimental program whose purpose is to obtain data from turbulent luminous flames for comparison with theoretical flame models. Thus, many of the experimental difficulties discussed in Section 4 will be encountered here. The example envisages a combination of Raman diagnostics for major constituents and temperature, laser velocimetry (with which the Raman techniques are particularly compatible), and conventional probes for minor constituents. Spatial resolution to volumes smaller than 1 mm on each side, and overall time resolution of 1 μs are sought for repeated simultaneous measurements of instantaneous values of temperature and major constituents (e.g. N_2, O_2, fuels such as H_2 or CH_4 and product gases such as H_2O or CO_2).

5.4.1 Laser

Since we have elected to deal with a turbulent, luminous medium, we are led to choose a pulsed laser source. It is not, however, known with generality that *any* laser source will be suitable for all experimental situations. In some cases, no 'window' may exist between the lower laser power-density limit set by desired spatial and time resolution and background limitations, and the higher limit set by measurement perturbations. However, keeping within the confines of viable experimental goals, we have selected a dye laser for these measurements. Commercially available units are capable of supplying 3 J per pulse at 20 pulses min^{-1} in spectral ranges about 30 nm wide in the regions of 470 and 590 nm. It is believed to be advisable to modify the optical cavity typically available, to the special configuration shown in Fig. 16 in order to filter out background light (as discussed in Section 4.2), to narrow and define the beam, and to facilitate alignment.

The tunability of this laser allows avoidance of narrow absorption regions and background flame-emission structure and, as an added benefit, increases the possibility that the Raman diagnostic equipment also can be used for fluorescence measurements of minor species. Use of a coaxial lamp configuration for the dye laser will provide a fast pulse (300–500 ns), relative to dye lasers using linear lamps, because of the correspondingly low flashlamp inductance. The fast pulse is more visible against a bright background, and may also help to minimize measurement perturbations due to laser/gas interactions.

Other pulsed lasers considered for this application are ruby, doubled ruby, doubled Nd:YAG and pulsed N_2. All of these lasers should be Q-switched in order to provide sufficient time resolution and discrimination against background, except the N_2 laser, whose pulse is naturally limited to about 10 ns. The ruby wavelength is inconveniently long for photomultiplier detectors unless measurements are confined to the anti-Stokes scattering. (It is possible that this combination will be useful in situations where high fluorescence background is encountered.) The Nd:YAG and pulsed N_2 lasers do not provide sufficient energy per pulse for single pulse measurements. All of the Q-switched lasers are much more expensive than the dye laser in terms of dollars per watt of average power. Thus, we believe that the coaxial dye laser is the optimum choice for this illustrative example.

5.4.2 Detectors and electronics

Interference filters appear to be the most likely candidates for use in providing the spectral channels containing density information. Such a device is illustrated in Fig. 21. The alternative configuration shown in Fig. 22 is convenient for BAM temperature measurements, which require adjacent channels that are particularly stable relative to each other.

In order to obtain good statistics, roughly 1000 laser shots are required for each measurement point and flame condition, consuming about one hour of measurement time. It is obvious that the number of points that can be observed in this way is limited by time and laser durability.

An image-converter vidicon detector can reduce this problem dramatically, because it allows observation of many spectral lines and spatial points simul-

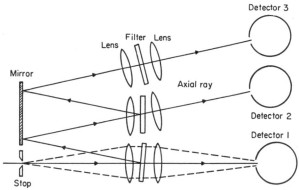

Fig. 21. Three-channel filter spectrometer.

taneously. Whereas cross-correlation with velocity components during a single laser pulse can be obtained at only one spectral point, full spatial correlation functions can be developed among constituent densities and temperature. This information is obtained along a line through the combustion zone that coincides with the incident laser beam.

We illustrate the advantages of this type of detector by referring to a commercially available unit, the OMA detector mentioned in Section 4.3.1. The photosensitive surface of the OMA detector extends over an area of 1.2×1.0 cm that can be divided into $500 \times M$ separately-addressable zones, where M can be varied from 1 to 256. The incident light is amplified by a vacuum image intensifier with an S-20 photocathode. The amplified light image is coupled to a silicon vidicon, where it induces a charge distribution that is read out by a scanned electron beam. The sensitivity of this system is such that one signal count is produced for each two photons detected (with S-20 response) per zone. The linear dynamic range is 750:1 and statistical fluctuations are essentially those of photon counting in zones where more than 10 photons are detected. The instrument can be gated to observation times as short as 10 ns, and the dark count for moderate-to-short observation times ($\leqslant 30$ ms) is much less than one count per zone. Vidicon read-out into the computer or onto tape requires 32.8 ms per 500 point line.

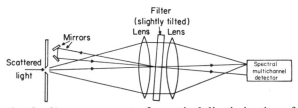

Fig. 22. Schematic of a filter spectrometer for optical discrimination of closely-spaced spectral channels. Although a spectral multi-channel detector is shown here, photomultipliers (with suitably placed deflection mirrors) or a split-cathode photomultiplier could also be used as detectors.

One informative and simple application of the OMA detector is to use a single filter to image the density of a particular constituent along a line (or to reflect the laser beam back and forth across a plane). For the optical parameters given in the standard example in Section 3.6, about 1800 photons can be detected as vibrational Raman scattering from a major constituent per millimeter of the incident beam. Suppose that subject-to-image magnification of the line system is $\frac{1}{2}$, the 500-zone direction of the OMA detector is aligned with the incident beam, and the zone width is set equal to the width of the image of the incident beam. Then these 1800 photons will be detected by 21 zones such that the average number of detected photons per zone is about 90 photons. Thus the OMA detector possesses ample sensitivity for this application, providing spatial resolution down to about 0.05 mm. In fact, sufficient intensity exists to observe, with an appropriate filter, the first hot band of N_2, yielding a display of temperature variations (weighted, of course, by nitrogen density). Other filters can be used to observe fuel and major-product densities. (If a dye laser or other broad band-tunable laser is used, the laser can be tuned to different wavelengths rather than the receiver.) Since the OMA detector is computer-compatible, full spatial analysis of the time-resolved information is facilitated. We expect that this kind of information will be very useful in the study of turbulent combustion.

Filter polychromators similar to those shown in Figs 21 and 22 can be used with the OMA detector to monitor several bands simultaneously as, for example, in temperature measurements. Fiber optics can be used, where necessary, to transfer spatially separated color-images to the desired positions on the detector's sensitive area. In this type of application spectral information can be displayed along one detector axis while one dimension of spatial information (the dimension that is parallel to the incident beam) is displayed along the other axis.

When many spectral channels must be observed, or when not all of the spectral channels of interest can be anticipated a priori, a diffraction grating can be used advantageously to disperse spectral information. The combination of spectral resolution, spatial resolution, and light economy considerations required for a typical application of this type can be established from the following considerations: For background rejection and separation of closely spaced spectral lines as in temperature measurements of the BAM type, spectral resolution of the order of 0.5 nm is desirable. The maximum polychromator entrance slit width W_{max} is limited by the desired spectral resolution $\Delta\lambda$, and the reciprocal dispersion of the spectrometer D, such that $W_{max} = (\Delta\lambda)/D$. Many fast spectrometers of conventional design have low reciprocal dispersion; consequently, slit widths less than 0.25 mm are required for 0.5 nm resolution. However, it is desirable to use larger slit widths in order to focus the incident beam within the slit without demagnification or extremely tight focusing of the incident beam. Tight focusing is undesirable because it increases alignment requirements and the possibility of measurement perturbations. Demagnification is undesirable because (as a simple ray-trace diagram will show) this results in a reduction of the solid angle over which scattered light is collected, in so far as this solid angle is determined by the acceptance cone of the spectrometer.

These considerations lead to the conclusion that an optimum spectrometer should be extremely fast (say $f/3$), and have high dispersion ($D \leqslant 1$ nm mm^{-1}) allowing large slit widths, but it does not need exceptional resolution (0.5 nm resolution is sufficient). Such a combination of requirements can be met at a reasonable cost using presently available gratings. For example, for applications where spectral overlap problems can be avoided, use of a coarse grating in high order allows good dispersion in combination with wide spectral range. For example, a 316 groove/mm grating blazed for 63° will place the nitrogen vibrational Raman bands, with shifts near 2331 cm^{-1}, in 11th order close to the corresponding hydrogen bands, with shifts near 4158 cm^{-1}, in 10th order, allowing simultaneous observation of both bands.

It is exciting to contemplate the extensive range of combustion applications beyond Raman scattering diagnostics for the OMA detector/grating spectrometer combination. For example, in addition to facilitating conventional optical techniques, such as sodium line reversal, this instrument can be used to observe laser-excited fluorescence, and to follow laser-excited chemical reactions.

6   STATUS OF THE FIELD

In this review, we have discussed the development of Raman scattering measurement techniques for measurements on combustion gases. These techniques are capable of accurate measurements of major-species density and temperature with good time and space resolution (e.g. 1 μs–1 mm cube). Potential limitations to the experimental implementation of RS methods have been explored and, within reasonable bounds imposed by these limitations, design criteria for some representative experiments have been given.

Much has been written in general terms concerning the necessity for new combustion measurements to advance the state of combustion science and technology. (See, for example, Goulard,[77] Boni,[78] Hartley et al.,[1,2] Oppenheim and Weinberg,[79] Glassman and Sirignano,[80] Swithenbank,[81] etc.) Additionally, reviews have appeared recently which are focused upon the application of Raman scattering techniques to fluid-mechanical and chemical systems such as flames. (See, for example, Penner and Jersky,[82] Lapp and Hartley,[83] Goulard,[84] etc.) Based upon these references, together with the material developed in the present review, we conclude by selecting some important areas of Raman scattering work related to combustion studies which, in our view, should receive strong emphasis in the next several years. We do not wish to convey an impression of completeness in these comments which are intended only as representative views of a rapidly growing area.

Firstly, in order to facilitate more widespread use of these diagnostic techniques, it is important to demonstrate the capabilities of Raman scattering for important combustion experiments. Thus, for example, vibrational RS measurements of turbulent fluctuations in temperature and constituent density in well-defined experimental configurations would be one reasonable choice. This study would utilize the combined spatial and time resolution provided by Raman scattering. (See, for example, Hartley *et al.*[1,2] and Gouldin.[85,86]) Another good choice would be Raman measurements of property variations across a flame front. With effort, this should be possible with atmospheric pressure flames, as has been pointed out by Stephenson.[87]

Another area suited to RS capabilities is the measurement of properties of systems that are not in thermal (or chemical) equilibrium. This type of effort can have a strong impact on flame-front studies, and has been implemented for electrical discharges,[88-90] as well as for chemical lasers.[91] It is hoped that additional work aimed at molecules and radicals of importance to flame studies will be carried out.

In order to implement properly RS diagnostics for flames for any of these experiments in an optimized fashion, experimental data must be obtained on the measurement of perturbation thresholds for laser-gas and laser-particle interactions. These thresholds determine the ultimate balance between spatial resolution and accuracy in time-resolved measurements using a pulsed laser, and are needed for different flame-gas compositions to determine the range of applicability of the various measurement methods. Such perturbation studies should have high priority.

Next, in order to advance the state of the art in Raman diagnostics, several new techniques should be explored to their limits in order to map out the various ranges of applicability and desirability for these methods. Perhaps the most promising of these are:

(i) CARS[38-48,94]—Can this process be used for quantitative flame probing? What is the effect of turbulent fluctuations on CARS signals and on the interpretation of the experimental signatures? What are the limits to the use of CARS for high-resolution Raman line-width studies?

(ii) Raman Photon Correlation Spectroscopy[67]—What are the ultimate limits in practical situations for the time resolution provided by the correlation functions? What are the effects of significant flame luminosity on such measurements? How useful is the type of information they supply?

(iii) Interferometric Rotational Raman Scattering[9,10]—Can this technique be applied to hot, multi-component gases, many of which often possess relatively similar rotational spectroscopic constants? What are the problems in experimental design and signal processing for achieving rapid time response with good spatial resolution?

For each of these methods, we could also ask: What are the prospects for implementing this technique with good experimental stability and at a reasonable cost for flame studies? And also, what advantages does this technique possess over competing measurement methods (such as ordinary RS, Rayleigh scattering, absorption/emission techniques, etc.) that might induce us to carry forth the development work? (This last question is not simple to answer. See, for example, Goulard[92] for a discussion of an index of merit for application of RS to different problems.)

In order to complement studies of new Raman techniques, additional work should be initiated on basic data common to all the methods. For example, we should ask the question: Can total hydrocarbons or important fuel fragments be traced by monitoring vibrational Raman bands corresponding to an appropriate common chemical bond (such as CH)? What are the values of scattering cross-section for important flame species not yet observed? (See, for example, the theoretical calculations of Coll and Melius.[93])

This partial list of opportunities at the forefront of Raman scattering experiments illustrates the present status of this field, emerging from early developmental stages to engineering applications, motivated by the growing demand for detailed combustion measurements, and accelerated by steady improvements in laser sources and detection systems.

ACKNOWLEDGMENT

We are grateful to Project SQUID (Office of Naval Research) for support of portions of the ongoing research program upon which this review has been based. We also are pleased to acknowledge support for part of this study from the National Bureau of Standards, U.S. Department of Commerce. Valuable discussions concerning laser-induced gas breakdown were held with Dr. A. A. Boni.

REFERENCES

(1) D. L. Hartley, D. R. Hardesty, M. Lapp, J. Dooher and F. Dryer (eds), in *Efficient Use of Energy*, American Institute of Physics Conference Proceedings No. 25, American Institute of Physics, New York, 1975, p. 153.
(2) D. L. Hartley, M. Lapp and D. R. Hardesty, *Phys. Today* **28**, 36 (1975).
(3) M. Lapp, *Proc. Soc. Photo-Opt. Instrum. Eng.* **61**, 42 (1975).
(4) D. L. Hartley, in *Laser Raman Gas Diagnostics* (M. Lapp and C. M. Penney, eds), Plenum Press, New York, 1974, p. 311.
(5) M. M. Sushchinskii, *Raman Spectra of Molecules and Crystals*, Israel Program for Scientific Translations, New York, 1972.
(6) A. Anderson (ed.), *The Raman Effect*, Volumes 1 and 2, Marcel Dekker Inc., New York, 1971, 1973.
(7) M. Lapp and C. M. Penney (eds), *Laser Raman Gas Diagnostics*, Plenum Press, New York, 1974.
(8) M. Lapp and C. M. Penney, *Appl. Opt.* **13**, A14 (1974).

(9) J. J. Barratt and S. A. Myers, *J. Opt. Soc. Am.* **61**, 1246 (1971).

(10) J. J. Barratt, in *Laser Raman Gas Diagnostics*, (M. Lapp and C. M. Penney, eds), Plenum Press, New York, 1974, p. 63.

(11) M. Lapp, C. M. Penney and J. A. Asher, *Application of Light-Scattering Techniques for Measurements of Density, Temperature, and Velocity in Gas-dynamics*, Aerospace Research Laboratories, Wright-Patterson Air Force Base, Report No. ARL 73-0045, 1973.

(12) R. S. Hickman and L. H. Liang, *Rev. Sci. Instrum.* **43**, 796 (1972).

(13) J. A. Salzman, W. J. Masica and T. A. Coney, *Determination of Gas Temperatures from Laser-Raman Scattering*, NASA TN D-6336, 1971.

(14) J. A. Salzman and T. A. Coney, *Remote Measurement of Atmospheric Temperatures by Raman Lidar*, NASA TN X-68250, 1973.

(15) J. A. Salzman and T. A. Coney, *Atmospheric Temperature Measurements Using Raman Lidar*, NASA TN D-7679, 1974.

(16) J. A. Cooney, *J. Appl. Meteorol.* **11**, 108 (1972).

(17) J. Cooney and M. Pina, *Appl. Optics* **15**, 602 (1976).

(18) M. Lapp, C. M. Penney and L. M. Goldman, *Optics Commun.* **9**, 195 (1973).

(19) M. Lapp, in *Laser Raman Gas Diagnostics*, (M. Lapp and C. M. Penney, eds), Plenum Press, New York, 1974, p. 107.

(20) M. Lapp, *Raman Scattering Probe for Water Vapor in Flames*, AIAA Paper No. 74-1143, 1974.

(21) R. H. Tourin and P. M. Henry, *Infrared Spectral Emissivities and Internal Energy Distribution of Carbon Dioxide at High Temperatures. Part I. Internal Energy Calculations*, Air Force Cambridge Research Center Report, AFCRC-TN-59-262, 1958.

(22) J. L. Bribes, R. Gaufrès, M. Monan, M. Lapp and C. M. Penney, *Appl. Phys. Lett.* **28**, 336 (1976).

(23) D. A. Leonard, *Point Measurement of Density by Laser Raman Scattering*, Project SQUID (Office of Naval Research) Technical Report AVCO-1-PU, 1972.

(24) F. Robben, Comparison of Density and Temperature Measurement Using Raman Scattering and Rayleigh Scattering, in *Combustion Measurements in Jet Propulsion Systems*, (R. Goulard, ed.), Project SQUID (ONR) Workshop Proceedings, Purdue Univ., Report PU-R1-76, 1975.

(25) M. Jyumonji, T. Kobayasi and H. Inaba, Measurement of Resonance Scattering Cross Section of Sodium D Lines and Laser Radar Detection of Sodium Layer in the Upper Atmosphere by a Tunable Dye Laser, given at the Fifth Conference on Laser Radar Studies of the Atmosphere, Williamsburg, Virginia, 1973.

(26) C. C. Wang and L. I. Davis, *Appl. Phys. Lett.* **25**, 34 (1974).

(27) D. K. Killinger, C. C. Wang and M. Hanabusa, *Phys. Rev.* **13**, 2145 (1976).

(28) C. C. Wang and L. I. Davis, *Phys. Rev. Lett.* **32**, 349 (1974).

(29) M. Birnbaum, J. A. Gelbwachs, A. W. Tucker and C. L. Fincher, *Opto-electronics* **4**, 155 (1972).

(30) C. M. Penney, W. W. Morey, R. L. St. Peters, S. D. Silverstein, M. Lapp and D. R. White, *Study of Resonance Light Scattering for Remote Optical Probing*, NASA Report No. CR-132363, 1973.

(31) C. J. Vear, P. J. Hendra and J. J. Macfarlane, *J. Chem. Soc. Chem. Commun.* **7**, 381 (1972).

(32) P. J. Hendra, C. J. Vear, R. Moss and J. J. Macfarlane, in *Laser Raman Gas Diagnostics*, (M. Lapp and C. M. Penney, eds), Plenum Press, New York, 1974, p. 153.

(33) R. H. Barnes, C. E. Moeller, J. F. Kircher and C. M. Verber, *Appl. Opt.* **12**, 2531 (1973).

(34) D. G. Fouche and R. K. Chang, *Phys. Rev. Lett.* **29**, 536 (1972).

(35) R. L. St. Peters, S. D. Silverstein, M. Lapp and C. M. Penney, *Phys. Rev. Lett.* **30**, 191 (1973).

(36) W. Holzer, W. F. Murphy and H. J. Bernstein, *J. Chem. Phys.* **52**, 399 (1970).

(37) P. D. Maker and R. W. Terhune, *Phys. Rev.* **137**, 801 (1965).

(38) P. R. Regnier, F. Moya and J. P. E. Taran, *AIAA J.* **12**, 826 (1973).

(39) P. R. Regnier and J. P. E. Taran, *Appl. Phys. Lett.* **23**, 240 (1973).

(40) P. R. Regnier and J. P. E. Taran, Gas Concentration Measurement by Coherent Raman Anti-Stokes Scattering and also J. P. E. Taran, Temperature Measurements by Coherent Anti-Stokes Scattering, in *Laser Raman Gas Diagnostics*, (M. Lapp and C. M. Penney, eds), Plenum Press, New York, 1974, p. 87.

(41) F. Moya, S. A. J. Druet and J. P. E. Taran, *Opt. Commun.* **13**, 169 (1975).

(42) F. Moya, S. Druet, M. Pealat and J. P. E. Taran, *Flame Investigation by Coherent Anti-Stokes Raman Scattering*, AIAA Paper No. 76-29, 1976.

(43) R. F. Begley, A. B. Harvey, R. L. Byer and B. S. Hudson, *Am. Lab.* (November 1974).

(44) R. F. Begley, A. B. Harvey and R. L. Byer, *Appl. Phys. Lett.* **25**, 387 (1974).

(45) A. B. Harvey, J. R. McDonald and W. M. Tolles, in *Progress in Analytical Chemistry*, Plenum Press, New York (to be published).

(46) J. J. Barratt and R. F. Begley, *Appl. Phys. Lett.* **27**, 129 (1975).

(47) I. Itzkan and D. A. Leonard, *Appl. Phys. Lett.* **26**, 106 (1975).

(48) J. E. Moore and L. M. Fraas, *Anal. Chem.* **45**, 2009 (1973).

(49) D. P. Aeschliman and R. E. Setchell, *Appl. Spectrosc.* **29**, 426 (1975).

(50) A. C. Eckbreth, *Laser Raman Thermometry Experiments in Simulated Combustor Environments*, AIAA Paper No. 76-27, 1976.

(51) S. Lederman and J. Bornstein, *Temperature and Concentration Measurements on an Axisymmetric Jet and Flame*, Project SQUID (Office of Naval Research) Technical Report PIB-32-PU, 1973.

(52) S. Lederman and J. Bornstein, in *Instrumentation for Airbreathing Propulsion*, (A. E. Fuhs and M. Kingery, eds), Progress in Astronautics and Aeronautics Series, Vol. 34, MIT Press, Cambridge, Massachusetts, 1974, p. 283.

(53) S. Lederman, *Some Applications of Laser Diagnostics to Fluid Dynamics*, AIAA Paper No. 76-21, 1976.

(54) S. Lederman, *Modern Diagnostics of Combustion*, AIAA Paper No. 76-26, 1976.

(55) D. A. Leonard and P. M. Rubins, *Laser Raman and Fluorescence Measurements Applied to Gas Turbine Exhaust Emissions*, ASME Paper No. 75-GT-83, 1975.

(56) R. E. Setchell, *Time-Averaged Measurements in Turbulent Flames Using Raman Spectroscopy*, AIAA Paper No. 76-28, 1976.

(57) C. M. Penney, L. M. Goldman and M. Lapp, *Nature (London) Phys. Sci.* **235**, 110 (1972).

(58) H. C. Hottel and A. F. Sarofim, *Radiative Transfer*, McGraw-Hill, New York, 1967, p. 244.

(59) A. A. Boni and D. A. Meskan, *Opt. Commun.* **14**, 115 (1975).

(60) C. DeMichelis, *IEEE J. Quantum Electron.* **QE-5**, 188 (1969).

(61) A. G. Gaydon and H. G. Wolfhard, *Flames. Their Structure, Radiation, and Temperature*, 2nd ed., revised, The Macmillan Co., New York, 1960, Chapter XIII. See also A. G. Gaydon, *The Spectroscopy of Flames*, 2nd ed., Wiley, New York, 1974, p. 273.

(62) D. A. Leonard, *Development of a Laser Raman Aircraft Turbine Engine Exhaust Emissions Measurement System*, AVCO Everett Res. Lab. Research Note 914, 1972.

(63) R. E. Setchell, *Analysis of Flame Emissions by Laser Raman Spectroscopy*, Sandia Laboratories Energy Report No. SLL74-5244; also Paper No. WSS/CI 74-6, Western States Section, The Combustion Institute, 1974.

(64) D. A. Stephenson, *J. Quant. Spectrosc. Radiat. Transfer* **14**, 1291 (1974).

(65) D. L. Hartley, *AIAA J.* **12**, 816 (1974).

(66) A. A. Boiarski, *Shock-Tube Diagnostics Utilizing Laser Raman Spectroscopy*, Naval Surface Weapons Centre (White Oak, Silver Spring, Maryland) Technical Report NSWC/WOL/TR 75-53, 1975.

(67) A. D. Birch, D. R. Brown, M. J. Dodson and J. R. Thomas, *J. Phys. D.* **8**, L167 (1975).

(68) D. R. Brown, J. R. Thomas, W. R. M. Pomeroy and J. M. Vaughan, *The Application of Laser Raman Spectroscopy to Transient Mixture and Combustion Measurements*, British Gas Corp., Research and Development Division Report MRS E 250, 1975.

(69) R. A. Hill and D. L. Hartley, *Appl. Opt.* **13**, 186 (1974).

(70) *RCA Photomultiplier Manual*, RCA Electronic Components, Harrison, New Jersey, 1970, p. 65.

(71) M. Bridoux, A. Chapput, M. Delhaye, H. Tourbez and F. Wallart, in *Laser Raman Gas Diagnostics*, (M. Lapp and C. M. Penney, eds), Plenum Press, New York, 1974, p. 249.

(72) M. Bridoux and M. Delhaye, in *Advances in Infrared and Raman Spectroscopy*, Vol. 2, (R. J. H. Clark and R. E. Hester, eds), Heyden, London, 1976, p. 140.

(73) J. R. Smith, in *Laser Raman Gas Diagnostics*, (M. Lapp and C. M. Penney, eds), Plenum Press, New York, 1974, p. 171.

(74) J. R. Smith, *A Rotational Raman Scattering System for Measuring Temperature and Concentration Profiles in Transient Gas Flows*, Sandia Laboratories Report SAND 75-8224, 1975.

(75) E. R. Schildkraut, in *Laser Raman Gas Diagnostics*, (M. Lapp and C. M. Penney, eds), Plenum Press, New York, 1974, p. 259.

(76) R. Bell, A. Carswell, S. Jeffers and W. Weller, *Image Intensifier Optical Multichannel Analyzer for Remote Sensing*. Report for Canada Centre for Remote Sensing, Department of Energy, Mines and Resources. Prepared at Centre for Research in Experimental Space Science, York University, Canada, 1975.

(77) *Combustion Measurements in Jet Propulsion Systems*, R. Goulard, (ed.) Project SQUID (Office of Naval Research) Workshop Proceedings, Purdue University Report No. PU-R1-76, 1975. To be published as *Combustion Measurements: Modern Techniques and Instrumentation*, Hemisphere Publishing Corp., Washington, D.C.

(78) A. A. Boni, ed., *Proceedings of the Workshop on the Numerical Simulation of Combustion for Application to Spark and Compression Ignition Engines*. Sponsored by NSF Rann Program. Science Applications Inc. Report, 1975.

(79) A. K. Oppenheim and F. J. Weinberg, Combustion R and D. Key to Our Energy Future, *Astronaut. Aeronaut.* 22 (November 1974).

(80) I. Glassman and W. A. Sirignano, *Summary Report of the Workshop on Energy-Related Basic Combustion Research*. Sponsored by NSF. Princeton Univ., Dept. of Aerospace and Mechanical Sciences Report No. 1177, 1974.

(81) J. Swithenbank, *The Unknown Fluid Mechanics of Combustion*, Keynote Address given at the ASME Fluid Mechanics of Combustion Conference, Montreal, 1974. Also, University of Sheffield (U.K.) Report HIC 220, 1974.

(82) S. S. Penner and T. Jersky, in *Annual Review of Fluid Mechanics*, Vol. 5, Annual Reviews, Inc., Palo Alto, 1973, p. 8.

(83) M. Lapp and D. L. Hartley, Raman Scattering Studies of Combustion, *Combust. Sci. Technol.* **13**, 199 (1975). Also in *Combustion Measurements in Jet Propulsion Systems*, (R. Goulard, ed.), Project SQUID (Office of Naval Research) Workshop Proceedings, Purdue University Report No. PU-R1-76, 1976.

(84) R. Goulard, in *Applications of Non-Intrusive Instrumentation in Fluid Flow Research*, AGARD Conference Proceedings No. CP-193, 1976.

(85) F. C. Gouldin, *Combust. Sci. Technol.* **9**, 17 (1974).

(86) F. C. Gouldin, *Combust. Sci. Technol.* **7**, 33 (1973).

(87) D. A. Stephenson, Laser Raman Analysis of Premixed Hydrocarbon Air Flames, Optical Society of America, Technical Digest, *Applications of Laser Spectroscopy*, Anaheim, California, March 19–21, 1975.

(88) L. Y. Nelson, A. W. Saunders, A. B. Harvey and G. O. Neely, *J. Chem. Phys.* **55**, 5127 (1971).

(89) A. B. Harvey, in *Laser Raman Gas Diagnostics*, (M. Lapp and C. M. Penney, eds), Plenum Press, New York, 1974, p. 147.

(90) G. Black, R. L. Sharpless and T. G. Slanger, *J. Chem. Phys.* **58**, 4792 (1973).

(91) J. M. Hoell, F. Allario, O. Jarrett and R. K. Seals, *J. Chem. Phys.* **58**, 2896 (1973).

(92) R. Goulard, *J. Quant. Spectrosc. Radiat. Transfer* **14**, 969 (1974). Also (M. Lapp and C. M. Penney, eds), in *Laser Raman Gas Diagnostics*, Plenum Press, New York, 1974, p. 3.

(93) C. F. Coll and C. F. Melius, *Theoretical Calculation of Raman Scattering Cross Sections for Use in Flame Analysis*, Sandia Laboratories Report SAND 76-8204, 1976.

(94) W. B. Roh, P. W. Schreiber and J. P. E. Taran, *Appl. Phys. Lett.* **29**, 174 (1976).

(95) *IES Lighting Handbook*, 5th ed., Illuminating Engineering Society, New York, 1972.

(96) R. T. Brown and D. C. Smith, *Appl. Phys. Lett.* **22**, 245 (1973).

(97) P. E. Nielsen and G. H. Canavan, *J. Appl. Phys.* **44**, 4224 (1973).

AUTHOR INDEX

A

Abbate, S., 99 (88); *123*
Abe, Y., 147 (77); 155 (77); *165*
Ackerman, M., 51 (41); *85*
Adamek, P., 101 (104); *123*
Adams, C. J., 182 (102); *200*
Adams, D. M., 88 (17); 99 (83); 100 (83); 105 (83); *121*; *123*
Aeschliman, D. P., 229 (49); 231 (49); *259*
Afsar, M. N., 60 (56); 61 (58, 59); 63 (61); 64 (62, 63); 65 (65); 66 (65, 67); 68 (68); 70 (69); *86*
Ahmed, I. Y., 190 (153); *202*
Akhmedzanov, R., 170 (6); *198*
Akopyan, S. K., 190 (149); *201*
Al-Baldawi, S. A., 192 (171); *202*
Albrecht, A. C., 129 (15, 18); *163*
Aldous, J., 99 (93); 107 (93); 111 (93); *123*
Alexander, C., 172 (39); *199*
Alexander, L. E., 172 (35); *199*; 127 (1); *163*
Aliev, M. R., 100 (96); *123*
Alix, A. J. P., 101 (105); 113 (152); 115 (159); 116 (170); 118 (188); 119 (195, 196, 197, 198, 200); *123*; *125*
Aljibury, A. L. K., 121 (210); *126*; 172 (21); *199*
Allario, F. 256 (91); *261*
Allemand, C., 22 (43); *42*
Allen, G., 127 (7); 138 (41, 42); *163*; *164*
Alway, C. D., 34 (64); *42*
Ananthakrishnan, T. R., 119 (199, 201, 202, 203); *125*
Anderson, A., 207 (6); 256 (6); *257*
Anderson, A. B., 91 (43); *122*
Anderson, R. J., 99 (85); *123*
Angelova, R., 172 (16); *198*
Aritomi, M., 194 (193); *203*

Aruldhas, G., 119 (199, 201, 202, 203); *125*
Arzoumanidis, G. G., 194 (194); *203*
Ashby, E. C., 187 (129); *201*
Åse, K., 190 (154); *202*
Asher, J. A., 215 (11); *258*
Atalla, R. H., 106 (126); 114 (126); *124*
Austad, T., 190 (154); *202*
Averbukh, B. S., 120 (205); *126*

B

Badilescu, S., 193 (185, 186); *202*
Bagus, P. S., 91 (39); *122*
Bailey, A. E., 61 (60); *86*
Bailey, G. F., 22 (42); *42*
Bailey, R. T., 141 (49); *164*
Bailey, T. A., 172 (49); *199*
Bakhshiev, N. G., 193 (187); *202*
Balkanski, M., 131 (25); *164*
Ballard, G. M., 138 (42); *164*
Ballein, K., 116 (165); *125*; 172 (45); *199*
Baltagi, F., 97 (71); *123*
Baluteau, J. P., 51 (42); *85*
Bamford, C. H., 142 (58); *165*
Baranova, G. I., 193 (187); *202*
Barker, C., 192 (170); *202*
Barnes, D. C., 66 (67); *86*
Barnes, R. H., 226 (33); 231 (33); *259*
Barnhart, D. M., 96 (66); *123*
Barratt, J. J., 215 (9, 10); 227 (46); 256 (9, 10, 46); *258*; *259*
Barron, L. D., 30 (48, 49, 50); *42*
Bartell, L. S., 95 (56); *122*
Barthelat, M., 196 (204); *203*
Bartlett, N., 182 (102); *200*
Basile, L. J., 4 (9); *41*; 88 (18); *121*
Bauder, A., 97 (71); *123*
Bauer, W. C., 64 (64); 66 (64); *86*

FORMULA INDEX

SUBJECT INDEX

A

Absorption coefficient, 59, 74
Absorption correction, 18
Absorption index, 59, 73, 74
Acetic acid, 189, 197
Acetone, 188, 192, 193, 195, 196
Acetonitrile, 173, 187, 188, 189, 190, 191, 192, 193, 194, 196
Acousto-optic modulator, 233
Addition Raman spectroscopy, 22
Aerosol, 230, 231, 233
n-alkane, 149
Amide, 145
Ammonia, 168, 169, 171–178, 187
Amorphous systems, 149–152
Amplifier, 13
Amplitude modulation, 49
Analog method, 100
Anharmonicity, 92
Anisotropic scattering, 28, 29, 31
Anomalous polarization, 131
Antimony(III) bromide, 172
Antimony(III) chloride, 172, 185
Antimony(V) chloride, 187, 190, 197
Antimony(V) fluoride, 172, 179, 180, 182, 183, 185
Anti-Stokes spectrum, 39
Approximate force constant, 112–121
Argon-ion laser, 8, 19, 26, 37, 135, 136, 160, 211, 213, 229, 233, 244, 245
Arsenic(III) bromide, 172
Arsenic(III) chloride, 172, 185, 196
Arsenic(V) fluoride, 179, 183
Atomic force constant, 100, 101
Autoionization, 169
Automatic scanning of the depolarization ratio, 22–30
Axial iteration method, 106

B

Balloon, 56, 57
Band area method (BAM), 216, 217, 252, 254
Beam divider, 76, 78, 80, 81
Benzene, 38, 39, 112, 136, 153, 154, 187, 192, 193, 196, 216, 242
Black-body, emission, 58, 231, 234, 235
  intensity, 77
  continuum limit, 78
  source, 84
Born-Oppenheimer approximation, 88
Boron-doped germanium photoconductive detector, 75
Boron trifluoride, 195
Bremsstrahlung emission, 75, 238, 239
Brewster angle prism, 230
Brillouin zone, 35
Bromine, 9, 196, 197
Bromine (III) fluoride, 169, 172, 182, 185, 186
Bromine(V) fluoride, 172, 182, 186
n-Butane, 242
1-Butene, 242

C

Caesium iodide, 170
Capillary cell, 4, 5
Carbohydrate, 106
Carbon dioxide, 9, 28, 29, 89, 216, 219, 220, 224, 226, 229, 236, 238, 241, 251
Carbon monoxide, 47, 48, 50, 90, 209, 216, 224, 238, 241, 242
Carbon tetrabromide, 10
Carbon tetrachloride, 10, 14–16, 18, 19, 22, 23, 25–27, 173, 179, 186, 192, 193
Carbon tetrafluoride, 170